Breeding Reptiles & Amphibians

A collection of papers selected from the

BRITISH HERPETOLOGICAL SOCIETY BULLETIN

1980-1992

Edited by

SIMON TOWNSON

Published by

The British Herpetological Society

c/o The Zoological Society of London

Regent's Park, London NW1 4RY

ISBN 0 9507371 51

CONTENTS

PREFACE

DEDICATION

LIZARDS

SNAKES

CROCODILES, ALLIGATORS, TORTOISES AND TURTLES

NEWTS, SALAMANDERS, TOADS AND FROGS

PREFACE

This book is the seventh in a series of miscellaneous volumes published by the Captive Breeding Committee of the British Herpetological Society (BHS).

Contained herein are 51 selected papers, specializing in the captive breeding and husbandry of reptiles and amphibians, which have been drawn together and reprinted from backnumbers of the *British Herpetological Society Bulletin,* 1980-1992. Unlike many of the glossy derivative books commercially available today, this volume contains invaluable original information written by experts with hands-on experience, many of whom are regarded as pioneers in their field, with some authors having contributed to BHS publications for more than a decade. Unfortunately the printing of some of the early photographs was not of very good quality and therefore reproduction here has been less than ideal; in addition, the high cost of colour plates has limited their usage. Nevertheless, I hope these factors do not detract too much from the overall value and appearance of the book.

In recent times there have been great leaps forward in the successful propagation of wild animals which were previously thought to be too difficult to breed in captivity; at the same time there has been a growing appreciation of the very positive benefits of captive breeding for conservation projects, scientific research and for the aesthetic interests of people worldwide. On behalf of the BHS Captive Breeding Committee, I hope this volume will make another useful contribution to the subject, and will encourage further collaboration and dissemination of information and ideas between herpetologists.

Dr. Simon Townson
Editor

DEDICATION

In memory of Mr. Steve Norrie, who tragically died in a diving accident in 1992. Steve was a long-standing member of the BHS Captive Breeding Committee and has contributed to this volume.

British Herpetological Society Bulletin No. 1. 1980

THE CAUCASIAN GREEN LIZARD, *LACERTA STRIGATA* EICHWALD 1831, WITH NOTES ON ITS REPRODUCTION IN CAPTIVITY

BERT LANGERWERF

**Agama International Rt 2, Box 285, Montevallo, Alabama 35115, USA*

DESCRIPTION

Length: 106mm (male) – 112mm (female). The characteristic colour of the adult is clear bright green over the first two thirds of the body, while the hind quarters including legs and tail, are olive brown. The female is similar, but the green is not as intense, and the body retains some of the spots and a trace of the stripes of the juvenile colouring. In the breeding season, the head, throat, and sides of the neck turn deep blue in the male; the throat of the female is greenish yellow. The belly of the male is greenish or greenish yellow, that of the female white. The juveniles are olive brown in colour with five clearly defined narrow, whitish, longitudinal stripes, between which are irregular small dark spots. The stripes fade and gradually disappear with the onset of the maturity, but may be retained longer in the female.

DISTRIBUTION AND HABITAT

N.E. Antolia; the Caucasus; West Central and N.E. Iran, and the south western extremity of Turkmenistan (Central Asia).

Lacerta strigata occupies a wide variety of habitats within its range. It is found in steppe, mountain-steppe, semi-desert, by the banks of rivers or small streams, in meadows, the borders of steppe-forest, windbreaks in cultivated land, the margins of vineyards and gardens, roadside and canal banks. Within these areas it avoids barren places or low vegetation, but lives by preference around small bushes, bramble, wild rose or dense weeds. Cover is sought in the holes of rodents or in rock piles, the lizards themselves sometimes dig burrows of 50-70mm in length. In the mountains, this species reaches an altitude of 3000 metres in some regions. In favourable localities population densities may be high. At Stavropol a density of 460 per hectare has been recorded (Bannikov and Darevski, 1977); in eastern Georgia 400 per hectare (Mus-gelishvili, 1970); by Lake Sevanin in Armenia, 27-34 individuals were counted in a walk of 1 km. (Bannikov and Darevski, 1977).

*Present address. This study was carried out in the Netherlands.

PERIOD OF ACTIVITY AND REPRODUCTION

The lizards emerge from hibernation in mid-March when temperatures reach 16-18°C. In mild winters in Georgia activity may commence in February. The adults usually begin hibernation in September, but the young remain active through October into November.

Mating begins early in May, with a peak period in the second half of May. Egg laying commences towards the end of May and extends until early July. Each female usually lays two clutches each of 6-11 eggs. The first clutch is normally laid at the end of May/beginning of June, the second at the end of June/beginning of July. The eggs measure 8-10 x 15-18mm. The incubation period is about six weeks. The young emerge from the end of July until mid-September. At hatching, the young have a snout-vent length of 30-32mm. Maturity is reached at an age of 22-23 months.

FOOD

Beetles (20-60% of stomachs examined), spiders (12-30%), woodlice (-25%), snails (13-22%), ants (-26%), flies (4-18%), bugs (-11%). Also grasshoppers, moths, cicadas.

PARASITES

Trematodes *(Brachylaemus)*, nematodes *(Physocephalus)*; ticks *(Haemaphysalis)*.

LACERTA STRIGATA IN CAPTIVITY

About four years ago I received from a friend in Eastern Europe 2 males and 1 female *L. strigata*. From the beginning they proved to be a very easy species to keep in my garden-terraria. *Lacerta strigata* is closely related to *Lacerta viridis*, *L. agilis* and *L. trilineata*, in that order. They have been crossed successfully with both *L. viridis* and *L. agilis* by Wolfgang Bischoff. The young are very similar in appearance to those of *L. trilineata*, and years ago *L. strigata* was regarded as a subspecies of *L. trilineata*. It was to be expected, therefore, that in captivity they would be as easy to keep as *L. agilis* and *L. viridis*. Breeding in garden vivariums proved to be very easy, almost exponential: in 1977 I was lucky to breed 6 *L. strigata*, while in 1978 26 young were born, and in 1979, 131.

I keep the lizards in different kinds of vivariums:

1) A brick-walled glass covered enclosure of 3 sq. m, facing south, in good weather 1/3 of the glass is removed.

2) A glass covered enclosure similar to the above, of 12 sq. m.

3) An open air enclosure of 600 sq. m.

The lizards thrive in all of these enclosures, where they live all year round, hibernating successfully. The winters within their natural range can be very severe, so the lizards are well able to survive the winters of North West Europe. In this regard, I noticed a most remarkable thing; in the warmest vivariums the lizards went into hibernation earlier than in the open-air enclosure; this applied particularly to the females. It seemed as if the females, after laying their three clutches of eggs automatically go into hibernation after a short period of activity of a few weeks. In the open air enclosure, of course, mating and egg laying are later. In the hot summer of 1976 the lizards in the glass covered enclosure had already disappeared by the end of August when temperatures outside exceeded 30°C (=90°F). Yet in the same enclosure I saw the first lizard emerge from hibernation on 29th January 1977 during sunny weather, at an outside air temperature of 10°C. In 1977 the *strigata* were hibernating by 17th September in beautiful weather. In 1979 in the warmest glass covered enclosure the lizards were gone by 28th August, while in the same year in the open air enclosure some females laid eggs on 20-22 September. In 1980 the first males appeared in one glass covered enclosure in February, and in another on March 25th. In the open air enclosure the animals did not appear until the beautiful weather of mid April.

Mating takes place mostly in the second half of April and in May. Eggs are laid from the end of May in the glass covered enclosures and a month or more later in the open air enclosures. A female may lay up to three clutches at intervals of about 3-4 weeks depending on food and weather. The number of eggs in a clutch varies from 8-10 in the case of young females to 10-15 in the case of old females. Therefore, one female can produce up to 40 young each year. My impression is that the more food the lizards are given, the more eggs are produced.

In the glass covered enclosures it is necessary to give calcium and vitamin D3 to the lizards, otherwise the eggs will not contain sufficient calcium for proper development; they may develop to the point of hatching but will die because the skeleton of the young lizard will be too weak to enable escape from the egg. This problem does not occur in open air enclosures. I give calcium in any way possible: egg shells in the enclosures, and calcium lactate in the drinking water are good methods. Vitamin D3 I give in amounts of 10,000-20,000 International Units per litre of water; the water is changed and a fresh mixture given each 2-3 days.

When the females are given good food, conditions and vitamins the incubation time is quite short. At a temperature of 28-30°C the incubation period is 50-54 days. The shortest incubation period I have observed was 44 days at 29-30°C. The sand in which the eggs are incubated must be fairly loose and not compacted, so that the eggs have sufficient oxygen.

Plate 1. Young *Lacerta strigata*. The two on the left are some months old, and have developed dark spots. The one on the right is less than two months old and has the characteristic pattern of the new-born.

Plate 2. Adult male (3-4 years old).

Plate 3. Adult female (3-4 years old).

The young grow very quickly; if they are kept warm and active through the winter they can reach maturity and breed the following spring. If the young (hatched in July-September) are kept outdoors during the winter in glass covered enclosures, they enter hibernation during November which is much later than their parents. They will reach maturity about a year after birth, and be ready to breed in their second spring.
Like other species of *Lacerta*, the males fight during the mating period. They can be kept with other species of lizards; I have kept them with smaller lizards; *Lacerta monticola, L. saxicola, L. praticola* and other small wall lizards; with species of about their own size; *Lacerta agilis, L. viridis, Agama stellio, Agama caucasia*, and also with larger ones: *Lacerta lepida pater*, adult *Gerrhonotus multicarinatus.*

I feed the lizards mostly on crickets, mealworms and flies.

CONCLUSION

Lacerta strigata is an excellent lizard for garden vivariums; they are easy to breed and can be kept with many other kinds of lizard. Another attraction is the variability of their own colour with different ages and sexes. It seems the conditions in glass covered enclosures in gardens in NW Europe are even more favourable for this lizard than its natural habitat.

REFERENCES

Bannikov, A.J., Darevski, I.S. Ishchenko, V.G., Rustanov, A.K., Cherbak, N.N., Moscow, 1977
Amphibians and Reptiles of the Soviet Union.

Mus-gelishvili, T.A. Tiflis, 1970.
Reptiles of Eastern Georgia.

Basoglu, M. and Baram, I., Izmir, 1977.
Reptiles of Turkey, Part 1, Turtles and Lizards.

Bischoff, W. Aquarien U. Terrarien, 1969,
"Lacertum bastarde".

Bischoff, W. Aquarien U. Terrarien, 1970.
"Lacerta strigata".

Bischoff, W. Zool. Garten Leipzig – 43 (1973).
"Lacerta bastarde".

British Herpetological Society Bulletin No. 2. 1980

THE ARMENIAN WALL LIZARD, *LACERTA ARMENIACA*, MEHELY 1909, WITH NOTES ON ITS CARE AND REPRODUCTION IN CAPTIVITY

BERT LANGERWERF

**Agama International, Rt 2, Box 285, Montevallo, Alabama U.S.A.*

INTRODUCTION

In the Caucasus there are five species of lizards which are known to be parthenogenic:

Lacerta dahli, Darevsky 1957
Lacerta rostombekovi, Darevksy 1957
Lacerta unisexualis, Darevsky 1966
Lacerta armeniaca, Mehely 1909
Lacerta uzzeli, Darevsky & Danieljan 1977

All of these species are rock lizards, and are closely related to other species with similar habits, such as *Lacerta raddei*, *Lacerta valentini*, and *Lacerta saxicola*.

The fact, alone, that these five species can reproduce themselves without the presence of a male makes them very interesting. They are particularly interesting for the terrarium keeper because it is possible to breed them from only one individual.

*Present address: This study was carried out in the Netherlands.

PARTIAL DESCRIPTION**

Length: 73 mm. The basic colour of the body, on the dorsum, is brownish green, dirty green, greenish yellow or olive yellow; the green colouration is more clearly developed on the anterior third of the body. A dorsal stripe is formed by small black or brown spots concentrated in a transverse manner along the centre of the back, not covering its entire width. Broad lateral stripes are formed by the merging together of dark irregularly shaped rings with light eye spots, one or two of which by the forelegs are blue. On the upper margin of the lateral stripes there is usually a row of clearly defined whitish spots. The venter is pale lemon yellow with alternating blue and small black spots along the edges of the ventral scales. The underparts of the head and the throat are white.

DISTRIBUTION**

The interior mountains of Armenia, within the borders of N.E. Turkey, Adzhar, southern Georgia, and northern Armenia, from where it extends into the adjacent mountainous parts of N.W. Azerbaijan.

ECOLOGY**

Lacerta armeniaca occurs in rocky areas, in stone piles, stony fields, and the sides of ravines in the wood and mountain-steppe zones at an altitude of 1700-2200 m. In the mountain-steppe zone it may also be found amongst vegetation a great distance from stony or rocky areas. Up to 200 or more individuals have been observed on a walk of 1 km. In Armenia the food consists chiefly of insects. Of the stomachs examined, membrane-winged insects were found in 45%, ants in 22%, beetles in 27%, orthopterans 26%, flies 33%, butterflies 19%, and spiders 11%. Also found were centipedes, earthworms and snails.

The population of this parthenogenic species is composed of females, which multiply without insemination. The number of eggs in one clutch is 2-5, most often 3-4; these measure, on average, 7.5-11 mm and are laid from mid-June to the middle of July. The incubation period is about 55 days. The young ones appear towards the end of July or early in August. At the time of hatching they measure 24.5-26.5 mm; by the following spring they reach 32-36 mm; by the end of the summer 45-48 mm; in the second spring, at a length of 47-49 mm they reach maturity. The maximum length of 65-73 mm is reached in the fourth year of life.

Plate 1. *Lacerta armeniaca* in captivity.

Lacerta armeniaca **in captivity**

I have kept this interesting species successfully for many years in my garden terraria. This species lives in nature in areas very similar to those inhabited by *Lacerta muralis* in the West, and can be kept in the same way that *L. muralis* can be kept. I have had success in both glass and gauze covered terraria. A rather small terrarium of 70 x 50 cm is sufficient to house about five individuals, because as there are no males (in nature there is said to be a ratio of one male to every thousand females) there is no fighting. The terrarium must always afford a frost-proof retreat in the winter and cool hiding places in summer. I provide these retreats with old roofing tiles inserted obliquely into the ground to a depth of about one foot. A layer of hay or leaves improves the situation. If kept under glass a dietary supplement of vitamin D3 is needed (see my article on *Lacerta strigata* in the BHS Bulletin No. 1, June 1980, for further details).

Kept in these terraria, the lizards have only a short hibernation: they may remain active until the end of November, and may emerge again early in February, depending on the severity or mildness of the winter. After hibernation there is of course no copulation, but the females become more beautiful in colour: the green and the small blue spots intensify. Then eggs begin to develop, each female usually laying two clutches between the middle of May and the middle of June. When the eggs are kept at a temperature of 30°C the length of incubation is about 40 days; the young emerge from the beginning to the end of July. The juveniles have blue tails with small black spots. After only one month the blue colour disappears; if kept warm and fed well they reach maturity in about one year.

Like *Lacerta strigata* this is an interesting lizard which can be kept here in Western Europe without extra energy costs. In the next Bulletin I hope to be able to discuss another lizard with the same qualities. By the time this article appears I will be the happy owner of some 10 *Lacerta unisexualis,* one of the other parthenogenic species, received from friends in the Soviet Union. Perhaps after some years I will also be able to write about this species.

** These sections are translated from the Russian, taken from the book: "*The Amphibians and Reptiles of the Soviet Union*" by A.G. Bannikov, I.S. Darevsky, V.G. Ishchenko, A.K. Rustanov, N.N. Cherbak. Moscow 1977. This is an excellent book of over 400 pages, comprehensively describing 400 species and subspecies of the Soviet herpetofauna. The book contains many illustrations, mainly in colour, and 135 maps.

REFERENCES

Darevsky, I.S. (1967) Leningrad. *Rock Lizards of the Caucasus.*

Darevsky, I.S. and Danieljan, F.D. *Zoological Institute of the Soviet Union, Herpetological Collected Papers,* P. 55-59. *Lacerta uzzeli.*

Darevsky, I.S. and Danieljan, F.D. (1968). Diploid and Triploid Progeny arising from Natural Mating of Parthenogenic *Lacerta armeniaca* and *Lacerta unisexualis* with bisexual *Lacerta saxicola* Valentini. *Journel of Herpetology 2.*

Bischoff, W. (1975). Aquarien U. Terrarien. Echsen des Kaukasus, *Lacerta armeniaca.*

Basoglu, M. and Baram, I. Izmir (1977). *Reptiles of Turkey, Part 1, Turtles and Lizards.*

British Herpetological Society Bulletin No. 4. 1981

NOTES ON BREEDING LILFORD'S WALL LIZARD *(PODARCIS LILFORD)* IN CAPTIVITY

STEVE NORRIE

14 Newtonwood Road, Ashtead, Surrey

My first encounter with this stunning lizard was over 20 years ago. It was in a mixed collection of lacertids belonging to a school friend. The striking coal black and royal blue livery stood out amongst the usual green and brown of the other occupants. Not knowing, caring or being aware of the scientific name at the time, I and many others knew this beauty as the "Spanish Black".

A hardy ground dwelling lizard, it originates from the sparsely vegetated rocky islets around the coasts of Majorca and Minorca, Spanish Balearic Islands. Some forms of *lilfordi* are green or brown in colour, but most – and the more spectacular – are melanistic or partially melanistic.

Although not so large as some of its relatives, (its maximum length snout to vent is approximately 8cms) a fully grown male in full breeding trim is indeed an impressive sight. Raised up high on its forelegs, the deep blue throat puffed out to its maximum and the head cocked in the direction of a male adversary, it almost pins the subordinate into submission with its piercing stare. Only the slow side to side weaving of its tail (like a cat about to pounce on a mouse) gives a clue to the tension about to explode. It is this deep rooted territoriality that ensures that a mixed group of these lizards in spring and summer will rarely be at rest. Females also may be drawn into the day to day dramas.

Recently, space and time allowed me to re-live those early days spent engrossed in the antics of a vivarium full of lacertas, so I acquired a small group of "Spanish Blacks". It was early summer, so food from the garden was plentiful: worms, beetles, woodlice, caterpillars, flies, centipedes, moths, plus hosts of others were given in copious quantities. Fruits of various sorts were also given to them but apart from licking at the juice they did not seem too bothered. Growth was excellent. Males and females were obvious at a glance, the males being much heavier and generally larger in size. The tails grew very thick, almost seeming not to be in proportion to their bodies. The summer had now passed and there had been no signs of aggression.

Plate 1. Adult female *Podarcis lilfordi.*

Plate 2. Three *Podarcis lilfordi* of different ages, 6 weeks old, 12 weeks old and adult male.

During the winter the lights were turned off in the vivarium and the temperatures allowed to fall to 10°C. With the raising of spring temperatures came a raising of aggressive temperament, the dominant male keeping his rivals out of the limelight of the females.

Courting of the females by the males is a very rough and tumble affair, being merely a raising of the chest from the ground, expanding the throat, then a rapid chase. The female is usually gripped at the base of the tail or by a hind limb.

Mating attempts of this kind were seen on a number of occasions during April/ May but only once was it seen completed. The male grasped the female's rear right leg after the customary chase, then brought his left hind leg over the female's tail and curved his body to come into contact with the female and complete copulation.

It became obvious after a while from their shape that the females were carrying eggs, and on the 22nd May the sudden loss of weight of one was an obvious sign that she had laid the eggs somewhere in the vivarium. The eggs were carefully buried in a damp spot but close to the heat of the overhead light bulb (the vivarium had a layer of sand and soil which had been deliberately kept damp in anticipation of egg laying). The three eggs were removed and incubated in vermiculite at 24-27°C. This procedure was again followed for a second clutch of eggs laid in July.

On the morning of the 57th day the first inquisitive snout protruded into the world and within an hour had completely emerged and was running about. The hatchlings were quite unlike the adults, being brown with dark brown streaks and dots, the flanks tending towards cream. The tails were a greenish blue. The head seemed much more pointed and narrower than in the adults. Sloughing of their skins took place within the first 48-73 hours, and then the job of feeding began. In fact this was quite easy, due to their fairly large size of 3.2 cm snout to vent. Baby crickets, fruit fly, wax worm larvae, greenfly, etc., were all very eagerly accepted. As they increased in size they gradually began to darken in colour and by October they were dark brown, including the tail. Even at this small size they show signs of display similar to that described for the adults.

As a matter of interest, no "True-lite" has been used on either adults or young at anytime, neither has the use of vitamin D, been necessary to maintain them in peak health. It may be possible that this species of wall lizard has a lower requirement for direct ultra-violet radiation than other species but it is my belief that it is the varied and naturally acquired garden food that ensures good healthy specimens.

Pordacis lilfordi is now a protected species as defined by the Berne Convention1979, requiring a licence to remove it from its habitat. In addition, Spain is advising that licences in future will not be granted except in special circumstances, thus making it less available in the future than it has been in the past.

It would be a great shame if this fascinating and hardy little lizard were to become unavailable to herpetologists in this country. Who knows, it could spark an interest in reptiles to young or not so young as it did to me in my school days.

British Herpetological Society Bulletin No. 32. 1990

AN ACCOUNT OF THE BREEDING OF THE SPANISH GREEN LIZARD, *LACERTA SCHREIBERI*, IN CAPTIVITY, WITH NOTES ON REARING

BERNARD LEWIS

34 Victoria Road, St. Peters, Broadstairs, Kent CT10 2UG

INTRODUCTION

During September 1988 I was fortunate to purchase a pair of adult Spanish Green Lizards. Both were received in good condition, albeit with regenerated tails. Their size approximated those of the European Sand Lizard, *Lacerta agilis*. The colour plates shown in A. Salvador's book on the Iberian reptile and amphibian fauna, typifies the female; however the male does not present the black marbling on its dorsal surface, rather a sprinkling of irregular black spots. The male in my possession may well be rather old judging by the deep sulcations separating head shields. Both sexes exhibit the same green ground colouration.

HOUSING AND ENVIRONMENT

Accommodation is a vivarium constructed of 13mm contiboard measuring 75 x 45 x 75 cm. Lighting is supplied by 2 x 18 watt "True-lite" flourescent tubes. Heating is via a 40 watt spotlight, positioned at one end of the vivarium. Fluorescent unit and tubes are housed in a detachable hood of contiboard and 5 plywood. Joints are screwed and sealed with silicone sealant. Ventilation grills have been installed in the back and hood. As *L. schreiberi* shows a preference for moister environments than others of the "green lizard" group, a terrace effect has been incorporated. A strip of acrylic sheet 40 mm deep has been sealed diagonally in place, thereby dividing the floor area in two. The area furthest from the light source has a substrate composed of a mixture of peat, sand and potting compost, topped with a generous supply of bark chippings. This area is kept moist by regular spraying. Within this area a small specimen of the Weeping Fig, *Ficus benjamina,* offers cover and also permits climbing – this allows the inmates to get within 5 cm of the "True-lite" tubes. A similar substrate is used at the opposite end of the vivarium, which is kept moderately dry. Branches are supplied to give the opportunity of basking under the spotlight. Cork bark provides ground cover. Water is supplied ad libitum in a shallow dish.

The vivarium is accessed by two sliding glass doors, running in plastic tracking, raised 8 cm above the base by a contiboard plinth. The combination of heating and lighting provides a temperature gradient of 20 - 30 ^{0}C. For their first winter, temperatures were maintained within that range, on a 12 hr cycle. With lights and heating turned off during the hours of darkness, temperatures did not drop below 15^{0}C.

DIET

Throughout the winter months a basic diet of crickets, *Acheta domesticus,* and various mealworm species, all dusted with a vitamin/mineral supplement is provided. Additional items by way of spiders, moths and other invertebrates were offered when available; most were readily accepted. Occasionally a "pinkie mouse" was accepted, usually by the male. Although suitably sized locusts were offered they did not find favour.

MATING

Early observations indicated only limited gregarious or social behaviour; whilst no conflicts were observed, each avoided the other. Only rarely would both be seen at the same time. This may have been due to the rather small area available, inhibiting normal interactions. During the first week of May '89, the pair was observed mating early one evening. No further copulations were noted although both stayed in close proximity to one another for a further two weeks. By late May it was evident that the female was gravid.

EGG INCUBATION

On the 30th May '89 it was noted that the female had regained her slim shape. Searching through the substrate revealed 12 eggs in a healthy hydrated condition. They were carefully removed and the upper surface marked before transference to a previously prepared incubator, as described by Elke Zimmermann. Temperatures within the incubator were kept at $29^{0}C \pm 2^{0}C$, controlled by an aquarium heater/ thermostat. Humidity was maintained at 95%. At relocation egg size ranged from 9-11 mm x 7-8 mm.

HATCHING

According to Norrie and Langerwerf (1987), the incubation period ranges from 41-65 days, the longer incubation periods relating to indoor incubation and a seasonally abnormal egg laying period. Forearmed with this information I had anticipated an incubation period of 50 days, in view of a seasonally normal egglaying and a relatively high incubation temperature. At 40 days, to allow better observation of hatching, eggs were transferred to a smaller incubator at the same temperature but with reduced humidity (75%). Eggs ranged in size from 15-21 mm x 13-17 mm at 40 days.

EGG	1	Shell collapse at 42 days; 2 days later no sign of emergence, egg opened; fully developed dead foetus. No abnormality detected.
	2	Shell swelled excessively at 43 days, at 46 days shell collapsed, at 48 days egg opened; large fully developed dead foetus.
	3 4 5	Shell collapse at 51 days, no emergence; at 53 days eggs opened all three contained recently dead fully formed foetuses
	6 7 8	Commenced hatching 53 days post laying, both assisted from shell 6 hrs post pipping.
	9 10 11 12 13	Successful assisted hatch four healthy active young, 53 days post laying

After dead embryos were found on day 53 and to avoid the risk of further fatalities, I decided with some trepidation to open the remaining eggs. This assistance resulted in six healthy and active young. A possible cause for the poor natural hatch may have resulted from the environmental change initiated at 40 days. Reducing humidity at 40 days may have prevented emergence by interfering with shell pliability. No foetus alive or dead presented a large yolk sac, indicating hatching was imminent.

HATCHLINGS

The six survivors were housed in a vivarium measuring 60 x 15 x 20 cm. Access was gained via a detachable hood in which was housed an 18" "True-lite" tube. A 25 watt pigmy bulb supplied heat. At hatching the young ranged in size from 30-35 mm SVL, with a tail length of approximately 45mm. Within 48 hrs all six were feeding avidly on young crickets and, especially, spiders, mainly *Zygiella x-notata* and *Enaplognatha ovata.* As the days passed these were supplemented with a regular supply of the small Magpie Moth caterpillar, *Eurrhypara hortulata* found in abundance on Convolvulus, *Calystegia sepium.*

By the end of September '89 all six were progressing well. Sizes ranged from 60-65mm SVL, with a tail of approximately 125mm. The distinctive juvenile pattern has gradually given way to the adult patterning, i.e. bold reticulations on a grass green or olive green background or a ground colour of green, speckled with irregular dark spots. There are two males and four females.

Six weeks after hatching they were transferred to a 120 x 30 x 45cm vivarium planted with Ivy, *Hedera helix.* When young these lizards are especially attractive and striking with broken white or yellow vertical bars on flanks over an olive green-brown background. The tail has a yellowish tint which stands out boldly. Unlike the parents, these young are friendly, climbing on fingers and taking food from them. However, slow movements are required to prevent them from dashing off into the undergrowth.

FUTURE GENERATIONS

My intention was to prepare all for hibernation during December '89, as growth had been considerable, with plenty of fat as reserve. Measurements at this time were, for males 80-90mm SVL, and females 65-75mm, tail lengths ranged from 150-170 (including one regenerated).

As both males had shown signs of territoriality I decided to transfer the whole group to a more spacious vivarium measuring 90 x 60 x 90cm high. Both males were in breeding condition; even this larger vivarium failed to stop the territorial disputes, on the contrary, only adding fuel to their fire. One male sustained a bite wound to its neck, posterior to the parietal shields. To prevent further injury he was separated. Attention of the dominant male was drawn towards the females and copulation was observed with one female (mid January '90).

The male received in September '88 died for no apparent reason, (possibly old age), this left the original female which was accommodated with her offspring where she became more tolerant of disturbance – taking food from forceps. The young remained tame.

Adult colour patterns have now been established. Both males are very similar and reflect that seen in A. Salvador's book mentioned earlier in the text. Each of the females is different; the larger shows large bold reticulations on a leaf green background; another has smaller black markings on a similar green background; the third shows an apple green back with a few scattered black spots; the smallest of the group has small black blotches on a light brown background.

Late January 1990 it was noted that two of the females were gravid. On 1st February '90 a female laid 5 eggs in damp vermiculite placed inside a margarine carton with a $2cm^2$ hole cut into its side. Another laid 7 eggs on 9th February in the dampened substrate. Both clutches were transferred to fresh dampened vermiculite for incubation.

GROWTH AND DEVELOPMENT, A SUMMARY

Rapid maturation, from hatching to achieving adult status in just six months, reflects the abundance of food on offer. This fare, dusted with a multivitamin mix, together with "truelight" illumination has resulted in six robust and apparently healthy young adults. Such rapid and substained growth may not be desirable as it is not a natural phenomenon. In the wild, with hatching in May-June, such speedy development is unlikely. Certainly, in their natural habitat, six months would coincide with the hibernation, sexual activity not occurring until the following Spring at the earliest. Therefore a minimum of twelve months is likely to be the norm, before the next generation is conceived. The omission of a hibernation period made early maturation possible, as photoperiod, temperature and food intake was maintained without interruption. Hopefully this does not give rise to a shortened life span. To reduce that possibility hibernation will be arranged for late October 1990. Throughout captivity I have attempted to optimize their microhabitat to approximate, as far as is possible within the confines of an artificial environment, a natural setting. In so doing one reaps the benefits of an aesthetically pleasing vision. In addition, valuable insights are gained from uninhibited behaviour.

In order to minimize inbreeding depression and/or genetic defects as a result of sibling matings, I would be happy to hear from anyone in the UK whom may wish to exchange information and/or specimens of *L. schreiberi* for continued breeding success.

PRODUCTS MENTIONED IN TEXT

"True-lite" fluorescent tubes, Duro-Test International Corp., 700 Goodwin Avenue, Midland park, NJ. 07432 USA.
"Cricket Plus", Monkfield Nutrition, Cambridge, England.

REFERENCES

Salvador, A. (1985) *Guia De Camp De Los Anfibios Y Reptiles De La Peninsular Iberica, Islas Baleares Y Canarias.*

Zimmermann, E. (1986) *Breeding Terrarium Animals.* T.F.H.

Norrie, S. and Langerwerf, B. (1987) *Lacerta schreiberi* in Spain, Portugal and captivity. In *Proceedings Of The 1986 U.K. Herpetological Societies Symposium On Captive Breeding,* Edited by Coote, J. British Herpetological Society, London.

British Herpetological Society Bulletin No. 16. 1986

THE CARE AND BREEDING OF COMMON BRITISH REPTILES AND AMPHIBIANS – PART V, THE VIVIPAROUS LIZARD *(LACERTA VIVIPARA)*

DAVID R. BILLINGS

Red House Farm, Brakefield Green, Yaxham, East Dereham, Norfolk

INTRODUCTION

This attractive little lizard is the most widespread and abundant British reptile and can still be casually encountered in most areas of Britain. However, as with all our native herpetofauna, its status has declined drastically since the end of World War II and the decline is accelerating due mainly to urbanisation and environmental degradation brought about by more efficient farming methods.

DESCRIPTION, DISTRIBUTION AND HABITAT

The viviparous lizard attains an overall length of 15-16cm. There is little difference in size between the two sexes. The body is moderately slender, the head rather short and flat. The neck and tail are thick but relatively short; the legs also are comparatively short.

Colour and pattern is very variable, being greyish, greenish or reddish-brown on top, with the back slightly lighter in colour than the sides. There is usually a stripe along the back which is often incomplete. There are often a number of light streaks and sometimes scattered light or dark spots or ocelli (eye spots) usually better developed in males. The sides have a dark band and are fequently speckled with yellowish or black spots. The underside is yellow or greyish in females; in males it varies from golden-yellow to orange or even red, spotted with black. Young specimens are very dark, almost black with a bronze hue.

The viviparous lizard is very widespread, occurring in most parts of Europe including Arctic Scandinavia, northern Spain, north Italy, south Yugoslavia and Bulgaria. It also occurs through much of north Asia through to the Pacific Coast but is absent from the Mediterranean area. In Britain it is the only reptile to be found in Ireland.

It is essentially a ground-dwelling species although it will occasionally climb in vegetation. A humid environment is favoured. Typical haunts are among tussocks of grass or dense herbaceous plants. It can be found at altitudes of up to 3000 metres; in the south of its range it is mostly montane and confined to moist places, alpine meadows, banks of ditches, marshes and the edge of damp woods. Elsewhere it occurs in woodland glades, field margins, heaths, bogs, grasslands, sand-dunes, sea cliffs and man-made habitats such as hedge banks, disused quarries and the embankments of railways or motorways.

CARE IN CAPTIVITY

Accommodation

An aquarium tank or garden cold-frame can be used to house viviparous lizards outdoors but the former has many disadvantages as permanent accommodation for lizards. If left uncovered outdoors it will rapidly flood during prolonged rainfall and the inmates will also be at the mercy of predators such as cats or birds. If covered and left in the sun the interior may become intolerably hot with disastrous consequences. Problems will also arise during the winter when the lizards wish to hibernate. Unless the tank is insulated, has a good depth of soil on the base and can be kept in an unheated but frostproof building for the duration of winter it is most unlikely that they will survive.

By contrast a cold-frame makes an excellent home for small lacertids although the initial expense is rather high. An aluminium framed type can be assembled easily and has the advantage of putty-free dry joints. The smooth sides of glass and aluminium minimize the chance of escape.

The frame is best stood upon concrete blocks or breeze blocks which are first cemented onto a permanent foundation. The blocks are then rendered over with cement to seal any gaps around the base of the frame and to improve the finished appearance. After the cement has dried out completely, soil is filled to the level of the frame's base. A light sandy soil or peat/sand/loam mixture is ideal for drainage and to facilitate burrowing down for hibernation in the winter.

In my own cold-frame, measuring 120cm x 75cm x 60cm, I have arranged large pieces of bark as basking sites which are surrounded by clumps of heath grass, heather and dwarf heath plants to provide a suitable micro-habitat. I have included a small shallow pond 30cm x 25cm, x 15cm using an off-cut from a butyl pond liner. The sides are gently sloping and the grass has been allowed to trail into the water to lessen the risk of drowning should the lizards enter the water. The pond provides humidity and drinking water although small lizards prefer to lap the dew from grass blades.

The great advantage of a cold-frame is that the glass protects the lizards from chilling winds (which they detest) while allowing the entry of light. During summer the top of the frame can be opened or removed altogether and replaced with a sheet of wire mesh to keep out predators. This will allow the entry of sunlight thereby reducing or obviating the need for vitamin D_3 supplement.

Feeding

Mealworms, woodlice, crickets, earthworms and spiders will all be accepted readily. I also periodically tip in the results of hedge-beating or grass-sweeping to provide more variety. A further source of food is the slugs and non-hairy caterpillars which infest lettuce and cabbage plants.

Viviparous lizards quickly become confiding in captivity once they have familiarised themselves with the topography of their new surroundings. Mine soon came to associate my presence with an imminent meal, racing towards my outstretched hand to look for the mealworms I hand-fed them and to test my fingers for edibility!

They will allow themselves to be gently handled but this should not be attempted until they have become tame enough to clamber onto the arm without taking fright. If handled roughly or grabbed at suddenly they may well resort to shedding their tail. This is a defence mechanism designed to baffle predators by creating a diversion. The severed tail writhes and twists conspicuously while the former owner escapes unnoticed. A new tail eventually grows but never to the same length as the original one.

Vitamin D_3 powder can be given as a supplement, very sparingly dusted onto their food, but if the top of the frame is removed this is not really necessary. The same applies to calcium which can be given in the form of crushed eggshell or powdered cuttlefish bone.

BREEDING

This should take place automatically in the type of accommodation described above; mating occurs during April or May with the females becoming progressively stouter until one day in July or August 4-10 fully formed young are produced. The babies at birth measure between 37 and 47mm overall, being almost black in colouration. From the outset they are able to fend for themselves but because of their tiny size I always remove the gravid females to a smaller vivarium furnished in similar manner to the cold-frame where they can give birth unmolested by the males and small amphibians which share the cold-frame.

When the young have been born I return the mothers to the cold-frame in order to feed the young intensively so that rapid growth is attained before hibernation. At first they will accept aphids, fruit-flies and other similar sized inverterbrates. Later they can be given small mealworms, baby crickets and small caterpillars. I usually end up with more young lizards than I can cope with and the surplus ones are released along a railway cutting nearby which already supports colonies of viviparous lizards. I have experienced no success in releasing young or adult viviparous lizards in our garden or a small open copse, both of which appear suitable. I suspect they were preyed upon by marauding cats or magpies.

HIBERNATION

Towards the end of October, viviparous lizards will gradually lose interest in food even though outside temperatures may stil be quite high. Some time during November they will disappear, burrowing under the grass tussocks or under the pieces of bark to re-emerge in early or late March depending on the mildness or severity of the weather. Within a week or so of emergence the skin is sloughed and interest is shown in food again.

CONCLUSION

The viviparous lizard is a very hardy, lively and intelligent little creature which thrives in captivity, breeding regularly when given favourable conditions. It is undemanding in its requirements and will live in amity with other similar sized lizards or small amphibians, such as *Bombina variegata, B. orientalis* or *Alytes obstetricans.*

The next article will deal with our only other relatively common British lizard, the slow-worm or blind-worm *(Anguis fragilis).*

REFERENCES

Arnold, E.N. & Burton, J.A. (1978). *A Field Guide to the Reptiles and Amphibians of Britain and Europe.* Collins: London, pp. 137 & 138.

Cihar, J. (1979). *A Colour Guide to Familiar Amphibians & Reptiles.* Octopus Books, p.122.

Hellmich, lW. (1962). *Reptiles & Amphibians of Europe.* Blandford Press: London, pp. 106 & 107.

Langerwerf, B. (1980). The Caucasian Green Lizard (*Lacerta strigata*), Eichwald 1831, with notes on its reproduction in captivity, *B.H.S. Bulletin* **1:** 23-26.

Smith, M.A. (1951). *The British Amphibians & Reptiles.* Collins: London, pp. 196 & 197.

Snell, C.A. (1983). Favoured haunts of native reptiles. *B.H.S. Bulletin* **8:** 40-42.

A CAPTIVE BREEDING AND RELEASE PROGRAMME FOR SAND LIZARDS AND NATTERJACK TOADS AT MARWELL ZOOLOGICAL PARK: AN APPEAL FOR SPONSORSHIP

PAUL EDGAR, Sand Lizard/Natterjack Project Co-Ordinator

Marwell Zoological Park, Colden Common, Nr. Winchester, Hampshire, SO21 1JH, England.

THE DECLINE OF THE SAND LIZARD

The Sand Lizard (*Lacerta agilis*) in Britain is confined to mature dry heathland in the south plus a few coastal dune systems, including the most northerly population on Merseyside (Frazer, 1983; N.C.C., 1983). Lowland heath is an endangered habitat and much has been destroyed by housing and industrial development, roadbuilding, agricultural reclamation, the planting of conifers, military activity and mineral extraction (N.C.C., 1983; Tubbs, 1985; Webb, 1986). The remaining areas are now fragmented and far more vulnerable than the vast heaths of Thomas Hardy's day to fires, trampling, erosion, motorcycle scrambling and the spread of bracken, scrub and trees. These factors together with illegal collecting (mostly by small boys), predation by cats and the gassing of rabbit burrows, often used for hibernation, can all lead to local extinctions of Sand Lizards (Corbett, 1988a; Corbett & Tamarind, 1979; N.C.C., 1983).

AS A RESULT THERE HAS BEEN A 73% LOSS OF SAND LIZARD COLONIES IN RECENT YEARS. In Dorset the known colonies (concentrations of breeding adults) have been reduced from 169 to 24 over 15 years. All known breeding populations in the New Forest are extinct and only a handful survive in Surrey and on Merseyside. Dorset remains the stronghold of the Sand Lizard but heathland is still being destroyed at an alarming rate there (Edgar, 1988). Some experts estimate that less than 5000 adult Sand Lizards remained in Britain in 1987 (Corbett, 1988a) and this figure is undoubtedly lower today as the pressures on their habitat have continued.

THE DECLINE OF THE NATTERJACK TOAD

The Natterjack (*Bufo calamita*) is confined to heathland and coastal dunes and marshes (Beebee, 1983; Frazer, 1983; N.C.C., 1983; Smith, 1973). It was once widely distributed on many sandy coasts in the south, east and north-west of Britain and some 70 inland heaths, in East Anglia and southern England. Many of the reasons for the decline of the Sand Lizard also apply to the Natterjack and, in addition, this amphibian has been affected by pollution, drainage, acid rain and increased competition from Common Toad and Frogs as a result of habitat changes (Beebee, 1983; N.C.C., 1983).

Plate 1. Male Sand Lizard (*Lacerta agilis*).

Plate 2. Gravid female Sand Lizard (*Lacerta agilis*).

THE NATTERJACK TOAD HAS SUFFERED A VERY SEVERE DECLINE OF 95% IN LESS THAN 40 YEARS. It is now confined to about 30 coastal sites in north-west Britain and East Anglia and just 2 inland heath sites, 1 in Norfolk (where the colony is all but extinct) and 1 in Hampshire (N.C.C., 1983).

THE B.H.S./MARWELL PROJECT

BACKGROUND. The endangered status of the Sand Lizard and Natterjack Toad is recognized in their protection under the Wildlife and Countryside Act 1981. It is illegal to disturb, catch, kill, possess or sell any individual without an appropriate licence, issued by the Nature Conservancy Council. Their habitat is also afforded some protection under this Act, but in practice a loop-hole clause allows destruction or damaging actions which were "the incidental result of an otherwise lawful operation and could not reasonably have been avoided ". Consequently the granting of planning permission on a heathland site overrides the Wildlife and Countryside Act and, for example, legalizes the destruction of an entire Sand Lizard colony (Corbett, 1988b; Edgar, 1988).

The continuing loss of colonies of both species (especially the Sand Lizard), through destruction or lack of management, places them in a more and more precarious position in Britain. Even National Nature Reserves are not immune to severe fires (Moore, 1976) and each accidental, or otherwise, local extinction threatens the status of these animals in Britain still further. Spellerberg and House (1982) describe the rescue of a Sand Lizard colony on a burnt heath by moving the surviving animals to a large, on-site vivarium where they were safely housed until the habitat had suitably regenerated. After several years the lizards were released and successfully recolonized the heath (Spellerberg, 1988).

In many cases, however, Sand Lizards and Natterjacks have already disappeared from heaths which are now surrounded by unsuitable habitat. Amphibians and reptiles have very poor dispersal abilities and often the only way they can recolonize such heathland "islands" is to be physically taken there and released by man. This practice, called translocation, is a proven conservation technique (N.C.C., 1983), already employed by the B.H.S. Conservation Committee with good results. Several Sand Lizard colonies, in particular, have been established in this way and are thriving many years after the initial releases.

CAPTIVE BREEDING. Translocations require a number of animals for starting new colonies and these can sometimes be obtained from areas that are being destroyed for development. Such rescues (Edgar, 1988) should not have to be necessary at all for a protected species and are a very poor alternative to actually conserving such sites. Hopefully, and perhaps over optimistically, this source of animals for translocations will disappear if the government and local councils start to live up to their self-stated green images, and take their conservation responsibilities seriously. Whatever the origin of the animals, it makes sense to attempt to breed some in captivity, so that larger numbers are available for translocations on a regular basis. If successful, captive breeding removes the need to take animals from the wild once the initial breeding stock has been obtained.

The B.H.S. Conservation Committee has bred Sand Lizards and, to a lesser extent, Natterjack Toads for many years, under licence from the Nature Conservancy Council. Most vivaria are in members' back gardens, which limits their size and the number of animals that can be housed. In 1989 the B.H.S. Conservation Committee established two large, outdoor, heathland vivaria in the grounds of Marwell Zoological Park, near Winchester, to increase its output of captive bred Sand Lizards and Natterjack Toads (Edgar, 1988).

THE MARWELL VIVARIA. The Sand Lizard vivarium is 12 x 5 m, while the Natterjack enclosure measures 6 x 5 m. The original chalky soil was excavated to a depth of about one metre and the holes filled with some 50 tonnes of brick rubble, slates and drainage pipes (to facilitate drainage and provide hibernacula) and 90 tonnes of sand. The sand was obtained from a development site on Canford Heath, Dorset which was also the source of the heather used and some of the Sand Lizard breeding stock. The vivaria were then planted with some 300 heather plants. A third of these are mature plants, which were delivered with the sand, and the rest are young plants, regenerating after a fire, which were dug up by hand. Smaller heathers seem to survive relocation better, probably because their root systems can be kept more intact. Despite the move, and the 1989 drought, only about 20 plants appear to have died in the vivaria.

Ling, *Calluna vulgaris*, dominates the vivaria, as it did the donor site, but Bell Heather, *Erica cinerea*, Cross-Leaved Heath, *Erica tetralix*, Dwarf Gorse, *Ulex minor*, and various heathland grasses (*Molinia* and *Agrostis*), flowers, mosses and lichens are also well established. The Natterjack vivarium has large areas of open sand (preferred by this species), stablized with logs, and a site for installing a butyl liner each spring, to create a shallow, temporary pond. The Sand Lizards have extensive vegetation cover and a patch of bare sand for egg-laying. The site is on a sheltered, south-facing slope and the vivaria have been landscaped to provide a varied topography for the animals (see Plate 3). The vivaria walls are constructed of perspex sheeting and both enclosures are protected from birds by a large fruit cage. This also has additional rat and rabbit-proof wire mesh round its base. There is some scope at Marwell for the building of further vivaria, depending on the success of the project and sponsorship appeals.

BREEDING STOCK. Every effort has been made to create optimum surroundings for the animals, and since Marwell is well within the normal climatic range of both species in Britain, breeding occurs naturally. Sand Lizards both rescued and captive bred by the B.H.S. Conservation Committee are providing the original breeding stock. Breeding will commence this Spring and it is anticipated that the colony will consist of about 5 males and 25 females (2 males and 5 females were obtained in 1989). Assuming an average clutch per female of 8 eggs (from previous B.H.S. captive breeding work) then the Marwell vivaria should produce some 200 or more eggs each year, depending on the size and age of the females.

Some clutches will be left in situ, to incubate naturally, while others will be removed from the vivaria and incubated artifically to avoid the vagaries of the British weather. Since eggs do not require sunlight for their development, this is the only stage when anything will be done indoors as artificial lighting, however successfully lizards can be bred and reared under it, is not considered suitable for this project. Animals to be released into the wild need to be acclimatized as fully as possible in outdoor vivaria (the overall health and vigour of the parent lizards is also important) and there is simply no artificial substitute for natural sunlight.

The hatchling lizards will be reared in a separate heathland enclosure, within the main vivarium, so they attain a larger size and are better able to survive in the wild. As with current B.H.S. releases, some will be released in their first year (September) and the rest overwintered until their release the following Spring. The construction of the Marwell vivaria allows other B.H.S. Conservation Committee vivaria to concentrate on breeding, for example, the much rarer Surrey "race" of the Sand Lizard.

Natterjack toadlets were obtained in 1989 from a North East Surrey College of Technology/Sussex University project, looking at competition between anuran tadpoles. A limited number of eggs were removed, under licence, from the only natural Natterjack site in southern England for this project. Once they had metamorphosed, some tadpoles went to Marwell and the rest were used for a re-introduction in Surrey. The Marwell Natterjacks (16 in all) are being reared to breeding size, which should be attained in 1991 or 1992, because mature adult toads are just too rare to take from the wild.

The use of ephemeral water bodies by breeding Natterjacks negates the installation of a permanent pond in their vivarium. A shallow depression has been made and a butyl liner can be laid here and filled with water each Spring, once breeding commences. When breeding has ceased this liner can be removed to create a large patch of open sand again. Spawn strings, tadpoles or toadlets can all be used for translocations of Natterjacks. The mortality rate in the early stages of Natterjacks' lives is very high (Beebee, 1983; N.C.C., 1983) so as many tadpoles as possible will be reared outdoors through to metamorphosis and several months beyond. The excess spawn can be moved to translocation sites soon after it is laid. As long as enough food is provided, the rearing of Natterjacks is relatively easy and growth can be rapid (Jones, 1984). Survival can be greatly increased by rearing tadpoles and toadlets in the absence of predators. Some individuals, however, lack vigour, despite abundant food, and grow slowly, feed poorly and die at an early stage (pers. obs. and R.A. Griffiths, pers. comm.). This may be an artifact of intro-and/or interspecific competition in the tadpole stage, or be a genetic phenomenon.

RESEARCH. The rearing of "weak" individuals for release, i.e. those that are weeded out of a wild population by predation etc., is a criticism sometimes levelled at this type of project. Long-term monitoring of both Sand Lizards and Natterjacks at the release sites is therefore imperative. Conducted properly, such research will provide information about the survival rates and dispersal of captive bred animals, released at different ages, in varying numbers and on a variety of sites, as well as the overall success of translocation as a conservation tool. It is often difficult, costly and time consuming to achieve significant, worthwhile monitoring results in the field, and there are also numerous variables to be taken into consideration, but this is one aspect of the project that cannot be ignored.

In addition, research on the reproductive biology and behaviour of captive animals can be valuable, especially when they are housed in semi-natural conditions and the results are compared to those obtained in the wild. The B.H.S. Conservation Committee is experienced in the captive breeding of Sand Lizards, and members have already made many useful observations. Producing hatchlings of this species is relatively straightforward. Breeding Natterjack toads, however, has proved to be a more hit and miss affair (T.J.C. Beebee pers. comm.). Research is planned on their husbandry, reproduction and behaviour in captivity, with the aim of improving the breeding results for this species.

TRANSLOCATIONS. Sites for the release of captive Sand Lizards and Natterjacks have to be very carefully selected, meet several criteria, and then be approved by the Nature Conservancy Council. They should be fully protected and in areas where the species once existed. The habitat should be suitable, and properly managed, and it is essential to ensure that the factors contributing to the previous extinction are now absent. It is also important that the various local races of each species (e.g. Surrey and Dorset Sand Lizards or heathland and coastal dune Natterjacks) are maintained as discrete populations, and are not able to interbreed, either in vivaria or the wild. Agreed translocation policies (B.H.S. Conservation Committee, 1973; N.C.C., 1983) will be adhered to when Marwell bred animals are released.

Plate 3. The B.H.S. vivaria at Marwell Zoological Park. The Sand Lizard vivarium is shown and partially obscures the Natterjack enclosure in the background.

Plate 4. Mature heather (*Calluna vulgaris*) in the New Forest (for scale; the dog is sitting up). The burning of heather too frequently, so it cannot reach this stage, is suggested as one of the causes of the Sand Lizard's extinction in the New Forest. This practice is now more strictly controlled.

Plate 5. Heathland nature reserve in Dorset, with a south to southwesterly aspect, mature heather, few invasive trees or scrub, and an adjacent wet heath. An increasingly endangered habitat, often viewed as either wasteland or prime real estate.

Only one natural Natterjack colony has survived in southern England, but B.H.S. translocations are now re-establishing this species. Toads bred at Marwell in the future will be utilized for release in Surrey, and possibly Hampshire and Dorset if suitable sites can be identified. In the case of Sand Lizards, the Conservation Committee's work has already been very successful in the Weald. It is proposed that Marwell bred lizards be used to re-introduce this species to the New Forest. This is to be a joint venture, combining Sand Lizards from Marwell with those bred by the Forestry Commission at Holidays Hill Reptiliary, near Lyndhurst, and by Martin Noble, Head Keeper (New Forest South).

HEATHLAND MANAGEMENT. Maintaining the natural and complete life cycle of heather, and preventing scrub and woodland succession, is the object of present heathland management for these species. Both Natterjacks (Beebee, 1979) and Sand Lizards (Corbett & Tamarind, 1979) require the maturer stages of heather development (see Plate 4) where they occur on heathland. Although fire is an often used method of managing heathland (Webb, 1986), it tends to have disastrous consequences for these species, especially on isolated fragments of habitat. Sandy fire breaks therefore reduce the risk of a whole site going up in flames at once. As Sand Lizards require unshaded areas of bare sand for egg laying (Corbett & Tamarind, 1979; Strijbosch, 1987), firebreaks also act as an important habitat feature. Small patches of open sand, abundant before myxomatosis reduced the rabbit population, are also created for this purpose.

Plants which would ultimately shade and kill the heather, such as pine, birch, gorse and bracken, are removed from the best areas, leaving some for other wildlife to use. Succession in its early stages may increase the density of invertebrate prey, and have a sheltering effect, but must be brought under control by management before a release can occur. Overgrowth of heather by introduced pines, or other species, is detrimental to both Sand Lizards (Corbett & Tamarind, 1979) and Natterjacks (Beebee, 1977). In the latter case, not only do physical habitat changes adversely affect the Natterjacks, but may also favour Common Toads and lead to destructive competition. Before releasing Natterjacks onto a site with suitably managed terrestrial habitat, it may be necessary to create shallow ponds for breeding and monitor the water pH to ensure it is kept at a suitable level for the toads.

Some heathland owners are increasingly sympathetic towards these management techniques. The only Natterjack colony in southern England, for example, has survived because of the co-operation of the Ministry of Defence, which owns the site, and the local Council with conservationists. The Forestry Commission is now very supportive towards herp conservtion and is carrying out extensive management, in its New Forest enclosures, to prepare sites for Sand Lizard reintroductions. The attitude that heathland is waste ground is still widespread, however, and planning proposals have to be fought every step of the way, often unsuccessfully. Despite the fact that lowland heathland is extremely scarce on a world scale, and that Britain possess more than any other country, current British wildlife laws still do not give this internationally important habitat the type of protection needed to prevent further losses.

HEATHLAND PURCHASE. Captive breeding is merely an adjunct to habitat protection and management: there is not much point breeding a species if there is no habitat for it in the wild. The only sure way of safeguarding heathland sites is to purchase them. The B.H.S. Conservation Committee Land fund (Banks, 1987; Edgar, 1988) was established to buy and lease areas of heathland as rare herp. reserves. Such reserves secure heathland against future development and benefit the full variety of plants and animals that depend on this important habitat for their survival. Sponsorship in excess of the Marwell project's requirements, estimated at £3-4000 per annum, will be donated to the Land fund at the end of each year. Marwell Zoological Park already has an outstanding record for the captive breeding of foreign animals, and their return to the wild, and was very keen to help the Conservation Committee's work on two endangered British species and their habitat.

EDUCATION. Few members of the public have much sympathy for, or knowledge of, amphibians and reptiles so education is very important in their conservation. Marwell Zoological Park has over 250,000 visitors a year, and generates a lot of media coverage, and makes an excellent venue for publicizing the Conservation Committee's efforts on behalf of rare herps and heathlands. The main vivaria are off-exhibit (except to sponsors), to avoid disturbance from so many visitors, but a display about the project is on view to the public. It is hoped that a walled vivarium will be built in the future to house some of the captive bred Sand Lizards for public view. The Education Department at Marwell is very involved in the project, and has prepared lectures for visiting schools about British amphibians and reptiles and their conservation. The author has also visited several schools to talk about the project, which has resulted in a variety of fund-raising efforts organized by the children themselves. Finally, the Marwell Oryx Club (the junior version of the Marwell Zoological Society), which has over 400 members, raised most of the money to pay for the vivaria and provided several volunteers to help with their construction.

SPONSORSHIP. The Sand Lizard and Natterjack project at Marwell is funded entirely by sponsorship and is independent of the zoo's other activities (because it is off-exhibit). The B.H.S. Conservation Committee and Marwell Preservation Trust are only able to afford limited financial support, as this is just one of many activities with which both are concerned. To ensure that the work continues, the rest of the money needed must be obtained from members of the public, trusts, businesses, councils, and schools. Money is required for general running costs (enclosures maintenance, food bills, incubators and so on), expenses for those working on the project, research equipment, education, publicity, administration and monitoring of released animals.

If you would like to help support this B.H.S. project, donations of any size will be most welcome. The Marwell Preservation Trust Ltd. (M.P.T. Ltd.) is a Registered Charity, No. 275433, so please indicate if you would like a deed of convenant form.

Please make cheques payable to **"M.P.T. Ltd., British Herpetofauna Fund".**

All sponsors receive regular information about the progress of the project. Remember that only sponsors are able to see the vivaria at Marwell, a good chance to see and photograph Sand Lizards and Natterjacks in a semi-natural setting. You should indicate if you would like to attend a lecture about the project and view the breeding facilities in the warmer months. It is important to give prior notice of your visit so that the author or another Conservation Committee member can arrange to meet you. Financial constraints mean that you must pay the normal entrance fee when visiting Marwell to see the vivaria, although the rest of the zoo makes a good day out. However, those donating a minimum of £25 will be sent complimentary tickets, which allow you to enter Marwell free of charge. This does not include a car but there is a large, free car park at the entrance gate. Sponsors will also receive an acknowledgement in the public display, in the Marwell Zoo News and in updates in this Bulletin. commemorative plaques, publicity and P.R. advice can also be arranged for companies or others interested.

ACKNOWLEDGEMENTS

The total sponsorship received, to February 1990, for this project has been just under £4600 (now all spent). Several companies also supplied materials for vivaria construction at a considerable discount. Grateful thanks are therefore due to the following:- Agriframes Ltd., Ark Aid, D. & M. Ashe, C. Ashton, Association for the Study of Reptilia and Amphibia, C. Beadle & Family, B.H.S. Conservation Committee, Bournemouth School, R. Buckland, D. Chapman, A. Clark, J. Compton, S. Curry, East Hampshire District Council, R. Eaton, A. Foden, B. Ford, Formerton Ltd., Mr. & Mrs. J. Foulston, Freemantle First School, Friends of Poole Aquarium, C. Gardiner, W. George, R. Grimond, Horndean Parish Council, W. Jupe, Liphook Junior School, A. Lloyd, H. MacKenzie, Marwell Oryx Club, Marwell Preservation Trust Ltd., Metwood (of Fareham) Ltd., M. Miller, D. Ormond, Petersfield Post, K. Pickard-Smith, Pink & Son Ltd., K. & I. Randall, J. Sanidson, P. Thorpe, W. Urry, Vauntberry Ltd. and C. Weatherby.

REFERENCES

Banks, B. (1987). Conservation Committee Land Fund. *B.H.S. Bulletin* **20:** 12.

Beebee, T.J.C. (1977). Environmental change as a cause of natterjack toad *(Bufo calamita)* declines in Britain. *Biol. Conserv.* **11:** 87-102.

Beebee, T.J.C. (1979). A view of scientific information pertaining to the natterjack toad *(Bufo calamita)* throughout its geographical range. *Biol. Conserv.* **16:** 107-134.

Beebee, T.J.C. (1983). *The Natterjack Toad.* Oxford University Press, 159 pp.

B.H.S. Conservation Committee (1973). Herpetological translocations in Britain – a policy. *Brit. J. Herpetol.* **6:** 314-316.

Corbett, K.F. (1988a). Distribution and status of the sand lizard, *Lacerta agilis agilis,* in Britain. pp. 92-100 in Glandt, D. & Bischoff, W. (1988). Biologie und Schutz der Zauneidechse *(Lacerta agilis). Mertensiella* **1:** 1-257.

Corbett, K.F. (1988b). Conservation strategy for the sand lizard *(Lacerta agilis agilis)* in Britain. pp. 101-109 in Glandt, D. & Bischoff, W. (1988). Biologie und Schutz der Zauneidechse *(Lacerta agilis). Mertensiella* **1:** 1-257.

Corbett, K.F. & Tamarind, D.L. (1979). Conservation of the sand lizard, *Lacerta agilis,* by habitat management. *Brit. J. Herpetol.* **5:** 799-823.

Edgar, P.W. (1988). Conservation matters: a review of herp conservation issues in the news during the period July to November 1988. *B.H.S. Bulletin* **26:** 32-35.

Frazer, J.F.D. (1983). *Reptiles and Amphibians in Britain.* Collins, 256 pp.

Jones, M. (1984). Captive rearing and breeding of Norfolk natterjacks. *B.H.S. Bulletin* **10:** 43-45.

Moore, P.D. (1976). Fire on heathland. *Nature* **264:** 112-113.

N.C.C. (1983). The ecology and conservation of amphibian and reptile species endangered in Britain. Wildlife Advisory Branch, Nature Conservancy Council, London, 93 pp.

Smith, M. (1973). *The British Amphibians and Reptiles.* 5th ed. Collins, 322 pp.

Spellerberg, I.F. (1988). Ecology and management of *Lacerta agilis* L. populations in England. pp. 113-121 in Glandt, D. & Bischoff, W. (1988). Biologie und Schutz der Zauneidechse. *Mertensiella* **1:** 1-257.

Spellerberg, I.F. & House, S.M. (1982). Relocation of the lizard *Lacerta agilis:* an exercise in conservation. *Brit. J. Herpetol.* **6:** 245-248.

Strijbosch, H. (1987). Nest site selection of *Lacerta agilis* in the Netherlands. Proceedings of the 4th A.G.M. of the Societas Europaea Herpetologica, Nijmegen: 375-378.

Tubbs, C. (1985). The decline and present status of the English lowland heaths and their vertebrates. Focus on Nature Conservation No. 11, Interpretive Branch, Nature Conservancy Council, Peterborough, 20 pp.

Webb, N.R. (1986). *Heathlands.* Collins, 223 pp.

THE CARE AND BREEDING OF COMMON BRITISH REPTILES AND AMPHIBIANS
PART VI – THE SLOW WORM *(ANGUIS FRAGILIS)*

DAVID BILLINGS

Redhouse Farm, Brakefield Green, Yaxham, East Dereham, Norfolk, NR19 1SB

INTRODUCTION

The Slow Worm *(Anguis fragilis)* is also known as the blindworm, but both these applications are inappropriate for this species is neither slow in its movements, blind or even poor-sighted. It can move through long grass or burrow into light soil with surprising speed and is keen-sighted enough to spot intended prey or potential predators from several feet away.

It is rather secretive by nature, being often overlooked in areas where it is reasonably plentiful. Perhaps this is fortuitous for the slow worm as it is still occasionally killed when encountered in the mistaken belief that is it a venomous snake. Although it is in fact a limbless lizard it does superficially resemble a serpent, an attribute which has been the main reason for widespread persecution in the past.

Wood (1865) informs us that "according to popular notions, the blindworm is a terribly poisonous creature, and by many persons is thought to be even more venomous than the viper whereas it is perfectly harmless, having neither the will nor the ability to bite, its temper being as quite as its movements, and its teeth as innocuous as its jaws are weak. The origin of this opinion may be found in the habit of constantly thrusting out its broad, black, flat tongue with its slightly forked tip: for the popular mind considers the tongue to be the sting, imagining it to be both the source of the venom, and the weapon by which it is injected into the body and so logically classes all creatures with forked tongues under the common denomination of poisonous".

More than 120 years on, there are, unfortunately, some who still subscribe to these beliefs. Anyone examining a slow worm carefully would note that its movements are altogether stiffer, less supple than a snake and that it possesses eyelids which snakes do not.

DESCRIPTION, DISTRIBUTION AND HABITAT

Slow worms average 40-45cm in overall length when fully grown although some specimens may attain 50cm. Adult males are fairly uniform in colour above and on the sides; brown, grey, reddish or coppery, occasionally with blue spots. The underside is usually greyish with dark grey or black mottlings.

Females frequently have a dark brown or black vertebral stripe; the sides are dark and often flecked or striped dark brown or black. The underside is usually black. Males have larger heads than females. In both sexes the scales are very smooth, the individual scales quite small in size.

The range of the slow worm is extensive, almost the whole of Europe with the exception of south Iberia, Ireland and north Scandinavia. It is also found eastwards as far as the Ural Mountains, in south-west Asia and north-west Africa. It is fairly widespread in the U.K., being most numerous in the south and south-west of England. In north and east England it is less plentiful and in many parts of Scotland local.

The slow worm likes well vegetated areas with good ground cover. It favours a range of habitats: heaths, common, hedgerows, pastures, open woodlands, gardens, scrub-land and railway embankments. It may occasionally be found basking in the sun especially during spring, but is more likely to be discovered under sun-warmed objects such as flat stones or sheets of discarded iron. It can also be found under piles of rubble or scree, in dry stone walls and even among the crumbling and fallen gravestones in churchyards.

In late summer gravid females can be observed basking in the open; this assists incubation of the developing eggs inside her body.

CARE IN CAPTIVITY

Accommodation

Slow worms can be kept successfully outdoors in a walled enclosure or under glass in a greenhouse or cold-frame. If the former mode is used, a good layer of soft soil must be provided to a depth of at least 50cm to enable the slow worms to burrow down a sufficient depth to escape winter frosts. The enclosure should be covered with netting to prevent predation by cats or large brids.

If a greenhouse is used it must be well ventilated as slow worms do not like excessive heat. A cold frame is probably the best form of outdoor housing; it can be set up and maintained in exactly the same way as I described for keeping viviparous lizards in my previous article.

Slow worms enjoy burrowing in soft soil, spending much time with just their heads protruding; in captivity they will quickly make a network of underground tunnels. Within a short space of time they will become confiding enough to allow gentle handling, weaving themselves around the fingers to gain anchorage.

By contrast a wild slow worm when first caught will thresh wildly about, quite often voiding the contents of its cloaca. Males will sometimes extrude their penes. The tail will be readily shed (the specific name, "*fragilis*" refers to this propensity). It regenerates but as little more than a stump.

Feeding

The slow worm is inordinately fond of slugs, particularly the small, greyish-pink garden slug, *Agrolimax agrestis.* When this species is in plentiful supply all other prey is likely to be ignored. Other types of slug will be eaten when *A. agrestis* is not available and earthworms, leatherjackets (crane-fly larvae), maggots, spiders and small snails will also be taken but usually with little relish. I have found that some specimens will eat mealworms while others will refuse them completely.

Slugs or earthworms offered can be occasionally dusted sparingly with multi-vitamin powder to provide all the necessary nutritional requirements.

Periodically during the year food will be refused; in a healthy slow worm this is a sure sign it is about to slough its skin. After this has occurred feeding will recommence.

BREEDING

This is not difficult even in a fairly small vivarium; mating takes place during late April, May or June. Males will fight during this time and can inflict serious injuries upon each other in confinement, so it is best to keep one male with several females or at least segregate the males during mating time.

When the females become noticeably gravid it is advisable to remove them to a nursery vivarium, smaller than the main accommodation but furnished in a similar way. They can then give birth unmolested by the males after which they can be returned to their permanent quarters leaving the young in a safe environment.

The slow worm is ovo-viviparous, giving birth to an average litter of 6-12 young in late August, September or early October depending on the warmth or coolness of the summer. The young are born in a protective membrane which they rupture and escape from either at birth or a few minutes afterwards.

They measure 65-90mm in overall length; the dorsal colouring is quite variable, pale golden brown or light yellowish, greenish or silvery. The sides of the head and body and the undersides are jet black. There is a small black parietal spot just behind the eyes which is continued as a stripe down the middle of the back to the tip of the tail.

New born slow worms are very lively little creatures which appear to enjoy burrowing into soft soil even more than the adults. I have experienced difficulty in rearing them in captivity because I can never seem to find enough tiny slugs and earthworms. However, I have partially overcome this problem by introducing a handful of garden compost into their vivarium every day. This provides many small invertebrates for the baby slow worms as well as providing an excellent flooring medium which retains a certain amount of heat. This is beneficial to the baby slow worms which love to burrow into this warmth, there to remain for long periods.

Fruit flies, whiteworms, baby mealworms and hatchling crickets were all ignored by my baby slow worms but small spiders and caterpillars captured by grass-sweeping were accepted, albeit rather reluctantly. The same slug, *Agrolimax agrestis* was as much relished as it was by the adults.

I never try to raise more than 3 or 4 young at a time; the remainder are released on a nearby railway embankment.

HIBERNATION

During the latter part of October, activity will slow down and the slow worms will cease feeding. They will shortly disappear from view burrowing into the soil for the duration of the winter often using a communal hibernaculum as they do in the wild.

They will re-appear the following year about mid-March; actual dates will, of course, vary with temperatures outside. It may well be a week or two after emergence before they start feeding. Water for drinking is very important at this time of year.

CONCLUSION

The slow worm is an interesting and unusual lizard which will live happily for many years in captivity, breeding readily if the correct conditions are provided. Young slow worms are comparatively difficult to rear in confinement unless enough tiny slugs or very small earthworms can be provided. It is therefore not advisable to attempt raising more than a small number at once. Slow worms can be safely housed with viviparous lizards, wall lizards and small amphibians such as *Bombina variegata* .

All our native herptiles are under threat due to the rapid changes taking place in their environment by man's activities. The situation is likely to become far worse in future years as increasing pressures are exerted on the resources of our small and very overcrowded island.

Responsible herptile keeping, where surplus offspring are used to boost existing wild colonies or to pioneer new ones can go a long way to ensure the continued survival of our indigenous herptiles for future generations to see.

FOOTNOTE

I have not included the adder *(Vipera berus)* in the series of articles although it is our most widespread British snake. Its care in captivity is realistically beyond the scope of the average herpetologist and best left to zoological institutions or specialist breeders.

Jones (1985) adequately described the stringent legal requirements for keeping this species in captivity, which I feel sure is enough to deter all but the most determined individual.

The Grass snake *(Natrix natrix helvetica)* is rather more difficult to maintain in captivity than any of our common amphibians or lizards. It is also under intense pressure in the wild due mainly to changes in land usage. However, to complete the series an additional article on keeping grass snakes with the emphasis on conservation will appear in the *"Bulletin"* soon. I am indebted to Marcus Langford of the BHS Conservation Committee who has agreed to co-write this article with me.

REFERENCES

Arnold, E.N. & Burton, J.A. (1978). *A Field Guide to the Reptiles and Amphibians of Britain & Europe.* Collins, London. p. 175.

Billings, D.R. (1986). The care and breeding of common British reptiles and amphibians – Part V, the Viviparous Lizard *(Lacerta vivipara) British Herpetological Society Bulletin* **16:** 30-32.

Gilpin, H.G.B. (1966). Breeding Slow Worms in confinement. *The Aquarist and Pondkeeper,* Vol. XXXI, No. 9.

Jones, M. (1985). Some effects of the Dangerous Wild Animals Act, 1976, with regard to the British Adder *(Vipera berus)* in captivity. *British Herpetological Society Bulletin* **11:** 36-38.

Smith, M.A. (1951). *The British Reptiles and Amphibians.* Collins, London. pp. 171-182.

Wood, J.G. (1865). *The Illustrated Natural History Vol. III.* George Routledge & Sons. London. p. 62.

British Herpetological Society Bulletin No. 3. 1981

AGAMA STELLIO, WITH OBSERVATIONS ON ITS CARE AND BREEDING IN CAPTIVITY

BERT LANGERWERF

**Agama International, Rt2, Box 285, Montevallo, Alabama 35115, USA*

INTRODUCTION

The genus *Agama* is usually regarded as being very difficult to keep alive in captivity. This is probably because the species which are usually kept are the tropical African species, such as *Agama agama*, which are delicate. However, there is a group within this genus which is more hardy and much easier to keep; one could call this the *stellio* group, consisting of the following species:

*Present address: this study was carried out in the Netherlands

Agama stellio from Turkey, Syria, Israel, Egypt and some of the Greek Islands.

Agama caucasia from the Caucasus and the mountains of N. Persia and Afghanistan.

Agama himalayana from the mountains of the Himalayas, southern Tibet, northern India, eastern Afghanistan.

Agama erythrogastra from N.E. Persia, N. Afghanistan and S. Turkmenia.

Agama lehmanni from the mountains of S.E. Turkmenia, E. Uzbekistan and S.W. Tadzjikistan.

These five species have several characteristics in common, such as their rough, ringed tails and their ability to survive hibernation in cold climates: all of them, except *Agama stellio*, experience winters more severe than those of Western Europe.

I have kept *Agama stellio, Agama lehmanni* and *Agama caucasia* for several years in outdoor enclosures, and have bred them all.

DESCRIPTION OF *AGAMA STELLIO*

Agama stellio is a rather large lizard with a total length of up to 35 cm. The back, legs and tail are covered with spiny scales. The scales on the tail are arranged in rings. The body is rather flattened in appearance, but less so than in *Agama caucasia* and *Agama himalayana*. The males are easily distinguished by a longitudinal band of distinctly large scales along the belly; they also have larger anal scales than females.

The background colour is grey, varying from clear grey to almost black individuals. Males are often predominantly black, and may have blue spots on the head and body. Examples from western Turkey often have extensive blue spots, and are particularly beautiful. On individuals with a grey colouration there are black and white dots, and the throat has a reticulated pattern. The belly is greyish-white. Young individuals have clear black spots behind the head and 4-5 vertebral spots. Along the tail are about 6-8 smaller white vertebral spots or white rings.

Agama stellio brachydactgyla from southern Israel and Sinai is more yellow or orange in colour and has shorter digits.

AGAMA STELLIO IN CAPTIVITY

I keep this lizard in different types of terraria, but mostly glass-covered ones. Also, in the summer, I keep some individuals in my large open air enclosure of $600m^2$. Some of them are left in the enclosure over the winter. This year, the first *Agama* emerged from hibernation on 8 March, having survived without difficulty the mild winter of 1980-81. In this enclosure there is a south-facing slope with large basalt stones, beneath which roofing tiles penetrate up to 1.5m into the ground. It is here that the animals retreat to during frost periods.

Plate 1. Adult male *Agama stellio.*

Although the Agamas are beautiful to watch in the big enclosure, jumping from rock to rock, catching flies and butterflies in flight, climbing the tall ruin I built there, I really do have most success in a warmer terrarium. This is a terrarium of 4m x 4m. It has a rear wall built of bricks in an East-West direction; on the other northern side of the wall earth is piled about a metre high; the southern inner side is painted black to absorb the heat of the sun. The terrarium ($16m^2$) is covered by glass sloping down to the south.

From April to September only 10% is covered. Inside the terrarium is a slope to the south with numerous rocks, stones and logs. As in the larger enclosure, there are refuges made of roofing tiles entering the ground to afford protection from extreme heat and cold. In summer, the temperature can rise above 40°C, and in winter it can freeze. During very cold weather I cover the glass with such things as old carpets. In the autumn I spread some large plastic bags of dead leaves over and between the rocks and logs inside the terrarium which reproduces more natural conditions, gives added protection against frost, and offers warm basking sites in the early spring. Towards the end of January each year I plant one or two large curly Kale plants in the terrarium. These plants grow there and the Agamas like to eat the leaves and flowers through the spring and summer. It is a very easy way to feed them! The Agamas also eat crickets, and as I put quite large numbers of crickets in the terrarium each week, those which are not eaten immediately by the lizards can feed on the Kale plants; it is better for the lizards that they eat insects which have their stomachs full of plant material, as they do in nature.

In this terrarium the lizards may be active during any month of the year in sunny weather, but they usually remain dormant for a period of about two months from mid-December to mid-February. This past winter (1980-81) was not very cold, but it was long, and the first *Agama stellio* did not appear until 8 March, when the outside air temperature was 12°C, during a sunny interval of a quarter of an hour after rain. In 1980 the first *Agama stellio* appeared on the 9th February at an air temperature of 12°C in sunny weather.

In this terrarium, the *Agama stellio* have bred every year since 1973. Mating takes place in spring. I once observed copulation on 16th February, but usually it takes place in April-May. The eggs are laid in June and July. A female lays two, sometimes three clutches of eggs per season. These are normally 10-15 eggs in a clutch. I incubate the eggs in moist (not wet!) sand at 29-30°C; they hatch after 50 days.

As mentioned in my earlier articles, the Agamas must be given extra vitamin D3 and calcium. Fortunately, some calcium is also obtained from the Kale.

Plate 2. Newly hatched *Agama stellio.*

Rearing the Young

In past years I kept the young *Agama stellio* warm and active through the winter, but as there were many lizards and heating costs are high in winter, I was forced to keep the lizards in rather high densities. This had no, or almost no, bad results with *Lacerta sp.,* but in *Agama sp.* it resulted in a sudden cessation of growth, usually in January; the lizards would then grow thin and show a deposit of white uric-acid under the tail. The Agamas then suffered from parasites – flagellates – which could be successfully treated with a solution of 250mg of Emtryl (Dimetridazole 40%) per litre of drinking water for a period of 8 days. The problem would recur after one or two months.

It was clear that the flagellates were mostly a result of stress in the overcrowded terrarium: in summer the illness, in still rather young Agamas (10 months old) could often be cured without Emtryl simply by releasing them in the large enclosure of 600m^2. For the past two winters I have let my young Agamas, born before the beginning of September, hibernate in the garden terraria, and in this way avoided the stress problem. The young lizards eat all kinds of small insects, such as small caterpillars, flies, cockroaches and crickets, and also the small leaves of several kinds of plants.

SOME PROBLEMS IN KEEPING AGAMAS

I first found that I could keep this species in a terrarium on 2m^2, but only one pair. In a larger terrarium of 16m^2 I was able to keep a maximum of 1 male and 3 females only.

If more individuals are kept together, they are no longer able to live in their own territory, creating stress which results in illnesses.

The larger *Lacerta* sp. and *Gerrhonotus multicarinatus*, however, do not disturb the Agamas. Three females in a terrarium of this size is an absolute maximum, particularly during the egg-laying season, as the females always fight with one another in defence of egg-laying sites.

A very serious problem in keeping Agamas can be outbreaks of parasitic nematode worms in the intestines. To avoid this, I inject the Agamas with a dose of 10 mg per kilogram body weight of Ripercol (Tetramisole).

CONCLUSION

Agama stellio is a lizard which should be kept in a rather large terrarium in a sunny place in the garden. The terrarium does not need to be heated: it is only necessary to create a favourable micro-climate. They will not cause trouble, and give the terrarium keeper much fun: they jump from one high point to another, and will nod their heads constantly. Though exotic in appearance, they can be kept outside throughout the year. It can also be kept together with several non-agamid lizards such as *Lacerta strigata, Lacerta lepida, Lacerta viridis, Lacerta trilineata* and *Gerrhonotus multicarinatus.* Adult *Agama stellio* occasionally eat small lizards of the size of *Lacerta muralis.*

REFERENCES

Barash, A. and J.H. Hoofien, (1956). *Reptiles of Israel.*

Khaluf, K.T. (1959). *Reptiles of Iraq, with some notes on the Amphibians.* Baghdad.

Langerwerf, B. (1977). De Hardoen, *Agama stellio*, in hot terrarium. *Lacerta* 35, no. 6, pp. 84-86.

Marx, H. (1968). *Checklist of the Reptiles and Amphibians of Egypt.* Cairo.

Zwart, P. (1973). Ziekten van Reptilien V: infectgieziekten. *Lacerta* XXX17, pp. 116-117.

British Herpetological Society Bulletin No. 7. 1983

THE CARE AND BREEDING OF *SAUROMALUS OBESUS OBESUS* IN CAPTIVITY

BILL CROOKS

1B Clova Road, Forest Gate, London, E7 9AQ

INTRODUCTION

The Chuckwalla is a large herbivorous lizard from the desert regions of Mexico and south-west U.S. where water is scarce and temperatures extreme. They are very territorial and a given territory would contain a dominant male, adult females, subordinate males and juveniles. Its breeding habits are largely unknown and there are few recorded cases of it having bred in captivity.

A pair of sub-adults were acquired in 1980 in order to attempt captive reproduction.

DESCRIPTION

Adult males are of larger build than females, with broader heads and heavier jowls. The tail is thicker and shorter than in females of similar snout-vent length. Females tend to have lighter colouration and often show faint crossbands across the back. Males are normally darker, especially around the head and often have speckles of red on the flanks.

The colouration may vary from light grey to black giving it a drab appearance but this blends in well with the habitat in which they are found.

Maximum SV lengths are around 220mm in males and 205mm in females.

When acquired the male measured 155mm SV and the female 150mm and had probably just reached sexual maturity (Berry, 1974).

HOUSING

The Chuckwallas were housed in a 75 x 37 x 37cm vivarium which was illuminated by 3 Trulite tubes situated 35cm above the surface. These were controlled to give a daylight period which ranged from 14.5 hrs in the summer to 10 hrs in the winter. In addition, a spotlight was situated in one corner above a basking rock and was switched on for 6 hrs each day.

The floor was covered with a layer of sand about 5cm deep and numerous rocks were provided for cover. Supplementary heating was provided by an underfloor heater if required. A nominal day-time temperature of 28°C in winter and 36°C summer was maintained but this was allowed to rise several degrees while the spotlight was on. At night heating was only used if the temperature dropped below 18°C.

The Chuckwallas were fed mainly on a vegetarian diet. The main foods being peas, green beans, Brussels sprouts and lettuce. This was supplemented from time to time with broken grapes, sweet corn, bananas, grated carrot, mealworms and rice. Vionate was added to the food 3 times a week.

Both animals were healthy when acquired except for nematode infestation. This was cured in each case by a single dose of Fenbendazole (Panacur, Hoechst Pharmaceuticals) at a dose rate of 200mg/kg.

Chuckwallas derive their moisture from the food they eat and do not require a water bowl. Because of this they can rapidly deteriorate if they do not eat for sustained periods.

As with all animals deprived of natural sunlight, a well-balanced diet supplemented with multivitamins, especially vitamin D_3, and calcium is essential. Trulite is also beneficial due to its ultra-violet element promoting vitamin D synthesis in the skin, which helps the body absorb the calcium needed to sustain sturdy bone growth and for egg production during gestation.

BREEDING

During early April 1982 there was a marked increase in courtship activity culminating with mating on the 20th. Courtship display was typical of iguanids with much head-bobbing. Egglaying was expected about midday and trays of damp sand and vermiculite were placed in the vivarium but ignored. By the beginning of June the female began to look very heavy with eggs but still showed no sign of looking for a suitable laying place. On June 9th food was offered, as normal, in a 19cm plastic bowl. This was commandeered by the female who emptied it of food and sat inside. She began head-bobbing which the male seemed to take as his cue to disappear and so retreated under cover. After about an hour she began to lay her eggs. The first five were laid in the bowl and the next five on a wooden platform next to the bowl. The period between each egg laid varied from 3-37 minutes. Three of the eggs were very soft and she tried to eat one of these but it was removed before the shell was broken.

At no time did the female make any attempt to cover or conceal the eggs and once laid she showed very little interest in them. After all the eggs had been laid the female attempted to gain access to the cover where the male was. Each attempt was met with an attack by the male which drove her off. She eventually spent the night out in the open, something she had never done before.

The eggs were removed and placed in an incubator at 32°C on damp vermiculite and covered to a depth of 2cm to allow moisture absorption. The following day the top covering of vermiculite was removed. The eggs measured approx. 35mm x 20mm and weighed 10g, there was no noticeable increase in size during development.

During incubation seven eggs were lost, these were probably infertile.

After 67 days the first egg hatched and movement could be seen inside the remaining two. The hatchling took 15 hours to completely emerge from the shell by which time movement had ceased in the others. The following morning the remaining eggs were opened to reveal two fully formed dead embryos. There was no apparent reason why they had failed to break out of their shells.

SUMMARY OF BREEDING DATA

Mating – 20th April
Egglaying – 9th June
Gestation – 50 days
Hatching – 15th August
Incubation Period – 67 days
Incubating Temperature – 32°C
Eggs Laid – 10
Fertile/Developed – 3
Hatched – 1

CARE OF THE YOUNG

At birth the hatchling measured 100mm total length (53mm SV) and was extremely active, managing to escape on the third day and remaining at large for 20 hours despite an extensive search. On recapture it was healthy but sluggish due to the low temperature.

All food was ignored for three weeks although the hatchling would lap at a broken grape for moisture. Eventually some cress was eaten and once feeding, lettuce, grated carrot and peas were also accepted, but as yet no interest has been shown in insects.

Plate 1. Adult female and baby Chuckwalla.

Plate 2. Captive-bred baby Chuckwalla.

In mid-February, the young Chuckwalla was transferred to the adult vivarium, and apart from a little head-bobbing, was readily accepted.

In eight months the hatchling has grown 87mm, and now measures 187mm total length, 105mm SV.

DISCUSSION

After mating the adult diet was supplemented with a Vionate/crushed eggshell/ Brewer's yeast/calcium & vitamin D mixture. Although 3 of the 10 eggs were soft, the shell was not easily broken and the remaining eggs were very tough. It may well be that this was the reason why the other two embryos failed to break out of their shells.

REFERENCES

Berry, K.H. (1974). *The Ecology and Social Behaviour of the Chuckwalla, Sauromalus obesus obesus* Baird. University of California Publications in Zoology. Vol 101.

Johnson, S.R. (1965). An ecological study of the Chuckwalla, *Sauromalus obesus* Baird, in the western Mojave Desert. *Amer. Midl. Nat.* **73:** (1): 1-29.

Fitch, H.S. (1970). *Reproductive Cycles in Lizards and Snakes.* University of Kansas Museum of Natural History. Misc. Publ. No. 52.

British Herpetological Society Bulletin No. 40. 1992

THE REPRODUCTION IN CAPTIVITY OF THE NORTH AFRICAN SPINY-TAILED LIZARD, *UROMASTYX ACANTHINURUS*

TERRY THATCHER

61 Kennington Road, Kennington, Oxford

This impressive agamid has been kept for many years with very few, if any, successful breeding results in the U.K. During the winter of 1990 the author decided to try once more to "cycle" his animals, which were kept in two separate groups, one consisting of one male and two females, and the other of three males and one female.

From 25 September, 1990, the artificial day length in the lizards' cages was reduced in one hour units, from sixteen to eight hours. The cage (6' x 2' x 2') has a false floor to the front with an area of damp sand and peat immediately behind, into which is placed a drainage pipe at a 45^0 angle. The drier underfloor area to the front was used more by the lizards as the light periods decreased. At the same time the lizards were sprayed each morning with a hand held water spray. Day temperatures reached a high of 25°C, but were normally about 20°C. Night time lows of 12°C were not unusual. By 3 November 1990, the basking area provided by a Mercury Vapour Lamp, 125w (manufactured by "Sunlight Systems") was turned off, as well as a heater pad. One "Trulite" fluorescent tube (24 inches) was used for 8 hours per day during this period. The ambient room temperature was 14°-20°C. The cage of Group One experienced slightly lower night temperatures due to the cage being in contact with concrete floor of the room.

As this stage the lizards weighed as follows:

GROUP 1	
Male	475g
Female	200g
Female	250g

GROUP 2	
Male	120g
Male	210g
Male	225g
Female	150g

On 28 December, 1990 all lights and the heat pad were turned back on. The maximum temperature, beneath the Mercury Vapour Lamp, was 52°C. The ambient temperature was 28°C, the night minimum 16°C.

Food was offered immediately: Spring greens, sprouted seeds, lentils, grated carrot, and apple skins. The food was dusted with "SA 37" vitamin/mineral powder plus calcium carbonate. The lizards were weighed again on 30 December, 1990:

GROUP 1	
Male	375g
Female	160g
Female	160g

GROUP 2	
Male	70g
Male	130g
Male	220g
Female	85g

These figures show huge weight losses, an average of 76g per animal in Group 1 and 50g in Group 2.

Plate 1. Adult male *Uromastyx acanthinurus.* Green colour phase. Compare with red colour phase on front cover, and Plate 4.

Plate 2. Juvenile captive-bred *Uromastyx acanthinurus,* approximately 6 months of age.

Plate 3. Adult male *Uromastyx acanthinurus*, yellow colour phase.

Plate 4. Adult male *Uromastyx acanthinurus*, red colour phase. Father of juvenile shown in Plate 2. All photos courtesey of Stephen Pelz

COURTSHIP

By mid-January the male in Group 1 was chasing the females and biting their flanks. The same male was introduced to Group 2 in an attempt to stimulate sexual activity but this proved disastrous as the male attacked another male, biting it viciously on the head and causing a fair amount of bleeding around the ear drum. The Group 1 male was immediately removed. The victim's wound soon healed.

On return to its own vivarium the male began courting in earnest, performing "press ups" in front of the two females, chasing and biting them, but not aggressively, The females were obviously ready to accept a mate as they would greet the male head-on, tongue licking. The lizards did not touch at this point but it would appear that this was a passive gesture on the part of the females. Actual copulation was not witnessed, but by 21 February 1991, the male had very long waxy deposits exuding from his femoral pores, and the hemipenal bulges were obvious. This characteristic only shows up after a winter cooling period; the males' sexual organs are activated by a lowering of temperature. By mid-March the females were filling out slightly but it was difficult to be sure if they were gravid. During this time, and later in the year after egg laying, the male would dig into the burrow system, spraying sand everywhere.

At the beginning of May one female was obviously gravid, and on 7 May, 1991, 14 eggs were deposited in the sand and peat mixture at the end of the drainage pipe. The eggs were extremely large in relation to the size of the female, being 4.6 cm long x 2.5 cm wide. They were incubated at approximately 30-33^{0}C, 85% humidity. Seven eggs proved infertile after a month, but the remaining seven hatched on 1 August, 1991, following an incubation period of 87 days. The youngsters were perfect replicas of their parents.

Within a very short space of time the juveniles were eating all types of chopped greens, such as friese, spring greens and kale, as well as sprouted seeds, grated carrot, waxmoth larvae and crickets. The latter are a bit fast for the lizards to catch, but are accepted if offered on tweezers. Growth was good and the babies fed until they looked like footballs on legs. "Nutrobal" mineral/vitamin supplement and calcium carbonate were added to the food. A shallow dish of water was placed in the cage daily but not seen to be used. The cage was also sprayed with a water spray. The water was also sprayed directly on the lizards' bodies. Lighting consisted of a 40w spot light over a flat rock, plus a black light fluorescent tube, which was positioned in such a way that the lizards could actually touch it.

At the time of writing (10 January, 1992), the youngsters are doing well and there appear to be no problems in raising them. Unfortunately, female two did not produce any eggs and the female in the second group did not produce either. This could have been because of the ratio of three males to one female.

After this initial breakthrough it is hoped to reproduce these beautiful and interesting lizards annually.

UPDATE, SPRING 1992

Pre-hibernation weights 6 December, 1991:

GROUP 1	
Male	400g
Female (non-breeder)	240g
Female (breeder)	250g

GROUP 2	
Male (Green)	330g
Male (Large Yellow)	250g
Male (Small Yellow)	170g
Female (Red/Brown)	180g
Female (?)	175g
Female (Small Red)	85g

The last two animals were reared from wild hatchlings and introduced to the group.

Post hibernation weights, 30 January, 1992:

GROUP 1	
Male	450g
Female	235g
Female	235g

GROUP 2	
Male (Green)	310g
Male (Large Yellow)	245g
Male (Small Yellow)	165g
Female (Red/brown)	180g
Female (?)	175g
Female (Small Red)	85g

The weight loss in Group 1 was an average of 1.66g per animal, minimal in comparison to the previous year, and in Group 2, 7.5g per animal, average. One animal (Male, Group 1) actually gained 5g. These lower average weight losses were probably due to winter temperatures remaining generally lower in the current year. (Minimum recorded 10°C).

At the time of writing (16 April 1992), both groups have been extremely active and courtship plus numerous copulations have been observed since 29 February, 1992. The larger red male of Group 1 was seen to chase a female and circle in front of her several times, as if chasing its tail. This was followed by "press ups", eventually resulting in the male gripping the female on the side of the neck, with his tail under hers, both tails and cloacas lined up. Mating followed. The Group 2 males were seen to mate with different females, even the very small 85g animal. Two females are looking very gravid, but are still mating with the males.

REFERENCES

Schumacher, Eike Ortlepp and Rainer (1988). *Uromastyx acanthinurus* Bell 1825. Nachzucht der Afrikanischen Dornschwarza-gama. *Sauria* **10** (4): 17-19.

Thatcher, T. (1988). Ecology and captive maintenance of *Uromastyx* species (family Agamidae). *Proceedings of the 1988 U.K. Symposium on Captive Breeding,* John Coote (Ed.)

Wheeler, Scott (0000). Husbandry of the Spiny-tailed agamid, *Uromastyx acanthinurus,* at the Oklahoma City Zoo. *Herpetological Symposia on Captive Propagation and Husbandry,* 109-117.

PRODUCTS MENTIONED IN TEXT

Mercury Vapour Lamps, Sunlight Systems, 3 St. Marys Works, Burnmoor Street, Leicester LE27 JJ.

"SA 37" Vitamin powder for Dogs & Cats, Intervet, Cambridge.

"Nutrobal" Vitamin/mineral powder for Reptiles. Vetark Products Ltd., Winchester, Hampshire.

British Herpetological Society Bulletin No. 33. 1990

THE CHINESE CROCODILE LIZARD, *SHINISAURUS CROCODILURUS,* NOTES ON CAPTIVE BIRTHS AND HUSBANDRY

TERRY THATCHER

61, Kennington Road, Kennington, Oxon

INTRODUCTION

The Crocodile Lizard was not discovered until 1928, when it was found to inhabit a small isolated area of the Chinese province of Eastern Kwangsi in south-western China. It was first described in 1930 by the German herpetologist Ernst Ahl. From the little information available it would appear to inhabit the edges of rivers and streams with rocky bottoms, in damp montane forest. Rainfall in the area where it is found averages 2000 mm annually, and winter frost is not uncommon.

Shinisaurus is diurnal and basks on branches overhanging water, where it can dive in if threatened. It can remain submerged for a considerable time, emerging in thick marginal vegetation when "the coast is clear".

During May 1988 two females and one male living specimens were obtained by the author. Males have proportionately larger heads and predominantly orange colouration, especially ventrally.

The females obtained weighed 100g each, the male 50g – obviously underweight as it was about the same size as the females. In August 1988, two more animals were obtained: half grown, probably males, with a weight of 20g.

All the animals were treated with "Nilverm" worming solution 0.2 ml per 100g body weight, orally. For use as an injection the dose is 0.1 ml per 100g. Injection can be less stressful than forcing open the mouth, but in this case *Shinisaurus* were only too willing to open their mouths, in hope of biting a finger.

One adult female showed signs of a suspected *Pseudomonas* infection in its mouth, and was swabbed with a 5% hydrogen peroxide solution. This proved effective in curing the infection.

ACCOMMODATION

Housing consisted of a clear plastic container 600 mm (23¾") x 420 mm (16½") x 305 mm (12") high. ("Critter pen", manufactured by Rolf Hagen, Canada).

A Philips TL 2W/09N "Blacklight" was fixed across the rear of the unit 9" from the base and 2" from the rear wall. A 60w incandescent spot light was also provided, in an angled fitting 8" from the base near the front of the unit.

The entire base of the cage was covered with water to a depth of 23 mm. A rock projecting from the water below the spot light provided a "hot spot". A network of branches for climbing and basking above the water were inserted into the remainder of the cage. A drain was fitted in the base to enable fresh water to be flushed through daily, with ease: an important feature as the water is fouled regularly.

Bottom heat to the cage was supplied by a "Jemp" heating cable, at 23w per 10ft. This also served an adjoining vivarium. Temperatures were 38°C at the "hot spot", ambient air temperature 25-26°C, and water 26°C. Apart from the hot basking area, this is a similar regime to that used by San Diego Zoo (Schafer, 1986, 1987). At San Diego ambient cage temperatures were 27°C day, 21°C night, with a "hot spot" at 32°C. Day length was 12 hours. This compares to temperatures in the wild of an average 18.6°C, maximum 35°C, and minimum -2.1°C.

FEEDING

Food items offered and taken included "giant mealworms" *(Zophobas morio),* crickets, locusts, earthworms, and to a lesser extent fish, frogs, tadpoles and new-

Plate 1. Adult Chinese Crocodile Lizard, *Shinisaurus crocodilurus.*

born mice. Although not offered by the author, freshwater shrimps and various aquatic insect larvae are reputed to be popular. Slugs and snails were offered but refused.

In an environment such as described above many food items can drown before being eaten, so some items are best fed from tweezers if time, and the lizards permit.

The adults have generally been more erratic in their feeding habits than the younger specimens.

REPRODUCTION

Almost immediately after acquisition some interaction was observed between the sub-adults, with chasing and some head bobbing. One youngster incurred a wound on the neck, but no further aggression occurred and the wound healed quickly.

On 11 January, 1989, two live young were born, with some underdeveloped eggs. The young were removed to rear separately. On 5 March, 1989 a second female produced two live young, sometime before 10.30 am; unfortunately these were not removed immediately and an hour later had been eaten. During the course of the day four more dead young and one live were born. This time, the lesson learnt, the live animal was rescued. The last birth on that day was around 7.15 pm but the next day one more dead youngster was passed, making a total of 8.

Plate 2. Juvenile *Shinisaurus crocodilurus.*

Some of those born dead were enclosed tightly in their birth membrances, others lightly free but with the membrane constricting the neck. It seemed they were born dead but it is possible one or two may have drowned trying to release themselves from their birth sacs. There were no signs of deformities.

The females were suspected to be gravid when obtained, though this is not certain. the females measured 366 mm in total length, of which 200 mm was tail. The head width was 24 mm. The new-born young were 53-54 mm s.v. length, tails 59-65 mm, head width 9 mm. The young born in January had after two months reached 57 mm s.v., 72-73 mm tail.

In the collection of San Diego Zoo, mating was observed on 7 March 1986, and young were born on 22 November 1986 and 19 December 1986. The average litter size was nine.

Previous reports of clutch size are 2-7 (Lan-tian and Han-han, 1982; Murphy, 1986). Gravid females have been seen in the wild between July and September, but not giving birth until April or May of the following year, after a period of hibernation. The length of development would agree with the females in this collection. These were also exposed to fairly cool conditions during December, January and February.

These unusual lizards have proved reasonably hardy in captivity, provided the environment does not dry out, and access to water is available at all times. They take a while to settle down to an alien diet, but once this is achieved they feed well.

REFERENCES

Grzimeks Animal Life Encyclopedia (1975). Vol. 6. Reptiles. p.319. Van Nostrand.

Lan-tian and L. Han-Lan (1982). Notes on the distribution and habits of the lizard, *Shinisaurus crocodilurus Acta Herpetol. Sin.* **1**(1): 84-85.

Murphy, J. (1987). Chinese Crocodile Lizard born at Dallas Zoo. *A.A.Z.P.A. Newsletter* **28**(1); 12.

Schafer, S. (1986, 1987). Breeding the Chinese Crocodile Lizard, *Shinisaurus crocodilurus,* at the San Diego Zoo. *10th and 11th International Herpetological Symposium on Captive Propagation and Husbandry,* June 25-28th 1986 and June 17-20th 1987.

British Herpetological Society Bulletin No. 10. 1984

NOTES ON THE CAPTIVE REPRODUCTION OF THE AUSTRALIAN SKINK, *TILIQUA NIGROLUTEA*

R. D. BARTLETT

Reptilian Breeding and Research Institute, 1421 Olmeda Way, Fort Myers, Florida 33901, U.S.A.

INTRODUCTION

Tiliqua nigrolutea is a resident of the comparatively cool, higher elevations of southeastern Australia (Cogger, 1975; Jenkins and Bardell, 1980). While two colour phases of the lizard are generally recognized (the larger and more brilliantly coloured of which is considered to be truly an Alpine creature), they have persistently resisted subspecific designations.

The smaller morph of *nigrolutea* is clad in more muted colours and is a resident of the less lofty altitudes. It was this form that was chosen for our breeding programs in southwestern Florida. It was though that being of lower, hence warmer, ranges that they would be more tolerant of our uncomfortably hot, humid summer conditions than would the alpine form.

T. nigrolutea, which is quite appropriately commonly known as the "blotched blue-tongued skink", displays the darkest dorsal ground colour of any of the members of the genus. This may run from chocolate-brown through olive-black to black. Dorsally there is a series of roughly outlined, usually paired, russet to orange blotches. The dorsal surface of the head is lighter, the lips grey to russet. Colours pale laterally and take on a rather vague pattern of vermiculations. The throat is from off-white to grey and the venter is pale grey, the centre of each scale being slightly darker, hence forming a series of ill-defined stripes.

The blotched blue-tongue, while large, nearing or occasionally exceeding 25cm snout-vent length, and robust, gives the impression of being more serpentine than its more commonly seen relative, *Tiliqua s. scincoides,* the eastern blue-tongue, for its legs are proportionately shorter.

In fact, when frightened it relies little upon its limbs to effect its escape, resorting instead to a series of stiff lateral undulations.

Its tail is short, being barely 50% of the svl.

Our colony, which consists of 3.2 individuals, was obtained as half-growns.

Our geographic location makes it possible to maintain numerous species of reptiles and amphibians out-of-doors all year round. The facilities offered our various scincids consist of uncovered pens some 3m in diameter, formed by sinking sheet aluminium of 92cm height 32cm into the ground. Horizontal plastic piping is offered as sub-surface refugia, the entrances sloping gently from ground level. Additional areas of seclusion in the form of piles of coral-rock are available also. Into these the lizards retire during extremes of heat or cold or during periods of rain. Neither photoperiod nor heating are augmented.

Food is offered daily except during periods of winter cold which render the animals temporarily dormant. Mixtures of grated apple, grated pear, ripe banana, ripe melons of several varieties and numerous kinds and flavours of canned catfood are consumed eagerly. To this is added liberal quantities of such vitamin-mineral supplements as "Vionate", "Osteoform Improved" and powdered calcium lactate. Live crickets, young mice and an occasional garden slug or snail periodically augment the diet of prepared foods.

T. nigrolutea has so far proven to be an easily cared for, interesting lizard. Quite unlike two of their congeners with which we also work, i.e. *T. s. scincoides* and *T. gigas,* the *nigrolutea* have displayed no periods of excessive hostility towards cagemates, even during the breeding season.

Entirely diurnal during the colder months, breeding activity on warm February and March days has prolonged the activity period until darkness. Copulation has never been observed during the hours of daylight but rather is accomplished during the diminishing light at day's end.

Frequently more than one male is in attendance of a given female, trailing the one behind the other as the female leads the way about the pen. Copulation is usually, but not invariably, accomplished by the male immediately behind the female. Slowly overtaking the female, he begins courtship by nudging the female on her posterior sides and groin, all the while flicking the area with his tongue. Slowly he advances along her length, eventually grasping her nape or shoulder area in his jaws. Receptive females then cease moving. Continuing to grasp her, the male then forms a crescent with his body bringing his tail down and under that of the female's until their cloacal openings are juxtaposed. At that time a hemi-penis is inserted after which gentle periodic convulsive movements become noticeable. This position is maintained from 5 to 30 minutes.

Because of the several weeks long breeding period it has been impossible to ascertain gestation, but it was obvious that the females were gravid by late May.

The first of the two females gave birth on 15 June, parturition beginning at 1600 hrs with birth of a dead, slightly undersized baby. This measured 116mm tl, 84mm svl and 20mm hl (head length). The second, slightly larger and living baby was produced at 1700 hrs. Measurements were not taken of this neonate. The third and final baby, also alive, was born at 1730 hrs. Larger than either of its siblings it measured 128mm tl, 93mm svl, and 22mm hl.

Immediately after being born the neonates consumed the attached placenta and sought refuge among the profusion of plants. The young were removed, placed in a separate enclosure, and offered live crickets which were immediately consumed. The day following their birth they were offered small portions of our prepared "skink mixture" most of which was consumed during the day.

The second female gave birth to two healthy babies on 22 June.

The "lowland" morph of *T. nigrolutea* has proven compatible with the vagaries of Florida's weather. As surmized in literature, they are active at temperatures far lower than those which activate their congeners. They have left their refugia to thermoregulate on even our coldest winter day, the single criterion seeming to be ample sunshine in which to bask. Conversely, on hot summer days they return to cover long before their congeners in adjacent pens with similar conditions.

While not actually crepuscular, during the heat of summer they do display peak activity periods in early morning and late afternoon. They remain active throughout the day in cooler weather.

While no cloacal temperatures have been taken, it seems likely that the dark dorsal colouration of *nigrolutea* makes them more efficient baskers than their lighter coloured relatives. Certainly they become "warm" to our touch while congeners basking for similar duration under identical conditions remain "cool".

The clutch size, averaging 2.5 young per female, is significantly smaller than those of the other three *Tiliqua* species which we have succeeded in breeding. As a comparison, *T. s. scincoides* averages 15.5, *T. gerrardi* 18 and *T. gigas* 7. We hypothesize that *nigrolutea* produces larger clutches with increasing age. This has proven so with the allied *Egernia cunningham kreffti,* most of which have produced 2 young in their first brood and up to 7 in those subsequent.

REFERENCES

Cogger, H.G. (1975). *Reptiles and Amphibians of Australia.* A. H. & A. W. Reed, Sydney. pp. 341.

Jenkens, R. and Bartell, R. (1980). *A Field Guide to the Reptiles of the Australian High Country.* Inkata Press, Melbourne. pp. 196-197.

British Herpetological Society Bulletin No. 4. 1981

THE SOUTHERN ALLIGATOR LIZARD, *GERRHONOTUS MULTICARINATUS* BLAINVILLE 1935: ITS CARE AND BREEDING IN CAPTIVITY

BERT LANGERWERF

**Agama International Rt 2, Box 285, Montevallo, Alabama 35115, USA*

INTRODUCTION

The Alligator Lizard belongs to the family Anguidae, which is distributed over the Americas, Eurasia and Africa. There are three subfamilies:

1. Diploglossinae, to which belong the genera *Diploglossus, Sauresia, Wetmorena, Ophiodes,* and *Celestes;* these are all confined to the Americas.
2. Gerrhonotinae, to which belong the genera *Gerrhonotus, Abronia, Coloptychon* and *Ophisaurus.*
3. Anguinae, to which belongs *Anguis.*

Subspecies, their distribution and biotypes

1. *Gerrhonotus multicarinatus multicarinatus* occurs in central and west-central California.
2. *Gerrhonotus m. scincicauda* occurs in the north-west of California, through westcentral Oregon into southern Washington about the latitude of Kennewick.
3. *Gerrhonotus m. webbi* is found to the south of *multicarinatus* in southern California, east-central California, and the north western part of Baja California.
4. *Gerrhonotus m. nanus* is restricted to the Los Coronados Islands, Mexico.

* Present address. This study was carried out in the Netherlands.

In nature they live in dry rocky areas, open grassland, chaparral, and woodland. In particular, they prefer oak woodland on the lower slopes of the coastal mountains. They climb very well, are frequently seen in trees, and will even rob birds' nests.

THE ALLIGATOR LIZARD IN CAPTIVITIY

I have kept this lizard in captivity since 1975, in various kinds of terraria. My animals came directly from California. As the males were very intolerant of one another, I had to keep them isolated in different terraria. The males could be distinguished by their fighting and their relatively large, broad heads. Further, their hemipenes could be exposed rather easily by gently pressing the base of the tail.

One vivarium in which I keep the lizards is the one of 16m^2 which I described on page 34 of the BHS Bulletin No. 3, June 1981. In winter (October-March) this enclosure is totally covered with glass. In summer, 90% is glass-covered. By this means, the animals are provided with a microclimate similar to that of California. The Alligator Lizards live in this enclosure for the whole year. On the southern slope of the enclosure, between the Mediterranean shrubs planted in it, is a layer of dead leaves (easily collected in Autumn). In the middle of the enclosure is a trench or depression running from east to west, thereby creating a cooler north facing slope, also covered with leaves or hay. Throughout the enclosure, there are large pieces of logs. There is 1m^2 only of exposed sand, kept slightly moist, in the north-west corner. Here there are no leaves, but some flat stones. This is the area used for egg laying.

In these conditions, the lizards are most active in April-May, and copulation takes place during this period. Later in the summer the males climb less often in the bushes and stay hidden in the hay and leaves; they are active, but are mostly not directly visible. The females also are not seen at this time as they are protecting their eggs (see later). In September, they can be frequently seen again basking in the sun.

I have kept the Alligator lizard with other species of lizards without problems: *Podarcis lilfordi, Lacerta strigata, Lacerta lepida pater, Lacerta t. trilineata, Agama stellio, Agama caucasia, Agama lehmanni* and *Ophisaurus apodus.* To keep Alligator lizards with smaller species could be dangerous.

I have also kept this lizard successfully in other terraria, both larger and smaller. I released one male in my large open-air enclosure where it survived two Dutch winters and summers! In a large glass house of 50m^2 and 4m high I often observed the animals in the bushes at a height of 2-4m.

In the 16m^2 terrarium the Alligator lizards disappear into hibernation in October, beneath the piles of hay, and emerge again at the end of February. This year I saw the first one on February 23rd, and in 1977 on February 14th.

REPRODUCTION

I have bred this species from the beginning, but from 1976-1980 it was never very successful (see Table 1).

As I have described in my earlier articles, I always give calcium and vitamin D_3 to my lizards in the drinking water. This had a clear effect on the reproduction of all species except the Alligator lizards. Each year there were 20-40 eggs, but the number of births declined to zero in 1980. This caused me to rethink my methods. I thought that the lizards, active climbers that they are, might drink condensation droplets from the glass, and so receive no intake of calcium and D_3. This year I added the calcium and vitamin D_3 directly to the food itself: on about 1kg of crickets *(Gryllus bimaculatus)* I dusted one spoonful of calcium lactate and about 10 drops of highly concentrated vitamin D_3 (1 million units per ml.).

As a result, success was high = only 5 of 75 eggs died. This is the breakthrough necessary to be able to breed them in hundreds annually in the near future.

Table 1. Details of captive breedings of *Gerrhonotus multicarinatus* over the past 6 years

Year	date of copulation	date of egg-laying	number of eggs	date of hatching	number hatched	incubation temperature	length of incubation (days)
1976	Apr 8	June 6	23	Aug 10,11,12	6	28°C	50-52
	Apr 8	Jul 2	30	–	–	28°C	50-52
1977	Apr 4	Jul 11	24	Aug 20,21,22	13	30°C	40-42
1978	?	?	?	Sep 9	7	29°C	?
1979	Apr 13 May 5	) before) Jul 1	?	Aug 8	3	29°C	about 40?
1980	Apr 17 Apr 30 May 5	) before)) July 7	22	–	–	29°C	–
1981	Apr 24	June 20	20	Aug 1,2,3	20	27°C	42-44
		Jul 9	55	Aug 18,19, 20, 21	50	27°C	40-43

Copulation takes place mainly in the second half of April; the eggs are laid at the end of June or the beginning of July. Hatching takes place in August. Full information is given in Table 1. Alas, as I have over 1000 lizards of about 40 species, I cannot notice everything that happens in the 50 terraria.

From the Table it is clear that incubation is rather short, between 40-45 days. One may think, when reading the Table, that the higher incubation temperature of 20-30°C may be the cause of poorer results in earlier years, but this is very unlikely: there were traces of calcium deficiency in the hatchlings of the years prior to 1981, such as a short lower jaw, parietal up-valuting, weak feet and curved tail.

From the Table it can be seen that in the worst years the incubation period was significantly longer than in 1981, even though the temperature was higher. I have also noticed the same tendency in *Lacerta* and *Agama* species, where eggs deficient in calcium take noticeably longer to hatch than good eggs.

A female usually lays about 20 eggs; the highest number I observed was 24 in 1977. There is only one clutch per female per year.

In 1976, two hatchlings were measured. Both had a snout-vent length of 37mm and total lengths of 97mm and 102mm respectively. In 1970 one hatchling was measured, total length 96mm. In 1981 a single hatchling was measured, snout-vent 34mm, total 90mm. It is remarkable that the hatchlings of the best years were the smallest, as usually, in other lizards, I have observed the opposite: eggs from females in poorer conditions produce smaller hatchlings.

I measured a single egg just after laying 1976; this measured 17 x 10mm.

I have observed very remarkable behaviour in the females in almost every year: they remain with their eggs after laying to protect them. This year (1981) I have been able to make the best observations of this behaviour. In one terrarium there was a large flat stone beneath which three females together made a chamber and passage to it (see Plate 2). In the chamber and entrance to it I found 55 eggs on 9th July. When I tried to remove the eggs the females became very aggressive and constantly tried to bite me. This is contrary to the behaviour of the related *Ophisaurus apodus,* which never bites when I take away the eggs, though it also protects them in a chamber like *Gerrhonotus.* I removed 50 of the eggs and left 5 in the chamber for two reasons: to see if and for how long the females remain to protect them and, because of the poor results of previous years, I thought that this protection might be necessary for the successful incubation of the eggs. I examined the chamber again on July 30th; the three females were still defending the 5 eggs. These eggs were probably all from one female, as they were all close together. I made a second examination on August 14th (after the first 20 eggs, of those which had been removed earlier, had hatched), and found only one female still with the eggs. One of these had died already, and so I considered it best to transfer the other 4 into the incubator; none of them hatched. All 50 of those which I had removed on July 9th, however, hatched successfully. The eggs left in the chamber until August 14th could have died for the following reasons: the defending females may disturb the eggs too much, though this seems unlikely to me; the eggs may be more sensitive to mechanical and/or thermal changes/ disturbance at a later stage of development.

Plate 1. Copulation of *Gerrhonotus multicarinatus.*

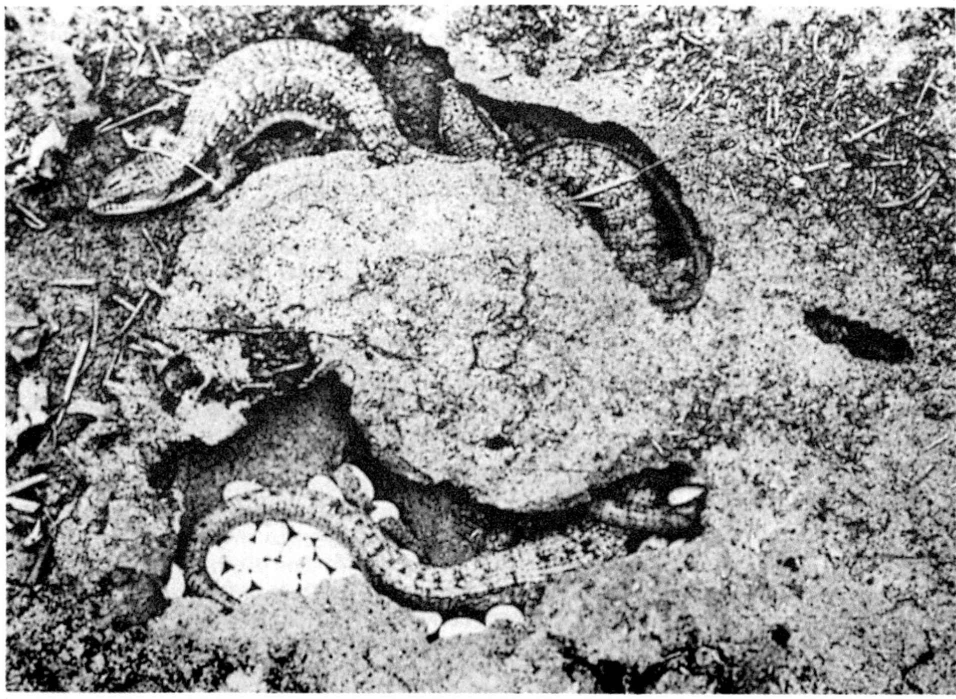

Plate 2. Three females *Gerrhonotus multicarinatus* protecting their eggs in a chamber beneath a flat stone.

Plate 3. *Gerrhonotus multicarinatus:* hatching time.

RAISING THE YOUNG

On the first six hatchlings – hatched on August 10th, 11th and 12th 1976 – I made notes on growth and behaviour as this was the first time that I bred this species.

At hatching, they had a total length of about 10cm (see above). They lived secretively, spending most of their time hidden in dead leaves and hay. They would bask in the hay, hardly visible. I noticed the same behaviour in *Ophisaurus apodus* hatchlings. They would feed on all kinds of small insects: fly larvae, small cockroaches, small crickets and so on. Water was given by spraying the hay daily, from which the lizards would drink. The water contained vitamin D_3 and calcium lactate (see my other articles for details). These lizards were not hibernated in their first year. By the following August (1977 – at one year of age), they measured 35.5cm, of which 23cm was tail. By this time the males were clearly distinguishable, as they had well developed hemipenes: there were 3 males and 3 females. In 1978, after their first hibernation during the winter of 1977-78, they copulated, but the resulting eggs were then bad.

From these observations, I expect to breed many *Gerrhonotus multicarinatus* from 1983 onwards, if I keep a good number of the 708 young of this year.

SOME GENERAL POINTS AND CONCLUSIONS

So far, I have lost none of these animals from disease; some only were lost because of accidents or fighting. It is an ideal lizard to keep in glass-covered garden terraria, where reproduction is possible if they are given enough food, minerals and vitamins.

Because of the ease of breeding this lizard, this is another species for which we will not depend on importation if we have a good population spread over terraria in Western Europe; it looks as though we may have achieved this already.

The Alligator Lizard does not tolerate great heat; at high temperatures it will die more quickly than, for example, *Lacerta* or *Agama* species. The critical upper temperature must be close to 40^{0}C.

A favourable factor for many terrarium keepers may be the rather short incubation period of the eggs.

If the lizards are kept in an indoor terrarium, they may reproduce if they are kept a little cooler and darker (less daylight hours) in wintertime. But of this manner of keeping them, I have no experience.

REFERENCES

Burrage, B.R. (1965). Notes on the eggs and young of the lizards *Gerrhonotus m. webbi and Gerrhonotus m. nanus. Copeia* 4:512.

Hultzsch, W. (1928). Noord Amerikaanse Reptielen en Amfibien *(Gerrhonotus scincicauda). Lacerta* 6:24.

Petzold, H.G. (1971) *Blindschkiche und Sheltopusik Die neue Brehm* – Bucherei 448, p.85-86.

Rekum, M. van (1962) *Lacerta* p.58.

British Herpetological Society Bulletin No. 8. 1983

BREEDING AND GROWTH OF THE PLUMED BASILISK *(BASILISCUS PLUMIFRONS)* AT THE ROYAL MELBOURNE ZOO

CHRIS B. BANKS

Keeper-in-Charge (Reptiles), Royal Melbourne Zoo,
P.O. Box 74, Parkville, Victoria 3052, Australia

INTRODUCTION

The Plumed or Green crested basilisk *(Basiliscus plumifrons)* is an attractive iguanid species inhabiting tropical, wet, evergreen forests of Costa Rica, Central America (Heyer, 1967).

The first specimens to be exhibited at Melbourne were received from Brookfield Zoo, Chicago in November, 1976. Unfortunately the female did not survive the journey and we were left with a solitary male until February, 1980 when two females arrived from Rotterdam Zoo.

ACCOMMODATION

Soon after arrival the male was transferred to a large exhibit, measuring 2x2x1.8m high, which also housed a small group of Star tortoises *(Geochelone elegans).* As with all our reptile enclosures, the interior walls and floors are of simulated rock, with numerous resting ledges. The heated floor maintains a temperature of 24-31°C, higher in summer than in winter due to the influence of outside weather conditions. It is also covered with a thick layer of coarse sand and contains a centrally-located plant pocket which presently holds two *Ficus lyrata.* A palm, *Kuntea* sp., is situated to the rear of the exhibit. These plants, together with an open network of branches in the upper areas, provide adequate cover and perching sites for the lizards.

To one side of the enclosure is a $0.5m^2$ shallow pond which is used extensively by tortoises and lizards alike. Clear perspex sheets in the roof above the wire-topped exhibits result in natural lighting and seasonal photoperiod changes. The enclosure is also lit by a 40W "True-lite" fluorescent tube which is switched on from 0810-1650 hours daily.

The females were introduced to this exhibit soon after their arrival in 1980 and settled in well with the resident male.

ADULT DIET

For the most part, the adults in this report were fed small mice, locusts *(Locusta migratoria*) and Northern field crickets (*Telegryllus oceanicus*), the last two usually being dusted with a mixture of bone flour and "Petvite" prior to feeding. On occasions the male will also take pieces of tomato and fruit from the tortoise's food tray. This is a similar feeding regime to that noted by Bloxam (1980) for this species at the Jersey Wildlife Preservation Trust, but contrasts with the more fruit/vegetable oriented diet offered at the Brookfield Zoo (Pawley, 1972).

BREEDING

The two females were placed on display with the male 10 days after their arrival in late February 1980, and commenced feeding the next day. They were designated female 2 and female 3. Female 2 laid two eggs whilst in transit and No. 3 laid four infertile eggs eight days after arrival. The latter female was also observed digging in the enclosure floor on 22nd and 28th March but no eggs were laid.

The male was seen attempting to mate female 3 from 9-16 April and 10 eggs were laid on 19th May but again all were infertile (see Table 1).

Female 2 was removed from the exhibit on 1st May due to her dominance by female 3 and on no further occasion were the two females placed together. Female 3 laid a further 13 eggs on 15th September and 7 on 27th November during a brief period of display. Female 2 laid 4 eggs on 30th October. None of these 24 eggs were fertile.

In 1981, female 3 was seen digging in mid-January but it was not until 22nd July that she oviposited. During the week prior to laying, the female appeared to present herself to the male – she positioned herself about 0.5m from the male, lowered her forebody to the sand and raised her pelvic region and tail. This behaviour has not been observed at any other time.

A total of 14 eggs was laid 150mm below the surface and next to a large branch. The tortoises had been removed from the exhibit to prevent them disturbing the lizard and laying took place from 1300-1400 hours. The eggs were immediately removed for artificial incubation. After being weighed and measured they were placed in a container of moist Vermiculite which was positioned in an incubator set at 28°C. Five infertile eggs were discarded after 15 days and a further two after 28 days. The remaining seven eggs were carefully measured after 35 days and were found to have increased in size (see Table 1). All seven eggs split on 26th September with a healthy lizard emerging from each the next day after an incubation period of 67 days. At hatching they averaged 43mm S.V. (41-44), 135mm total length (126-143) and 2.06g (2.01-2.12).

Table 1. Ovipositional data for *B. plumifrons* at the Royal Melbourne Zoo

Clutch laid (No. eggs)	No. eggs fertile	Mean egg weight at laying (g)	Mean egg length at laying (mm)	Mean egg width at laying (mm)
22 Feb, 1980 (4)	0	Not	recorded	
19 May, 1980 (10)	0	Not	recorded	
15 Sept, 1980 (3)	0	1.8	22.3	11.6
20 Oct, 1980 (4)	0	Not	recorded	
27 Nov, 1980 (7)	0	Eggs	dehydrated when found	
22 July, 1981 (4)	7	2.3	22 (25*)	14 (19.5*)

* size after 35 days

GROWTH OF YOUNG

Hatchling *B. plumifrons* have been adequately described by Pawley (1972) and Bloxam (1980) and suffice to say that these individuals showed no appreciable differences. They were placed in an all glass aquarium measuring 1.0 x 0.4 x 0.5m high. The floor was covered with a layer of coarse sand, and leaves were provided for cover. A pot plant, *Stromanthe sanguinea,* and small branches running the length of the tank were included for resting and climbing. A 200W heat lamp was suspended over the wire top, producing a maximum temperature of 32-36°C on the uppermost leaves and branches. The lizards spent most of their time in these areas. As the tank was situated on a heated table, floor temperature did not drop below 24°C. A 40W fluorescent "True-lite" was also placed above the tank enabling the lizards to bask within 200mm of the tube. As with the display enclosure this was switched on from 0810-1650 hours daily.

The lizards were sprayed each morning with a fine mist spray and always drank readily from droplets on the vegetation. A shallow bowl of water was also present at all times. Feeding commenced the day after hatching with small mealworms being accepted without hesitation. Growth was very slow over the first month and two deaths occurred after 21 and 28 days respectively. Overheating was thought to be the cause and consequently the maximum temperature was reduced to 33°C. This may have been only part of the problem as further deaths occurred 54 and 69 days after hatching. In order to make servicing of the tank less traumatic for the lizards and to enable the tank to be carried to a sunny, off-limit area outside the Reptile House each day, the lizards were transferred to a small tank (600 x 300 x 300m high) in late November. In early December, as feeding still consisted solely of small crickets and mealworms dusted with boneflour and Petvite, it was decided to attempt careful force-feeding of small pieces of fruit and hard-boiled egg. Although this was carried out on four occasions over a two-week period, it did not appear to reduce the lizards' reluctance to accept such food and the practice was discontinued.

After overcoming the initial difficulties, the two remaining lizards grew steadily and by the end of the sixth month, the larger individual began to develop the large crests which are characteristic of the male *B. plumifrons.* A further seven months elapsed before the smaller lizard exhibited similar development. Although the lizards still accept live crickets with relish, since the 14th month they have taken increasing amounts of chopped fruit, pieces of hard-boiled egg and moistened Puppy Chow.

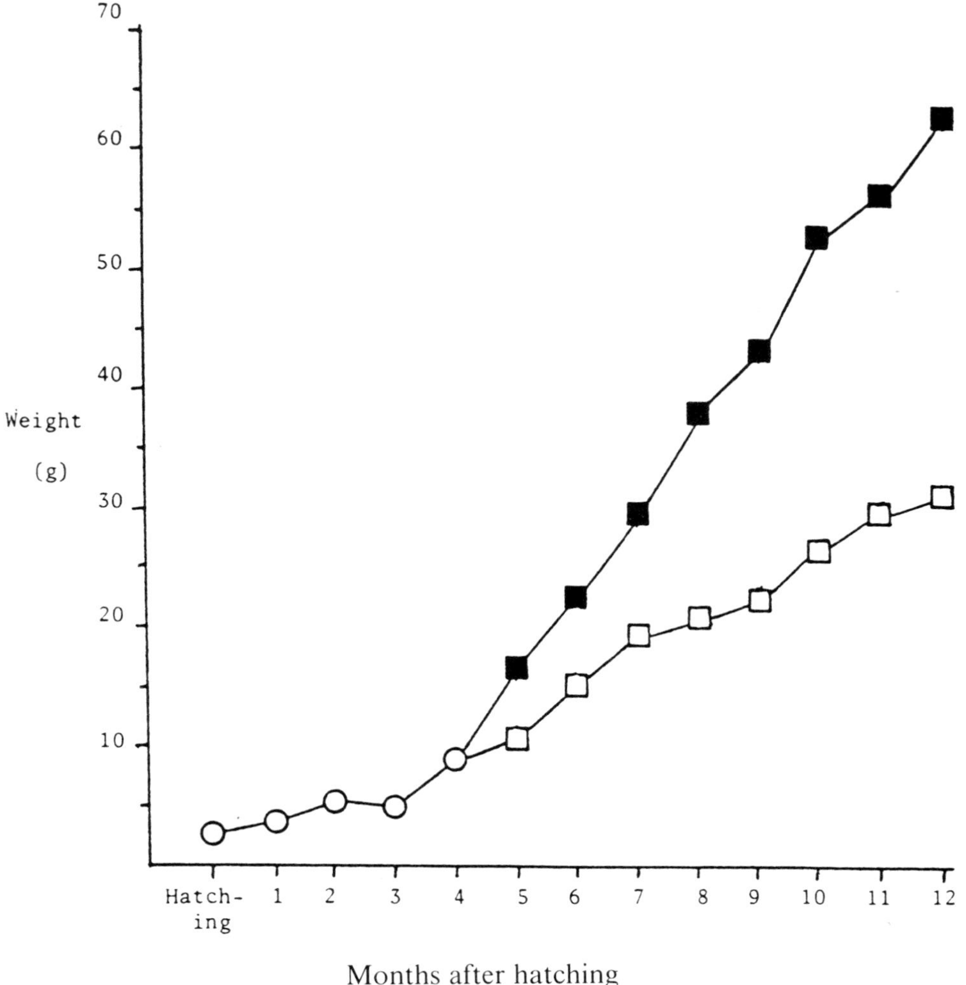

Figure 1. Weight increase in grams from hatching to 12 months of age for *B. plumifrons* at The Royal Melbourne Zoo. O – mean; ■ – male 1; □ – male 2.

DISCUSSION

The two previously published accounts of captive breeding of *B. plumifrons* (Bloxam, 1980; Pawley, 1972) differ in the breeding seasons shown by the respective animals. Those at Jersey (Bloxham, 1980) oviposited from November-July while those at Brookfield (Pawley, 1972) oviposited from May-September, with corresponding differences in times of hatching. Both are northern hemisphere collections, but in both instances the period from which data was drawn did not extend into the second breeding season and it may well be that long term studies will reveal a

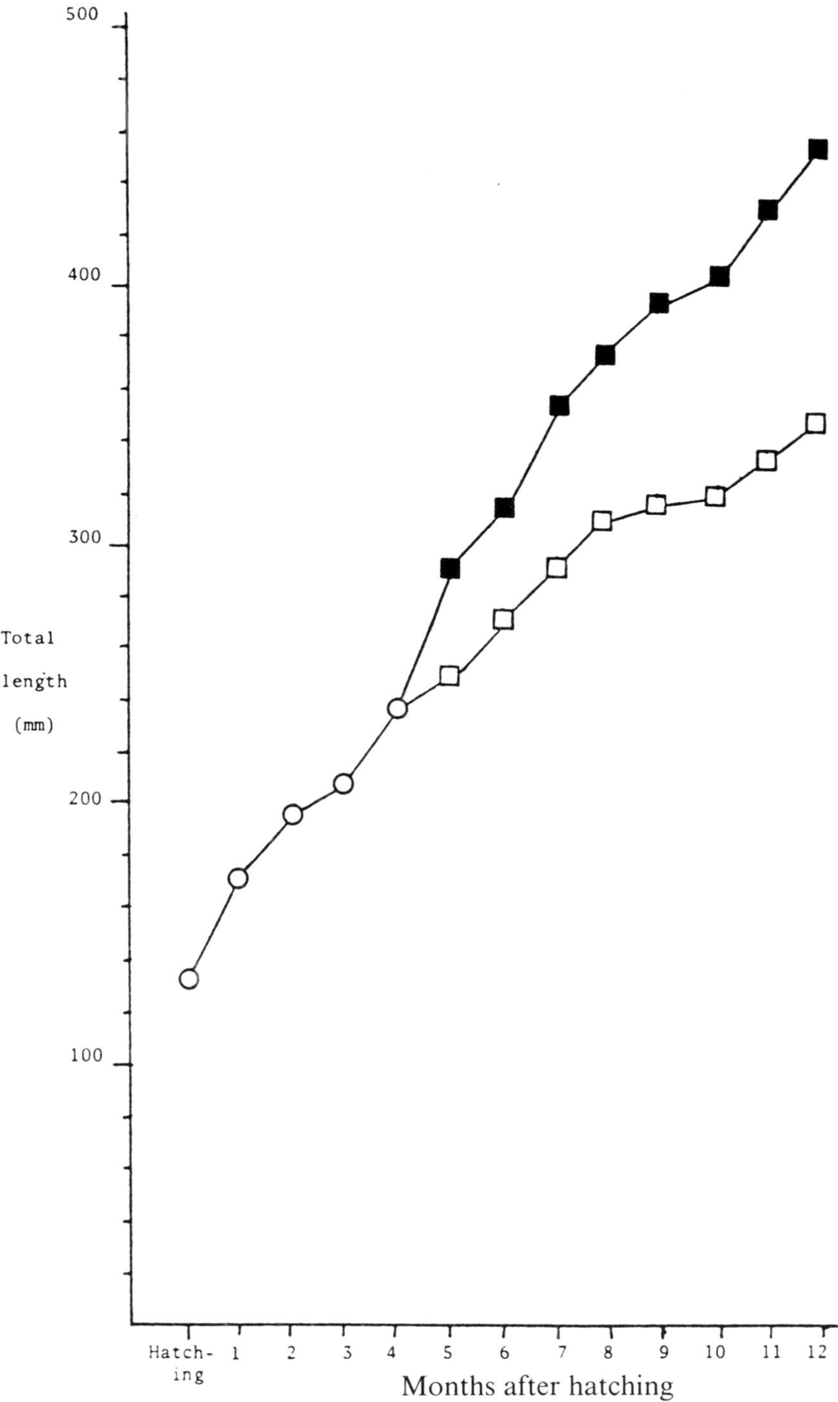

Figure 2. Increase in total length in millimetres from hatching to 12 months of age for *B. plumifrons* at The Royal Melbourne Zoo. O – mean; ■ – male 1; □ – male 2.

more specific breeding regime. Indeed the ovipositional data in this report show elements of both previous accounts and are only from one season, as both females died in late 1981.

However, egg dimensions at laying and after 35 days incubation (Table 1) were similar to those previously recorded under similar incubation conditions. Incubation length also showed a similar correlation. Unlike the previously reported breedings, no humidity problems were experienced during incubation as the eggs were maintained at 90-93%.

As can be seen from Figures 1 and 2, the individual which first showed itself to be a male (male 1) grew at a faster rate than its sibling, from the point at which individual recordings commenced. This is despite no shortage of available food, space, or cover. It is also of interest to note the differing growth rates between these individuals and the Jersey animals; after about 200 days the latter weighed almost 40g while the Melbourne specimens averaged 24g (1 (18-30g). The weight at hatching was very similar for both groups; from 2-3g. Mean snout-vent length as a percentage of total length varied very slightly over the first 12 months – from 30.2% at 1 month to 26.1% at 12 months. That for the remaining adult male is very similar: 26.9%.

At the time of writing, both lizards are still very shy and it will be some time before they are introduced to the exhibit still occupied by the adult male after six years. As these are the only *B. plumifrons* in Australia at the present time, every consideration must be taken to ensure further successful reproduction.

Products mentioned in the text

True-lite (Vita-lite)

Duro-test International, 17-10 Willow Street, Fair Lawn, New Jersey 07410, U.S.A.

Petvite

I.G.Y. Manufacturing Pty. Ltd., 20 O'Briens Road, Hurstville, N.S.W. 2220, Australia.

Puppy Chow.

Robert Harper & Co. Ltd., 5 Dunlop Road, Mulgrave, Vic., Australia.

ACKNOWLEDGEMENTS

I am grateful for Roy Dunn's review of this paper, drafts of which were typed by Meg Braden.

REFERENCES

Bloxam, Q.M.C. (1980). Breeding and maintenance of the Plumed basilisk *Basiliscus plumifrons* at the Jersey Wildlife Preservation Trust. *Dodo. Journal of the Jersey Wildlife Preservation Trust* **17:** 88-96.

Heyer, W.R. (1967). A herpeto-faunal study of an ecological transect through the Cordillera de Tilaran, Costa Rica. *Copeia* 1967 **2:** 259-71.

Pawley, R. (1972). Notes on reproduction and behaviour of the Green crested basilisk *(Basiliscus plumifrons)* at Brookfield Zoo. Chicago. *International Zoo Yearbook* **12:** 141-44.

British Herpetological Society Bulletin No. 39. 1992

THE CARE AND BREEDING OF JOHNSTON'S CHAMELEON, *CHAMAELEO JOHNSTONI,* IN CAPTIVITY

STEVEN C. HALFPENNY

37 Cronton Lane, Widnes, Cheshire, WA8 9AR, England

INTRODUCTION

This species is found at high altitudes, 2000 ft to 7000 ft in the montane regions of central Africa (Witte, 1965). It possesses large, muscular limbs and a very strong grip, reputedly necessary to combat high winds in its natural habitat. I have been informed that specimens currently being imported into Britain are collected from Burundi, at an altitude of approximately 6500 ft (2000 m), and are thus specimens from the cooler and higher altitude range of this species.

DESCRIPTION

Chamaeleo johnstoni is an easily recognized species; the males possess three horns on their heads. Confusion often occurs between this species and *C. jacksoni,* however there are several distinguishing characters that easily differentiate the two. The dorsal crest in *C. johnstoni* is straight, whereas in *C. jacksoni* the dorsal is heavily serrated. *C. johnstoni* is the more colourful species, often showing vertical bands on the flanks in slate grey and yellow. Female *johnstoni* also show, to varying intensity, orange lips. An important point to consider is that few, if any, *jacksoni* exist in this country since Kenya, their country of origin, ceased exports some years ago. Any three horned chameleons offered for sale in this country are extremely unlikely to be *C. jacksoni.*

C. johnstoni is a medium sized chameleon, both sexes reaching 110mm snout to vent, with a 90mm tail.

Plate 1. Adult female *Chamaeleo johnstoni.*

ACCOMMODATION

I have housed this species in two quite different set-ups, both being successful. Gravid females are housed in a typical all glass vivarium, 120cm long x 40cm x 40cm. The floor is covered in a peat and leaf litter mix, which is piled up at one end to a depth of 20 cm, this providing a suitable laying area when covered with a few small branches. The rest of the vivarium is filled with branches, strategically placed to give various basking sites close to the heat and light source, some mention of which should be made. Heating is provided by an incandescent bulb, wattage adjusted to give the desired temperature. I also provide a source of ultra violet radiation, which I believe to be essential in captive lizards to enable them to produce their own vitamin D3. I use Actinic 09 tubes, 18" and 15 watts, situated vertically in the vivarium, allowing easy access for basking, and below any glass cover which would decrease the U.V. from the tube.

The other set-up used was a planted 2.4 m x 1.8 m x 1.8 m (8' x 6' x 6') high greenhouse. The glass is covered with greenhouse shading, to avoid any excess over-heating, and the floor is of concrete flags. The plants are container bound for ease of moving. The best types of plant to use are the Buddleias and the Rhododendrons. Both these plant genera contain half hardy species suitable for the cold greenhouse that also provide colour and fragance on their own.

Plate 2. Juvenile *C. johnstoni.*

ENVIRONMENTAL PARAMETERS

As has been previously mentioned, this species of chameleon is found in montane regions, and therefore requires a cooler temperature than one might expect. The specimens imported into Britain show signs of stress at a temperature of 85°F. Those specimens kept in the greenhouse show no ill effects at all with a night time temperature down to 45°F (7.2°C). Daytime temperatures should be around 75°F (23.9°C), with a drop of 10°F at night. A temperature difference of 5°F above or below this does no harm however 80°F (26.7°C) should be a maximum. The humidity needs to be quite high with this species, around 75%. This means a daily spraying of the enclosure used, and drinking water should be offered at this time, using a syringe, offering droplets to the chameleon's mouth. This is necessary as chameleons will not drink from standing water. One alternative is to use a water pump to create a simple waterfall, water being pumped from a reservoir to the top of a long piece of cork bark or slate. The water flows down this, and is "visible" to the chameleon which will drink at will. The water flows back into the reservoir for recirculation, but should be replaced with fresh water at regular intervals. The water used should be at the same temperature as the environment, so as not to chill the chameleon.

FEEDING

Food consists in the main of crickets, dusted with a mineral/vitamin powder. These can be placed in a smooth sided bowl from which they cannot escape but which the chameleon can feed from at will. Other food items include flies, hatched from maggots obtained from fishing tackle shops, locusts, wax worms, mealworms, and even pink mice. All food items should be fed a nutritious diet themselves as this will ultimately be utilized by the chameleon.

BREEDING

The gravid female searches out a nest site prior to laying, and suitable areas should be available in the vivarium. These consist of mounds of moist peat and leaf litter to a depth of at least 20 cms and in a secluded position within the vivarium, such as the corners. The female digs a pit the depth of her body and lays 2 or 3 eggs then moves up out of the pit a little and fills substrate around the eggs. This is repeated until the eggs are laid and the female then covers the tops of the eggs with substrate, leaving behind the eggs in a "tube", stacked on top of each other.

The eggs should be removed to be incubated in a controlled environment, taking care to mark the orientation of the eggs. They should be transferred to a suitably moist medium; the best seems to be "vermiculite", but only covered with the medium to 50% to allow inspection of the developing egg. The eggs are quite large in comparison to the size of the female, around 20mm diameter and only slightly oval. This large size results in a low number of eggs, usually 10 to 12, though they can number up to 20.

The incubation temperature for the eggs should be around 75^{0}F (21^{0}C). A little below this seems to do no harm, even to 65^{0}F (18.3^{0}C), but the temperature should not go above 75^{0}F, as this has proved detrimental to the developing embryos.

The eggs are reported to take around 100 days incubation (Schmidt *et al,* 1989). However I have had eggs hatch 10 days earlier at 85 to 90 days, but the incubation temperature increased to 85^{0}F in the latter quarter of incubation due to a fault on the temperature regulator. Some eggs did not hatch although they reached full term, and when opened revealed fully developed young. This is almost certainly due to the erronously high incubation temperature.

The young are quite large at hatching, 30 mm snout to vent, 45 mm total. Rearing the young chameleons has so far been relatively easy and problem free given that the temperature regime indicated above for adult specimens is strictly adhered to.

Feeding presents no problems as the young will take house flies and fruit flies, even within 4 hrs of hatching! The young grow quickly, and are soon feeding on crickets and other larger items. They can reach adult size in as little as 12 months.

Chameleo johnstoni has proved a very interesting and spectacular species which can be successfully bred and raised in captivity.

REFERENCES

Schmidt, W., Tamm, K. & Wallikewitz, (1989). *Chameleons Drachen unser zeit* Terrarien bibliothek

Witte, G. De. (1965). *Les Chameleons de L'Afrique centrale.* Mus. R.Afr.Cent.

British Herpetological Society Bulletin No. 41. 1992

THE REPRODUCTION IN CAPTIVITY OF THE NATAL MIDLAND DWARF CHAMELEON, *BRADYPODION THAMNOBATES*

BERT LANGERWERF

10514 Chilton Road 73, Montevallo, Alabama, 35115, U.S.A.

INTRODUCTION

The Herpetological Association of Africa invited me to their second Symposium held in Bloemfontein, 8-11 April, 1991. I gave a slide show there and met several interesting herpetologists from South Africa. One of them was Lynn Raw, from Merivale, Natal. He invited me to his home and introduced me to a dwarf chameleon,

Plate 1. Adult female *Bradypodion thamnobates.* *photo: Stephen Peltz*

Bradypodion thamnobates, described by him as a new species in 1976. When I looked at its habitat around houses and in gardens, and when I obtained information about the local climate, it appeared to me that I was dealing with a species which would be easily kept in captivity. At the locality where we were the animals were abundant, so that it was easy to collect a breeding group of 20 animals within an hour. Thanks to the help of wildlife authorities in Pietermaritzburg, Natal, I received CITES export permits. I promised to give information if I succeeded in breeding this species, which I do by writing this article.

CLIMATIC DATA

I obtained information on the local climate from *Climatic change and variability in Southern Africa* by P.D. Tyson, University of the Witwatersrand, Johannesburg, Oxford University Press, Cape Town. The following data I extracted by locating the range of *Bradypodion thamnobates* on the climate maps by Tyson:

(a) Mean annual rainfall: 100 cm
(b) Above 80% of rainfall in summer
(c) 120 days of recordable rain
(d) Between 20 and 30 days with over 10mm rain
(e) Frequency of 4-day rainy spells: 10
(f) Days with thunder: 60
(g) Days with hail: between 4 and 6
(h) Days when the temperature exceeds 30°C: 30
(i) Days when the temperature falls below 0°C: about 5.

Plate 2. Adult male *Bradypodion thamnobates.* *photo: Stephen Peltz*

Plate 3. Four different ages of *Bradypodion thamnobates* on one branch, from left to right: adult male; 3 months old; 5 weeks old; new born; 3 days old. *photo: Bert Langerwerf*

Plate 4. Habitat of *B. thamnobates* at Merivale, Natal, April 1991. *photo: Bert Langerwerf*

From all this we learn that this chameleon must be able to live at temperatures above 30°C and to be able to survive days with nightfrost, when they probably hide deep in high weeds and bushy vegetation.

The climate of Alabama is characterised by abundant rainfall and by hot summers with many days when the temperature rises above 30°C. In winter here the temperatures are comparable to those of March and April in England. Night frosts of -10°C are possible, but also days where the temperature reaches 25°C may occur. However, most days average about 15°C during the day, with more sunshine than in England.

ACCOMMODATION

The terraria in which I keep the chameleons in Alabama have a surface area of 1½ x 2½ m. They are inset into the ground and face south. The rear third is covered by a sheltering layer of concrete, overlaid by a 30 cm depth of earth. This feature gives extra protection against excessive heat or cold. Looking at pictures of the habitat, one can easily see that this animal in nature always has the possibility of hiding in shade or weed cover. Therefore these terraria are filled with weeds and fine branches in such a way that the branches extend from beneath the concrete cover to the open, sunny ⅔ of the terrarium. As the amount of weeds and branches affords plenty of living space for the chameleons, I had no problem keeping up to 2 males and 5 females in one terrarium.

The chameleons live all year round in these terraria. Only when there is a chance of nightfrost I cover them at night with old rugs. A tomato plant placed inside the terrarium is an indicator to check if it remains frost free. In January we had over 100 cm of snow.

REPRODUCTION

At the end of April, 1991 I returned to Alabama with my breeding group of Chameleons. It was immediately clear that I was dealing with a hardy animal, as between capture in Natal and arrival in Alabama was an interval of about 10 days, yet in spite of this all the animals survived. Only one male was later lost to disease, probably caused by stress. Also some may have escaped during a spring-time tornado when flying pieces of trees destroyed the wire-mesh at night.

During 1991 the females appeared gravid but no births were noted either here or in California (Sean McKeown of Fresno Zoo, who accompanied me to Natal, also kept some of the chameleons there). I discovered the first young on March 9, 1992, when somebody from Knoxville Zoo was visiting me and we were observing the terraria. There were about 15 new-born. Later, during March, April and May of this year, all 7 females I have gave birth, producing a total of 106 young. Also, the animals kept by Sean McKeown gave birth in May.

At birth the young are 20+20mm – 21+21mm in length. The best fed and strongest females gave birth to the largest young. The largest female gave birth to 20 young (21+21mm) on 29 May.

Table 1. Chameleon births in 1992

Female	Date	Number born	
1	9.3.92	15	Note: All terraria were
2	24.4.92	17	thoroughly searched,
3	2.5.92	16	but it is always possible
4	14.5.92	8	that I failed to find all
5	22.5.92	16	young so that these
6	22.5.92	14	figures may be slightly
			higher.
7	29.5.92	20	

The young started to feed on fruitflies (*Drosophila)* and have been maintained in terraria of $1m^3$, 20-30 individuals to each terrarium. After several weeks I checked the terraria at night and removed and separated the 2 or 3 individuals which lagged behind in growth. The terraria are all covered with mesh screen and filled with twigs and weeds. The big leaves of the weeds provide shade for these small creatures. After some weeks small crickets (*Gryllus*) were added to the diet. No vitamin or mineral supplements were given as the animals were raised outside.

The growth rate is fabulous: those born in March reached adult size in June, and I expect all those born this spring will themselves breed next spring.

The adult chameleons are given a mixed diet of fruitflies, flies, crickets, and small "giant" mealworms (*Zophobas*).

ACKNOWLEDGEMENTS

I wish to express my thanks to all my South African friends, who were so helpful to me, especially Mr. O. Bourguin, Mr. R. Douglas, Mr. A. Lambiris, Mr. J. Marais and Mr. L. Raw.

REFERENCES

Raw, Lynn R.G. (1976). A Survey of the Dwarf Chameleons of Natal, South Africa, with Descriptions of three New Species. *Novitates*, Durban Museum, **XI**, 7.

Branch, Bill (1988). *Field Guide to Snakes and other Reptiles of South Africa.* Cape Town.

British Herpetological Society Bulletin No. 2. 1980

CARE AND CAPTIVE BREEDING OF THE NORTHERN PINE SNAKE *PITUOPHIS M. MELANOLEUCUS*

RAYMOND A. HINE

P.O. Box 992, Wickford, Essex SS12 9EW

DESCRIPTION AND RANGE

The Northern Pine Snake is one of the U.S.A.'s most impressive serpents, both in size and colour. The record length is 83" (210.8cm), with an average of over 60" (152cm).

The background colour ranges from a light buff to a dirty or almost pure white. This is overlaid with dark brown or jet black saddles, to give a very striking effect. The scales are keeled.

Youngsters are similar to adults, but have more of an orangey or pinkish tinge to the background colour and the saddles are brown, thus giving it an appearance which could mistake it for its western cousins, the bull and gopher snakes.

The range of this species is S. New Jersey (where it is a protected species), W. Virginia, S. Kentucky, Tennessee, N. Alabama, N. Georgia, S.W. and S.E. N. Carolina and S. Carolina.

HABITAT AND HABITS

It is found mostly in dry flat sandy areas, or dry mountain ridges in or near to pine woods. Being so large and diurnal one would think it would be a common sight to herpetologists in its range, but this is not so. Probably because of its feeding habits it is rarely seen. Being an avid rodent eater it no doubt spends most of its active life down rodent burrows searching for food. Birds, nestlings and eggs are also eaten and for this prey item the Pine snake will climb trees. In hot weather the snake may be encountered at dusk.

CARE IN CAPTIVITY

Housing

The cage should be quite roomy, 36" (91.4cm) x 18" (46cm), being a minimum for one adult. The furnishing should be simple; a hide box, a sturdy branch and a water pot. The floor should be kept clean and dry; newspaper is excellent, although some people use wood shavings, pine needles, pea gravel, heavy aquarium gravel or bracken.

The cage should have good air circulation and a bulb at one end to give a heat gradient. Two hide boxes can be used, one at each end, to give the snake a choice of temperatures.

Feeding

Adults if of a good body weight, should be fed once a week on two mice. Males in breeding conditions will not feed and gravid females will not feed until after the eggs have been laid; nor will either sex feed during the winter 'cool off' period (which, if your aim is to breed Pines, is essential). Adults will also eat day old chicks and smallish fresh farm eggs. However, if fed solely on these, their faeces become very runny and smelly.

There are no hard and fast rules on how much an individual should be fed, as it will depend entirely on the condition of the specimen at that particular time. A female that has just laid eggs obviously needs feeding up before the winter 'cool off' period (which can last up to 5 months in my collection). Females will also need larger meals after the cooling period and before being mated by a male in the spring.

Hatchling Pines will generally eat baby mice from the start, so are very easy to rear. They do, however, tend to gorge themselves if the opportunity arises (as do most species of *Pituophis).* This should be avoided as they may regurgitate and this cannot do the snake any good.

REARING HATCHLINGS

I obtained my 5 specimens (2 males and 3 females) as hatchlings in autumn 1977. For their first winter they were kept in individual sandwich boxes with nylon mesh fronts. These boxes, in which I house all my hatchling snakes, were stacked three high in a 36" aquarium. The two 40 watt bulbs, fitted in the lid, were left on for 16 hours a day and a heat pad under the tank assured the temperature would not fall below 75°F (24°C) even on the coldest nights.

The youngsters fed throughout their first winter and it was not until their second winter that I allowed them a cooling off period. By this time all the youngsters had grown to between 42" (107 cm) and 48" (122 cm), and were living in 36" cages. The bulbs in the cages were wired up to an automatic timer, which switches on and off at pre-set times. The photo-period I use is governed by the natural day-lengths outside. I simply set the timer to come on about 30 minutes after sunrise, and go off about 30 minutes before sunset. This normally gives about 16 hours of daylight in the height of the summer, and 8 hours in the winter.

The room has no additional heat source, but as the house is centrally heated, and the room is an upstairs bedroom, a certain amount of heat is retained; even on the coldest winter nights temperatures never fall below 12°C.

The snakes stopped feeding about the end of September 1978, the males having fed for a couple of weeks longer than the females. Although feeding had stopped and temperatures were quite low, the snakes were still very active. My thoughts were that if the cage prowling activity carried on through the fasting period, a lot of energy and body fat would be used up before spring. At this point I changed all the 25w bulbs for 15w. This seemed to do the trick and they remained relatively inactive for the rest of the winter.

The snakes started feeding again in March 1979 and fed well until the middle of September. They were all in the region of 60" (152 cm) when they stopped feeding, and it was hoped large enough to breed the following spring.

BREEDING

They all saw the winter through without any problems and commenced feeding about the first week in February, a fast of 4 ½ months. The first sign of unusual behaviour was when the two males stopped feeding at the beginning of March. They both seemed very restless, continually nosing the corners of their cages and moving around both day and night. After a few days of this I put the larger male (M1) in the cage of the smaller male (M2). There was a very hostile reaction from both snakes and they spent the next 20 minutes arching their bodies and twining around each other, obviously in some sort of combat ritual. I separated them and a week later put them together again. After 30 minutes of combat they were separated and put with the two largest females.

Both males attempted to mate their respective females, but their approach was totally different. The larger male (M1), rubbed its chin slowly up and down the female's back, while trying to position itself for copulation. The second male (M2) grabbed the female in its jaws and they both flew around the cage at high speed, knocking everything upside down. After a couple of hours, they had all lost interest and were separated. On the 28th March they were reintroduced, this time the females were switched. The same approach by males took place as before. M2 was separated after a few hours, but M1 was left with his mate. Mating activity continued through the night, but copulation was not observed on the various inspections I made through the evening.

These introductions and separations continued until 10th April, but unfortunately copulation was not witnessed. However on the 16th April a mouse was offered and refused by the largest female, up until then a very greedy feeder. Further mice were refused over the next few days, and the body of the snake began to look swollen. It was confirmed that she was gravid when I ran the snake through my hands and felt several large lumps along her body.

On the 28th April she shed her skin, and by this time she was very triangular in shape and extremely heavy bodied. A receptacle, in the form of hand basin, was introduced a couple of days later for egg laying purposes. This was filled with damp sphagnum moss, and covered with some cardboard for added security.

Unfortunately, I had a holiday booked at this time, so I left a friend with instructions to look in a couple of times a week and remove any eggs should they be laid.

On the 15th May my friend found the female straining to pass her final egg. She had already laid five, two in the receptacle and the other three around the cage. Being an experienced herpetologist, he had seen females retain eggs before, so he left her overnight and returned to help her the next day. Unfortunately she was dead, with the two final eggs still inside her. She was probably so weak from laying the first five eggs, which were very large and probably overdue, that she had no strength left for the last two. (Never book holidays at egg laying time!).

The eggs were incubated in a sandwich box half filled with slightly dampened vermiculite. The box was placed on a shelf in my home made incubator and the temperature fluctuated between 26^0 and 31^0C.

Three of the eggs discoloured and went off within ten days of laying. The largest two looked good for about three weeks, until a thick mould grew over one of them. This mould was scraped off now and again, but still grew back, However, both eggs hatched on the 8th July, an incubation period of 55 days.

Plate 1. A newly hatched Pine Snake and eggs.

The young (both females) measured 18" (46cm) long, were very plump, and when picked up hissed and struck repeatedly. They were housed in the same sandwich boxes as their parents had been three years previously. On the 21st July both snakes shed, and each ate a baby mouse the following day.

It is hoped that some males can be bred next year for future captive breeding.

REFERENCES

Conant, R. (1975) *Field Guide to Reptiles and Amphibians of Eastern and Central North America.* Houghton Mifflin Co. Boston.

Kauffeld, C. (1969) *Snakes: The Keeper and the Kept.* Doubleday and Co. Inc. Garden City, New York.

Wagner, E. and Slemmer, G. (1976) Some parameters for breeding reptiles in captivity. *Proceedings of the 1976 Reptile Symposium, Frederick, Maryland.*

British Herpetological Society Bulletin No. 3. 1981

CAPTIVE BREEDING OF *ELAPHE RUFODORSATA* AND *RHABDOPHIS TIGRINUS* FROM THE KOREAN PEOPLE'S DEMOCRATIC REPUBLIC

PIOTR SURA

Department of Biology, Medical Academy,
Kopernika 7, 31-034 Krakow, Poland

Several specimens of living snakes were collected on 9th June, 1980, by Zbigniew Szyndlar about 50 km SW of Pyonyang in the vicinity of Taesong-ho Lake. They belong to the commonest species from this region – *Elaphe rufodorsata* and *Rhabdophis tigrinus.* Rice fields are their typical habitat and they spend the majority of time laying in the water.

Three females of *E. rufodorsata* (Plate 1) were placed in the terrarium of size 70 x 45 x 63 cm. The snakes got used to new conditions very quickly and began to eat frogs almost immediately thereafter. A month later they were bold enough to approach my hands searching for food and sometimes all three tried to swallow the same frog. This species constricts larger prey and swallows it as a rule from the head (Plate 2). Only smaller frogs can be eaten from behind. In the middle of July they began to refuse offered frogs, only occasionally eating young specimens. The snakes were however very thick and it was clear they were pregnant. It is quite possible that during constriction of prey the embryos could be damaged. This species is especially remarkable in being ovoviviparous, but there is not much information about this (Fitch, 1970). Bannikov *et al.* (1977) state that this species gives birth to 8-20 young of size 165-180 mm at the end of October, whereas Terentiev and Chernov (1949) report about 8-10 young at the end of September,

Plate 1. Adult female *Elaphe rufodorsata.*

Plate 2. *Elaphe rufodorsata* swallowing adult frog, *Rana temporaria.*

Plate 3. *Elaphe rufodorsata*, juvenile aged 10 days.

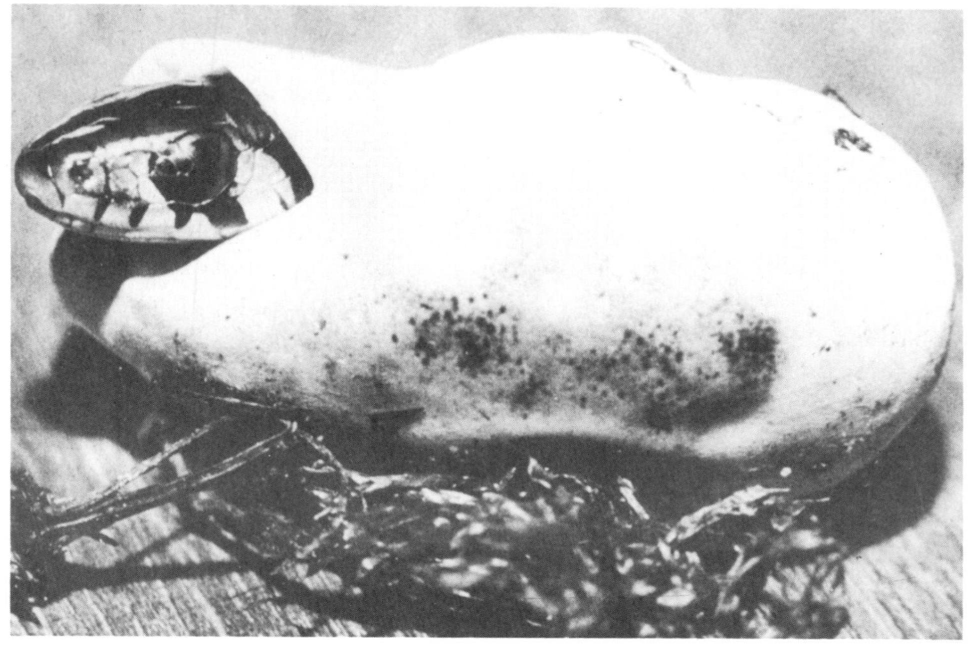

Plate 4. *Rhabdophis tigrinus* hatching from egg.

and up to 21 according to data of Pope (1935). Each of my females of size 50-60 cm produced 7 young on 2nd September, 29th September and 7th October respectively. The babies hatched in the oviducts of the female and the egg membranes emerged after the hatchlings. In the first two broods there was one embryo dead though fully developed, length 182 mm and 158 mm respectively. Freshly born snakes were shedding within 1-2 hours and they started to feed on small frogs after 2-3 days, constricting their prey in the same way as adult specimens. When disturbed they vomited a frog when even almost completely swallowed. Although this species is specialized in feeding on fish and amphibians, one of my females, however, eats weaned mice from tweezers even just before shedding. Also, a juvenile *Natrix natrix* kept in the same terrarium once was swallowed and then vomited. The preferred temperature of these snakes is 25-28°C in my terrarium.

R. tigrinus has been much more studied, especially in Japan. It is one of the several members of the aglyphic colubrids being potentially venomous and there is one report on human death caused by this snake (Mittleman and Goris, 1978; see also Minton and Mebs, 1978). Two specimens were brought to Poland. The female of about 1m long laid 2 eggs on 13th June in the bag during the journey back to Poland and were destroyed, then 13 eggs on 1st July which were incubated and 12 eggs on 18th July in the water pot which were also lost. In total it laid 27 eggs. Bannikov *et al.* (1977) report about 18-22 eggs depending on the size of female (see also review by Fitch). Fitch writes that at room temperature (20-30°C) incubation averages 37.6 (29 to 45) days. Trutnau ((1979) refers to Emilianov that incubation is about 46-47 days. According to my records the first snake hatched on 3rd August (after 34 days) and two others the day later (Plate 4). Unfortunately some eggs dried when I was out of Krakow and others were killed during checking the stages of the embryos' development. Their size was within the average size of hatchings (150-170 mm) known from the literature. The eggs were incubated in a big jar with earth and Sphagnum moss at about 20°C at night and about 30°C during the day. Such changes seem to be very important for the embryos. With eggs of *Chelydra serpentina* incubation at constant temperatures of 20°C resulted in females, whereas 26°C produces males; between these temperatures a mixture of males and females will be produced (Yntema, 1979; see also Limpus and Miller, 1980). Hatchlings began to feed on tadpoles of *Bufo viridis* days later, catching them in a dish of water. The first shedding occurred on 10th August. They became used to captive conditions quickly and it is very exciting to see animals with such an excellent apetite. It was impossible to put one frog in the terrarium, I had to give them all food at the same time; they also took frogs from my hands. Sometimes serious biting during competition for food took place, and they were so keen to feed that they would do so with milky eyes just before shedding. This species usually eats frogs from behind and when the prey is too large it is left. When this happens the frog dies quickly, suggesting that the venom is quite strong. These snakes also eat small fish and newts.

REFERENCES

Bannikov, A.G., Darevsky, I.S., Ishchenko, V.G., Rustamov, A.K., Scherbak, N.N. (1977) *A Guide to Amphibians and Reptiles of U.S.S.R.* Prosvieschenie, Moskow, 415 pp. (in Russian).

Fitch, H.S. (1970) *Reproductive cycles in lizards and snakes.* Univ. Kans. Mus. Nat. Hist., Misc. Pub. No. 62: 1-247.

Limpus, C.J., Miller, J.D. (1980) Potential problems in artifiicial incubation of turtle eggs. *Herpetofauna*, 12: 23-24.

Minton, S.A., Mebs, D. (1978) Vier Bibfalle durch Colubriden (Reptilia: Serpentes: Colubridae). *Salamandra*, 14: 41-43.

Mittleman, M.B., Goris, R.C. (1978). Death caused by the bite of the Japanese colubrid snake *Rhabdophis tigrinus* (Boie) (Reptilia, Serpentes, Colubridae). *J. Herpetol.*, 12: 109-111.

Terentiev, P.V., Chernov, S.A., (1949). *A Guide to Reptiles and Amphibians.* Sovietskaya Nauka, Moskow, 340 pp. (in Russian).

Trutnau, L., (1979) *Schlangen im Terrarium. Band I Ungiftige Schlangen.* Verlag Eugen Ulmer, 200 pp.

Yntema, C.L. (1979). Temperature levels and periods of sex determination during incubation of eggs of *Chelydra serpentina. J. Morph.*, 159: 17-28.

British Herpetological Society Bulletin No. 7. 1983

THE SECOND GENERATION OF CAPTIVE BRED *RHABDOPHIS TIGRINUS*

PIOTR SURA

Department of Biology, Medical Academy, Kopernika 7, 31-034 Krakow, Poland

Two males and one female hatched at the beginning of August 1980 and raised together successfully reproduced in 1982, but sexual activity had already occurred one year after hatching (on 10 August 1981) when the female reached about 70cm in length. Both males were smaller and one of them started to court the female by flicking his tongue over her dorsum and pressing his lower jaw against her body in order to stimulate her to crawl, and coiling his tail around hers. The movement of the female induced increased activity in the male. This behaviour continued until the end of September. However, in October the snakes became apathetic and stopped feeding, so I decided to put them into the refrigerator (on 1 November).

They were removed on 18 February, 1982 and courtship occurred the next day. A week later the second male also showed interest in the female – its interest increased noticeably after the female shed its skin. Mating activity was continuous until the end of February, and was not interrupted even when the female was swallowing frogs. The female ate the last frog 10 days before egg laying. Twelve eggs were laid on 20 April (age of female 1 year 8 months and 17 days) between 5.30 pm and 7.00 pm. The mean size of the eggs was 29.0 x 16.0mm. All of them were fertile. Courtship behaviour and mating recommenced immediately after egg laying and continued until the end of April. At the beginning of June the eggs reached their maximum size. The largest one reached 39 x 27, $\bar{x}$ =35.0 x 24.7mm, so their volume increased about three times (max 3.8). Seven young of about 180mm in length emerged from the eggs on 4-7 June after 35-38 days of incubation. A further 5 died just before hatching (their lengths were: 183, 187, 181, 166, 187mm $\bar{x}$ = 180.8mm). Shedding occcurred a week later (compare Sura, 1981.)

The second clutch of 9 eggs was laid in the afternoon on 8 June, of which one was infertile and another not properly developed. Their sizes: 36 x 16, 33 x 17, 33 x 16, 33 x 17, 34 x 17, 31 x 17, 34 x 18, 35 x 17 ($\bar{x}$ = 33.6 x 16.9mm) and 22 x 144mm (undeveloped), a little larger than the previous clutch. The period of incubation was slightly longer because I had to leave Kraków for some time and the heating was switched off. Two juveniles only hatched on 21 July, after 43 days; the others died before hatching. Their sizes: 152, 160, 190, 181 and 177 ($\bar{x}$ = 172.0mm). The last one was removed from the biggest egg on 19 July. It measured 42 x 25mm (the egg volume increased 2.7 times). This low reproductive success may have been caused by inbreeding and/or vitamin deficiency. In spite of this, the hatchlings were in good condition and started to eat without difficulties – they prefer "jumping" frogs – tadpoles did not stimulate them in the same way.

In August courtship commenced again, but with less intensity, and continued with intervals until the end of October. The female's last ecdysis occurred on 18 October, when she was noticeably gravid. Oviposition took place at night on 2 November but only 8 eggs were found (one abnormal – 7 with $\bar{x}$ = 30.6 x 17.7mm). Unfortunately the female was very weak and died in the afternoon of the following day. Her oviduct contained a further 13 eggs of similar size, so the total number of eggs produced in 1982 was 42. The total length of the female was 870mm (SVL 735mm); growth rate of 558mm in the first year and 142mm in the second. The eggs failed to develop, only one contained an embryo in an early stage of development.

According to the literature known to me, *Rhabdophis tigrinus* produces one clutch of eggs in one season, at the end of July. However, it is quite possible that the period of reproductive activity may be extended or at least this may happen in captivity. Male snakes determine the productive stage of the female on the basis of an estrogen-dependent pheromone produced by glands in the dorsal skin (Crews,

1976). However, it was stated recently that the sex attractant pheromone of the female red-sided garter snake *(Thamnophis sirtalis parietalis)* is produced in an active form in the liver under the control of estrogen and is present there and in the circulation, reaching its active site on the skin by passing through the keratinized outer skin cells in an active process associated with courtship (Garstka and Crews, 1981; Crews and Garstka, 1982). Female *Thamnophis* are not attractive to other males after copulation and this change of female attractivity is a consequence of the deposition of a mating plug by the male (Crews, 1979; Crews and Garstka, 1982).

It is difficult to ascertain the reasons for the last unsuccessful clutch. The female apparently produced sex pheromone for an abnormally long time and, in the light of the above facts, this may not have resulted in the deposition of a seminal plug. Such a situation is probably caused by lower testicular activity by the males in autumn. However, the asynchronization of the time when eggs could be fertilized with the time of insemination should not be excluded. Of course, the physiological factors regulating reproductive function and behaviour of *Thamnophis* may differ from those in other snakes, even closely related, so these noteworthy discoveries of American herpetologists could be extended to other species after special research. But one thing can be pointed out now. A striking correlation exists in European *Natrix natrix* between the size of the ovaries and the abdominal fat body. In females with undeveloped ovaries the fat bodies are very large. When ovaries increase in size the fat bodies show an opposite reaction, so after ovulation only rudimentary fat bodies can be found. This may be explained by the theory of Crews and Garstka. Gonadotropic hormone causes the follicles in the ovary to secrete an estrogen which in turn causes the abdominal fat bodies to release fatty molecules incorporated in the liver into vitellogenin. The vitellogenin is deposited (with other fatty molecules) deep in the skin serving as the pheromone that attracts the male for mating. Not going into details, after mating an increased production of vitellogenin is noted. Now it is gathering in the ovary being a precursor of yolk. Thus, a smaller size of fat body is correlated with advanced development of eggs.

Summing up, *Rhabdophis tigrinus* is a very attractive species, simple to maintain in captivity where it readily reproduces. Some failures described here could be avoided though the reproductive cycle of this snake and possible endocrinologic anomalies are still not satisfactorily known.

REFERENCES

Crews, D. (1976). Hormonal control of male courtship behavior and female attractivity in the garter snake *(Thamnophis sirtalis sirtalis). Horm. Behav.* **7:** 451-460.

Crews, D. (1979). Endocrine control of reptilian reproductive behavior. In: *Endocrine Control of Sexual Behaviour,* ed. C. Beyer, Raven Press, New York, pp. 167-222.

Crews. D. and Garstka, W.R. (1982). The ecological physiology of a garter snake. *Sci. Amer.*, **246:** 159-168.

Garstka, W.R. and Crews, D. (1981). Female sex heromone in the skin and circulation of a garter snake. *Science,* **214:** 681-683.

Sura, P. (1981). Captive breeding of *Elaphe rufodorsata* and *Rhabdophis tigrinus* from the Korean People's Democratic Republic. *Brit. Herpetol. Soc. Bull.* **3:** 20-24.

British Herpetological Society Bulletin No. 4. 1981

NOTES ON THE CARE AND CAPTIVE BREEDING OF THE SINALOAN MILK SNAKE *(LAMPROPELTIS TRIANGULUM SINALOAE)*

MIKE NOLAN

Willow Cottage, 48 Tikhurst Lane, Dorking, Surrey RH5 4DZ

INTRODUCTION

Lampropeltis triangulum with its twenty-three subspecies has one of the most extensive geographical ranges of any species of snake. In fact a distance of 3,600 miles, from Canada down throughout most of the United States and Central America to Colombia, Venezuela and Ecuador in South America. The subspecies range in size from the pretty and diminutive Scarlet King Snake *(L. t. elapsoides)* with a maximum recorded length of 686 mm (Conant, 1975) to the relatively gargantuan *L. t. micropholis* which can reach a length of nearly 2 metres. The Sinaloan Milk *(L. t. sinaloae)* is one of the Mexican geographical races.

Description

The Sinaloan Milk reaches a maximum length of about 1220mm with an average adult size of between 600mm and 1000mm long. With its classic red, black and white bands it is one of the tricoloured King snakes. The pattern consists of between 10 and 16 dark red to orange broad body rings which are separated by black rings which in turn are split by fine white rings.

The head, which is indistinct from the neck, is black with variable amounts of white flecking on the snout. The subspecies most likely to be confused with the Sinaloan Milk is Nelson's King *(L. t. nelsoni)* with a range adjacent to the Sinaloan Milk. The chief difference being on the Sinaloan Milk, the first black ring which crosses the throat midventrally is usually unbroken forming a V, whereby in the Nelson's King it is usually broken or narrowly connected in a straight line.

Range

Williams (1978) gives the range as: the southwestern corner of Sonora, southeastward through the broad coastal plain and foothills of Sinaloa to near the southern border of Nayarit and up the Rio Fuerte into southwestern Chihuahua.

HUSBANDRY

Housing

The main bank of cages I keep my *Lampropeltis* spp. in consists of twelve units in four rows of three, each one measuring 610mm x 380mm x 380mm, with access by sliding glass fronts. They are made of contiplas and all the seams inside the cages are silicon sealed, which makes for easy cage cleaning and good hygiene. Substrate is white newsprint and each cage is furnished with a water bowl, a length of terracotta half piping (which I use instead of hide boxes) and odd pieces of driftwood and green plastic plants for aesthetic reasons.

Heating and lighting is by means of a 15 watt pygmy light bulb in each cage, which in my room is more than sufficient to bring temperatures up to the required levels. The light bulbs are connected to a timeswitch and a dimmer switch, which gives me control, not only of how long the bulbs are on, but the amount of heat and light given off by them.

The lights are on for 16 hours a day during summer and reduced to 8 hours during winter, with a simultaneous dimming of the bulbs to reduce temperatures. In fact the lights are turned off completely for about six weeks during the midwinter, through temperatures in the cages never drop below 15°C. As most of my *Lampropeltis* spp. stop feeding during the winter period the lowering of temperatures help to reduce loss of body weight. Temperatures in summer vary between 22-30°C, and in winter 16-24°C.

For incubating eggs and to keep hatchling snakes feeding through the winter period, I use an environmental chamber. This is a purpose built cupboard made of contiplas with a glass panelled door and shelves inside to take the various sizes of plastic boxes I use. It is 2000mm tall and 610mm square. Heating is by means of two 50 watt heater pads attached to a thermostat to give an average temperature of 28°C; it is lit by a five foot "True-Light" flourescent tube which is on a time-switch to give a 16 hour day light period all the year through. During summer this tube often has to be turned off because of excessive heat build-up. The chamber is ventilated by means of one 13 cm^2 vent in the top, and four smaller vents, one in each side, at the base.

Feeding

Bogert and Oliver (1945) mention two wild specimens, one containing two unidentified reptile eggs and the other an unidentifiable juvenile mammal. I think I can safely add lizards, small snakes and fledgling birds, with probably lizards and rodents forming the bulk of the diet in the wild.

In captivity they will feed on "pink" and DEAD ADULT MICE. I emphasise the word dead as they are not true constrictors in the normal sense, but kill prey (too large to be swallowed live) by getting a firm grip with their jaws and bracing themselves and applying pressure, with the prey being sandwiched between the snake's body and the ground or some solid object. Now, with an adult mouse in the close confines of a rodent burrow, where they probably spend a lot of their nocturnal prowling, this is obviously a very efficient method. But given the comparatively open spaces and unnatural smooth surfaces of the usual captive conditions, this can become a hair raising experience for all concerned, with the snake in danger of being badly bitten!

CARE AND CAPTIVE BREEDING

In the autumn of 1979 I purchased four wild caught adult Sinaloan Milk Snakes from a dealer. They consisted of two males and two females, their lengths varying between 620mm and 850mm, one pair being slightly larger than the other.

They were rather thin and so I decided to house them in a different room from the rest of my collection for a quarantine period which I do with all new stock of questionable health.

My suspicions were founded, as having fed avidly on "pink" mice they subsequently regurgitated.

Flagellated protozoa were suspected as the cause (Wagner 1979); they were all given Flagyl via a stomach tube, at the single dose rate of 250 mg per kg of body weight, after which there were no more regurgitation problems.

After about six weeks it was felt safe to introduce them into the room in which I keep the rest of my collection. Though gaining weight steadily, they were not up to full bodyweight, and as the main bank of cages were now on a decreasing light period and the occupants rapidly going off feed, it was decided to forgo any breeding attempts with the Sinaloans the following spring and concentrate on getting them into good condition. I separated them into four large plastic freezer boxes, which I put in my environmental chamber to encourage optimum feeding through the coming winter.

The following late spring the light cycle was back to 16 hours in my main bank of cages and the Sinaloans were then introduced into what was to be their permanent homes. The two females were put into one cage together and each of the two males given a cage of its own.

They were now in beautiful condition and feeding on an average of one freshly killed adult mouse a week each, having been weaned off the "pink" which they were consuming at an alarming rate.

They continued to do well during the summer, and in late autumn were cooled down with the rest of the snakes. As a point of interest, though the other *Lampropeltis* spp. in my collection stop feeding during the winter period, the Sinaloans continued to feed right through, though infrequently.

About the end of February the light cycle was increased weekly in hourly stages back to the summer levels by the end of April. With my *Lampropeltis* spp. the sexes are usually housed separately and the females introduced to the males at four or five day intervals until mating activity is observed.

With the other species of *Lampropeltis* mating activity was at its highest levels during April, but there was still no sign of anything happening with the Sinaloans despite alternating the females between the males. Then on the 18th May during late evening time the large female was put in with the large male for the umpteenth time, when this time his response was immediate; with short jerky movements he started to follow the newly sloughed female around the cage trying to pin her down. In fact for the first half hour he couldn't seem to work out which end was which and was trying to mate her in a head to tail position. Eventually after about one and a half hours of some frantic chasing round the cage, copulation was seen to be successful.

Mating activity was seen on various occasions over the following three or four weeks, with both males having successfully mated both females. As a point of interest, any sort of disturbance to the Sinaloans would trigger off mating activity (e.g. cage cleaning, feeding, etc.), in fact just removing them from their cages and putting them straight back in again was sometimes enough to get them started.

The larger of the two females was the first to show signs of being gravid with the typical pear shaped cross-section appearance, and the ventral surface, being normally flat, had a convex shape around the rear third of the body. On the 29th June she completed her pre-laying slough (Wagner, 1979) and a couple of days later a plastic box half filled with damp spagnum moss and with an entry hole in the lid, was put in the cage in readiness for egg laying.

Over the next few days she was encouraged to use the box and on the night of the 5th July she was discovered in the box in the act of egg laying. Having laid three already and in the middle of laying a fourth she was left alone for an hour. On returning she had five eggs and was examined to ensure there were no more left inside her. Though the eggs were adhering together, they were still moist enough for me to very gently separate them. The measurements of the eggs were as follows: 58mm x 23mm, 60mm x 20mm, 60mm x 23mm, 63mm x 24mm, 70mm x 20mm.

My preferred incubation medium being vermiculite, I mixed 8 oz of this with 8 fluid oz of water, which had been previously boiled and allowed to cool down. The only slightly damp mixture was put in the four litre size ice-cream containers, which are rather tall plastic boxes measuring 20mm x 150mm and 155mm high.

With the amount of vermiculite only occupying 25% of the box this left 75% for airspace. The eggs were half buried in the vermiculite and the tight fitting lid was put on (no air holes were made).

Plate 1. Hatchling *L. t. sinaloae* at 62 days old.

The box was put in my environmental chamber and twice weekly the lid removed to check the eggs and, in the process of doing so, they were gently fanned with the lid to exchange the air in the box. With this method, no extra water needed to be added and no fungal growth problems occurred throughout the incubation period.

The first sign of hatching was observed on the 7th September (64 days) when one of the eggs had split with a baby peering out, and by the 9th, all five youngsters had emerged from the eggs.

They were absolutely beautiful replicas of the adults, the only difference being the colour of the bands, which were bright yellow instead of the normal white of adults. Their lengths were as follows: 300mm, 310mm, 311mm, 320mm, 322mm.

They were separated into two litre capacity plastic boxes of the type the eggs had been incubated in, which had the same dimensions but were only half as tall. (The keeping of hatchling snakes in relatively small containers may be important to encourage optimum feeding levels). The boxes were vented, lined with newsprint and furnished with a small water bowl and a piece of cork bark for them to hide under. The hatchlings sloughed on the 16th September and within hours of doing so they all accepted their first meal of newborn pink mice.

The second female laid eight slightly smaller eggs on the 26th July. By the time they were discovered they were stuck firmly together in a cluster and could not be safely separated. They were buried in the vermiculite, with those at the bottom of the cluster completely buried and some at the top not touching the vermiculite at all.

Incubation procedure was exactly the same as for the first clutch, and they hatched on the 28th September (64 days) with another 100% hatch rate. The hatchlings were slightly smaller than the first.

After they had settled down to feeding regularly all the hatchlings were probed to determine the sexes. The first clutch comprised one male and four females, and the second clutch six males and two females, so overall the sexes were evenly matched and to date all are doing well.

REFERENCES

Conant, R. (1975). *A Field Guide to the Reptiles and Amphibians of Eastern and Central North America.* Second edition, Houghton Mifflin Co., Boston.

Bogert, C.M. and Oliver, J.A. (1945). A preliminary analysis of the herpetofauna of Sonora. *Bull. Amer. Mus. Nat. His.* 83, 297-426.

Wagner, E. (1979). Breeding King Snakes. *Int. Zoo Year Book* 19, 98-100.

Williams, K.L. (1978). *Systematics and Natural History of the American Milk Snake.* Milwaukee Public Museum, Publications in Biology and Geology No. 2.

HUSBANDRY NOTES ON THE ASIAN RAT SNAKE *GONYOSOMA OXYCEPHALA*

S. PICKERSGILL[1] and R MEEK[2]

[1] *Department of Pure and Applied Biology, University of Leeds, UK*
[2] *8 Mountfield Road, Waterloo, Huddersfield, UK*

The reproductive biology of rat snakes is relatively well documented although much of this data deals with the North American forms (e.g. Coote & Riches, 1978). However, there is little detailed information on the Asian rat snakes despite their rather frequent appearance in the pet trade. One Asian species often imported is *Gonyosoma (= Elaphe) oxycephala*, an arboreal form with a reputation in captivity for being "difficult" particularly when dealing with wild caught adults (Trutnau, 1986). It is found over a wide area in Southeast Asia where it principally inhabits regions with dense vegetation and very high humidity levels and indeed in captivity such conditions are apparently required if reproduction is to take place (Trutnau, 1986). However, whilst reviewing the recent literature on captive husbandry of snakes we were unable to locate any detailed descriptions of egg incubation techniques, or rearing of the hatchlings of this species. In this paper we provide this basic information, which concerns a clutch of eggs deposited by an imported adult.

Plate 1. Threat posture adopted by juvenile *Gonyosoma oxycephala.*

OBSERVATIONS

A clutch of seven eggs were deposited by an imported female *Gonyosoma oxycephala* on 18 November 1986. These were placed in vermiculite to which water was added and maintained at a weight ratio of three parts water to one part vermiculite. Temperatures during incubation were kept at 26-30°C. Hatching began on 30 March 1987 continuing over a three day period, thus giving an incubation period of approximately 132 days. This is considerably longer than that found for North American rat snakes at similar incubation temperatures (e.g. Coote & Riches, 1978: Meek, 1980). Table 1 shows total lengths and weights of the hatchlings and also the dates of the first sloughs.

The animals were housed individually in small plastic containers for ease of feeding. The containers were maintained at around 28°C, however, initially all the snakes refused food (small dead mice 1-7 days old) and were subsequently force fed on one small dead mouse per week, covered in a multivitamin paste (St Aubrey High Calorie Vitamin Concentrate). The mice were offered to the snakes in the afternoon and left in the containers overnight; those snakes which did not eat were force fed the following day. Voluntary feeding first occurred in snakes 6 and 7 on 15 June 1987 but eventually, by August, all were feeding of their own accord on approximately one small mouse per week which was usually consumed during night or late evening. Due to space limitations it was decided to retain only three snakes (numbers 3, 6 and 7 in Table 1) for exhibition purposes, the weights of which on 20 October 1987 are shown in Table 1 indicating an approximate two-fold increase in weight since hatching.

In contrast to adult *G. oxycephala* which can on occasions be somewhat docile, the juveniles were all rather fierce, adopting a threat posture of rearing up and inflating the throat and striking when approached (Plate 1). This behaviour has persisted to an age of seven months.

Table 1

Hatchling measurements of *Gonyosoma oxycephala* with secondary weight measurements of three retained snakes

	Weight hatching (g)	Weight on 20.10.87	Length at hatching (mm)	Date of first slough
1	19.5		560	12.4.87
2	16.1		510	16.4.87
3	18.8	29.5	565	13.4.87
4	15.6		530	17.4.87
5	18.3		550	12.4.87
6	19.1	31.5	560	13.4.87
7	17.3	37.5	540	14.4.87

REFERENCES

Coote, J.G. & Riches R.J. (1978) Captive reproduction in North American colubrids of the general *Lampropeltis* and *Elaphe. Cotswold Herpetological Symposium report,* **5**; 6-15. Burford: Cotswold Wildlife Park.

Meek, R. (1980) Reproductive behaviour of two temperate zone reptiles *Elaphe obsoleta* and *Lampropeltis getulus A.S.R.A. Journal.* **3**; 45-59.

Trutnau, L. (1986) *Nonvenomous snakes.* New York; Barron's.

British Herpetological Society Bulletin No. 29. 1989

ELAPHE MANDARINA (CANTOR 1842): A PROGRESS REPORT ON A PROBLEMATIC SPECIES IN CAPTIVITY

TREVOR SMITH

3 Juniper Close, Greasby, Wirral L49 3QX, UK

INTRODUCTION

Elaphe mandarina is considered by many herpetologists to represent the 'jewel in the crown' of Asian ratsnakes. It has also been the cause of much consternation as *E. mandarina* commonly languishes in captivity and often dies quickly. It is impossible to confuse *E. mandarina* with any other species. Their pattern and colours are unique and extremely distinctive. In appearance *E. mandarina* is typically grey with dramatic black saddles, each of which contains a bright yellow centre, bordered by yellow. The effect of this beautiful combination of colour and pattern is heightened by the polished appearance of the smooth scales. There can be a great variation between specimens and the grey body colour can show traces of red scales. Sometimes this occurs to an extensive degree and the animal appears to become bright reddish brown. The saddles are also variable in shape and intensity of pigment between specimens. Typically these saddles are diamond shaped and uniform; they can be so pronounced, however that they almost form tranverse crossbands, or so weak that the yellow pigment breaks through forming lacy patterns. There appear to be no geographical correlations regarding these variations. Specimens collected from one locality can exhibit a wide range of pattern and colour characteristics. The head is dramatically patterned with black bands, forming a typical 'bandit's mask and moustache' arrangement. The ventral surface is chequered with black, grey and white pigment. *E. mandarina* is a medium sized colubrid, growing to lengths in excess of 1m; its body form suggests a semi-fossorial life style. In its most attractive colour phases, *E. mandarina* rivals any of the *Lampropeltis* 'tri colour' complex for aesthetic beauty.

There is little useful literature appertaining to natural history, biotope and captive care for *E. mandarina* and regimes devised on its behalf have amounted to little more than intelligent guesswork. After maintaining a pair of *E. mandarina* with limited success for a period of six months I decided to submit an appeal to keepers of this species via society journals in Britain, Europe and America. The aim of this appeal was to determine the current status of *E. mandarina,* assess common factors regarding successful husbandry and disseminate this information in the form of an article. Many positive responses were received and this article represents a synopsis of this new information, supplemented by my own observations and conclusions. I hope that enthusiasts who are currently maintaining *E. mandarina,* or who are considering this enigmatic species, will find some useful information here.

NATURAL HISTORY

The range for *E. mandarina* has been given as Upper Burma, South China (including Chekiang, Fukien, Kwangtung, Kweichow, Szechwan), North Vietnam (including the apparently fertile region for *Elaphe* spp., Tong King). (Pope, 1935; Smith, 1931). It is acknowledged as a montane species occurring at elevations of 700-2300m. Little is known of *E. mandarina's* habits; high lying mountain woods are given as typical habitat, especially in the vicinity of water (lakes, etc.) By examining the habits of related species *(E. perlacea, E. conspicillata),* it is speculated that *E. mandarina* inhabits rodent burrows, also tunnelling beneath rocks and logs, and particularly matted grass.

Preferred prey items include small mice, voles and shrews.

Specimens are often nervously aggressive and extremely shy. Individuals can be decidedly feisty, striking and vibrating their tails; this may be considered a desirable trait when acquiring wild stock, as it is likely to reflect vigour.

SYSTEMATICS

There is common reference to *E. m. takasago* (Maki, 1931) as a distinct subspecies, restricted in its range to Taiwan. Reddish coloured specimens have been wrongly attributed to this form. The three specimens collected apparently possessed higher ventral scale counts than the mainland forms and were similar in colour to specimens collected from Fukien.

As far as I can discover, these are the only records for *E. mandarina* on Taiwan. This species has apparently not been recorded prior to, or subsequent to Maki's discovery and this may challenge its credibility.

The most closely related species to *E. mandarina* are *E. perlacea* (Stejneger, 1929) and *E. conspicillata.* They are found in Szechwan and Japan respectively. Neither species possesses the attractive markings of *E. mandarina,* but are similar in body form, habits and scutellation. The dramatic head patterns are similar in all three species.

CARE IN CAPTIVITY

A number of elaborate environmental regimes have been devised for *E. mandarina*. These have included naturalistic arrangements, outdoor vivaria, 'sweater box' type accommodation and foam rubber sheeting. A variety of substrates have been incorporated including soil, peat, bark mulch, sphagnum moss, pine shavings, vermiculite, etc. These have been selected to accomodate *E. mandarina's* fossorial habits.

There have also been many experiments regarding heating, lighting and humidity.

The consistent factors for successful maintenance appear to be:

a) Security
The psychological needs of *E. mandarina* are such that it requires to feel totally secure before offering a positive feeding response. This has been accomplished by a number of means.

1. Loose substrates (for burrowing purposes).
2. Natural substrates with secure hiding sites.
3. Foam rubber (specimens hide and feed between sheets of foam).
4. Minimal disturbance.

b) Temperature
E. mandarina is a montane species which requires cooler conditions than typically associated with *Elaphe* sp. 'Hot spots' can be provided within the vivarium, but in conjunction with much cooler areas.

Hatchlings have also been successfully raised at lower temperatures, although they appear to be more adaptable in this respect, with specimens thriving under conditions provided for other colubrid juveniles.

Most sources quote a temperature range of 20-27°C (day), 16-20°C (night). The ideal temperature considered by certain keepers is 25°C. When temperatures approach 29°C *E. mandarina* becomes very reluctant to feed.

It is possible to provide temperature gradients also. The ambient temperature in one keeper's vivarium was 27°C, while readings taken from hiding sites indicated 23-25°. Heat tapes/cables restricted to one end of a vivarium have also been employed with success.

c) Humidity
Humidity is a poorly researched aspect of reptile husbandry. The indications are that *E. mandarina* requires a damp environment. This has been achieved in a variety of ways, most commonly by providing permanently moist areas within the vivarium (a minimum of 25% floor area has been recommended). Again hatchlings are less demanding in this respect.

d) Feeding

E. mandarina possesses a light appetite and a preferrence for small prey items. "Pink" or 'fuzzy" mice and "pink" rats are the most frequently accepted food items, with certain individuals accepting weaned mice. Attempts to feed other prey items in captivity (e.g. amphibians) have been largely unsuccessful. Live prey is sometimes demanded by imported specimens. I have found them to react badly to forcefeeding attempts.

e) Lighting

The role that lighting plays in the successful husbandry of *E. mandarina* is speculative. Certain specimens remain entirely nocturnal, whereas others will regularly bask, especially in the early morning. Certain enthusiasts have felt that U.V. lighting has been beneficial, while others consider its influence to be inconsequential. My own experiments in this respect did not reach any firm conclusions.

f) Health

The acquisition of healthy specimens is an obvious prerequisite for the successful maintenance of *E. mandarina,* or any species. For such a shy and specialized animal the route *E. mandarina* must take before arriving in a collection represents an extremely stressful experience. This may lower their resistance to disease and parasitic burdens. Importers/exporters frequently house species from different global localities within close proximity and a degree of cross infection can also be anticipated. Factors which adversely affect the health of specimens often confound the efforts of enthusiasts.

Problems which have been related have included dehydration, endo- and ectoparasites, enteric necrosis, amoebic dysentery, bacterial infections and suspected organ removal. There have also been doubts raised over whether the disease or the 'cure' eventually killed certain specimens. Dehydration appears to be one of the major problems encountered by herpetologists. Individual specimens have suffered dehydration to the degree that they are beyond redemption, with certain organs being extensively damaged.

Recently imported specimens frequently experience problems with sloughing. One particular keeper found a specimen to have two previous sloughs still adhering to its body. Warm water soaking appears to be effective in cases such as these.

Oxfendazole and levamisole HCL have proved effective in the treatment of worms, however one specimen developed a secondary bacterial infection after treatment (Golder, 1974). This condition responded to treatment with Spectinomycin.

Although commonly alluded to, the practice of organ removal from live snakes before export (a practice personally witnessed by myself in a Chinese village) has not been substantiated by post mortem records. Veterinary advice I have received on the subject suggests that snakes thus mutilated (for their gall bladders) could survive for up to two months, and would exhibit the symptoms reported.

From my own observations it would appear that specimens of *E. mandarina* which have been imported into Britain recently have displayed an improvement in their physical condition. There are also more frequent shipments of this species it seems. I am aware of a number of recently imported animals, which have adapted well to captivity and their potential is promising. However, specimens such as these remain in the minority and are easily outnumbered by specimens which have languished and eventually expired over a similar period.

To summarize, the most consistent factors appear to be: Secure hiding sites; cool conditions; high humidity; small prey items; naturalistic furnishings.

BREEDING

As with many species it appears that captive bred *E. mandarina* present few, if any, of the problems associated with their wild caught counterparts. All indications are that they are hardy, adaptable and thrive in similar conditions to those provided

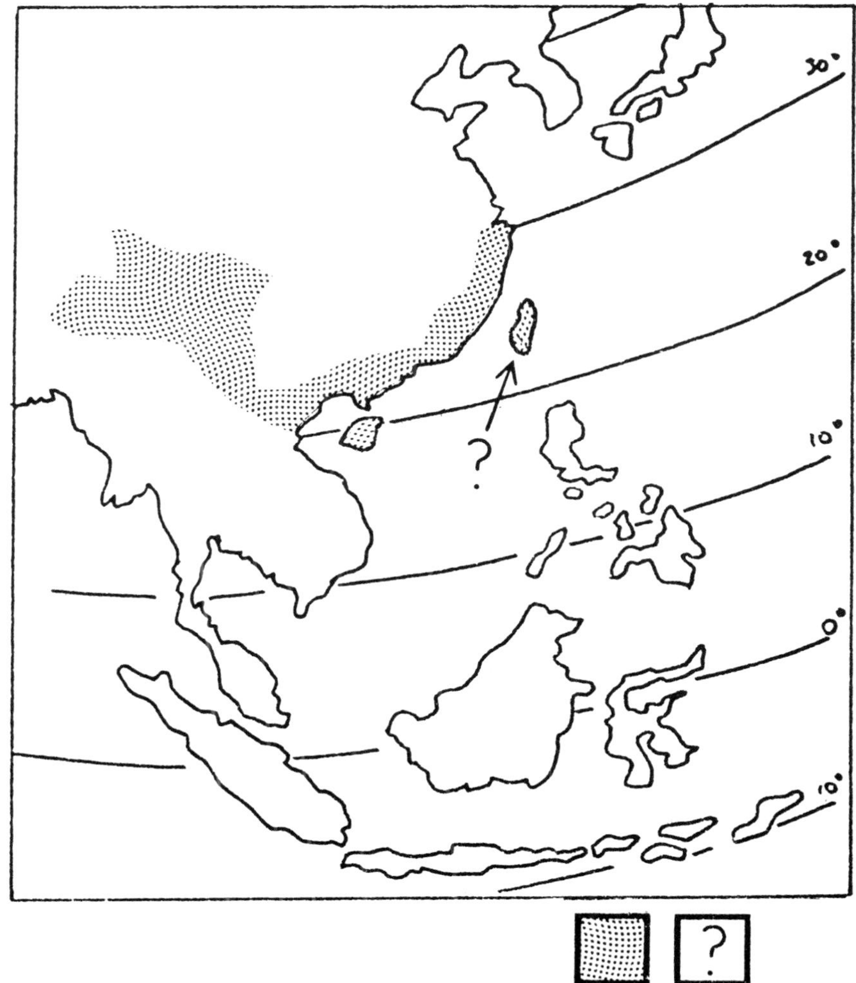

Figure 1. Distribution of *Elaphe mandarina. E. mandarina; E. m. takasago.*

for other *Elaphe* juveniles. They remain, of course, at a premium, but inevitably more will be produced each year and will eventually become available to herpetologists in limited numbers. Most examples of captive born specimens are the result of imported females which have been gravid before purchase. There appears to be a high incidence of fertility associated with eggs laid in this manner with 100% hatch rates being regularly recorded. I have heard of only one report where raising the resulting hatchlings has proved problematic.

To my knowledge there has only been one incidence of true captive breeding with *E. mandarina.* This was accomplished by Bill Gillingham of California in 1988. Bill acquired two pairs of long term captive specimens via three other keepers (initiated by Mike Nolan), which had been in captivity since 1982. It is not unusual for species from highly seasonal environments to take a number of years to readjust their cycles before breeding behaviour can resume. Romer states a case where a pair of *E. porphyracea nigrofasciata* required nine years of captivity before breeding. Originally four specimens (2.2) were obtained in May 1987 and were housed separately for their first month. One of the females died from a respiratory infection during this period. The remaining animals were housed together in June 1987. The vivarium consisted of an all glass tank arranged in a 'naturalistic' manner. The substrate consisted of damp bark mulch and sphagnum moss; this was decorated with living plants and pieces of slate afforded hiding sites. Illumination was provided by a four foot "Grolux" tube. The room was space heated to 26°C, with a 4-5°C drop at night. Temperature readings taken from beneath the slate pieces indicated cooler conditions of about 22°C. All three snakes shared one primary hiding site. "Pink" and "fuzzy" mice were scattered within the vivarium during the evening and would be eaten overnight.

The room was cooled during winter to 15.5-12°C. Heating was gradually re-instated from February onwards and feeding was resumed in March. By late March the female began to exhibit physical signs that she may be gravid. One of the males was not allowed to share the primary hiding site at this time. By April it was confirmed that she was indeed gravid. The post coital slough occurred on May 27th and the female was transferred to a plastic box containing damp vermiculite. Six eggs were laid on June 7th (eleven days after postcoital slough), which were removed for incubation. Incubation temperatures ranged from 27°C (day) to 24°C (night), lower than was provided for the other colubrids which were reproducing in the same room (28.3°C). Despite this cooler incubation regime, the first egg began to hatch on July 26th, 49 days after being laid. The remaining eggs all hatched over a 36 hour period.

The hatchlings were identical to their parents and represented a perfect sex ratio of 3/3. They weighed 10-12 g each and their total lengths were 30cm. Their neonatal skins were sloughed on August 4/5th (9 days after hatching) and they began to feed on "pink" mice without problems. The juveniles were raised in individual plastic boxes, containing damp bark mulch (later replaced by aspen bedding), a

Plate 1. Adult *Elaphe mandarina.* (Bill Gillingham)

Plate 2. Hatching *Elaphe mandarina.* (Bill Gillingham)

piece of bark as a hiding site and a small water bowl. A feeding regime of one "pink" mouse every 4-6 days was introduced; meals which were too large were rejected. They have continued to thrive and have attained lengths of 50cm after six months.

Factors which have contributed to true captive breeding;
a) Well acclimated and conditioned adults.
b) Favourable environmental and psychological conditions.
c) Hibernation.

Table 1. Breeding information

Source (keeper)	Clutch Size	Hatch Rate	Inc. Temp.	Inc. Period	Sex Ratio	Feeding
Gillingham	6	100%	24-27°C	49-52 d	3.3	+
Gillingham	2	100%	25.5.-27.7°	54 d	0.2	+
Bartz	N/K	N/K	N/K	N/K	1.0	+
Nolan	N/K	N/K	N/K	N/K	2.1	+
Schultz	N/K	N/K	N/K	N/K	3.2	+
Muezenmeir	6 + 5	100%	N/K	N/K	N/K	-

N/K = Not known

CONCLUSIONS AND COMMENTS

E. mandarina is arguably the most desirable Asian ratsnake in collections due to its beautiful colours and patterns. It is also one of the most demanding species to maintain successfully in captivity.

Wild caught specimens typically present problems regarding feeding, health and stress. Young specimens are most adaptable and less problematic than adults. Captive bred/born specimens present few, if any, problems, adapting well to captive conditions and feeding satisfactorily. Breeding captive reared specimens should be unproblematic.

E. mandarina exhibits variations in both colour and pattern. It is a montane species which requires cooler conditions than typically associated with *Elaphe* spp. It requires higher humidity levels than typically associated with *Elaphe* spp. It requires a high degree of security. Specimens are frequently aggressive.

E. mandarina possesses a light appetite and prefers small prey items. Specimens which feed voluntarily often do so on "pink", "fuzzy" or freshly weaned mice, or "pink" rats.

Breeding has been achieved following a prolonged period of captivity and hibernation.

As I had long suspected, the problems typically associated with *E. mandarina* have dissipated with the advent of an F.I generation.

A small population of captive raised juveniles are now in existence and represent a viable gene pool for future breeding programmes. This population will inevitably increase over subsequent years through the accomplishment of true captive breeding, and the further acquisition of gravid females from the wild. These specimens should establish a foundation of healthy, vigorous stock which will adapt well to captivity, and hopefully breed as reliably as other members of the genus. This can only represent a welcome development due to the desirability of *E. mandarina,* and in providing a viable alternative to imported animals.

ACKNOWLEDGEMENTS

I would like to express my gratitude to everybody who made contact during the research for this article, and who were willing to share their successes and failures with me.

Those who deserve a special vote of thanks inlcude Bill Gillingham (U.S.A.), Larry Keller (U.S.A.), Holger Bartz (W. Germany), Klaus Dieter Schultz (W. Germany), Ken Welch (U.K.) and Mike Nolan (U.K.) for their continued support and encouragement.

REFERENCES

Fleck, J. (1985). Bemerkuingen zur Haltung von *Elaphe mandarina. Salamandra* **21:** 157-160.

Golder, F. (1974). Zur kenntnis von *Elaphe mandarina. Salamandra* **10:** 22-26.

Maki, K.M. (1931). *A Monograph of Snakes of Japan.* pp. 105-107. Tokyo.

Pope, C.H. (19335). *The Reptiles of China.* New York. American Museum of Natural History.

Romer, J.D. (1979). Captive care and breeding of a little known Chinese snake *(Elaphe porphyracea nigrofasciata). International Zoo Yearbook.* **9:** 92-94.

Schultz, K.D. (1989). Asian Rat Snakes of the *Elaphe* genus. Part XII, *Elaphe conspicillata* (Bole 1826). *The Snakekeeper,* Feb. 1989.

Smith, M.A. (1931). *The Fauna of British India, Ceylon and Burma, Including the Whole of the Indo-Chinese Subregion.* Vol. IV, Reptilia and Amphibia: Serpentes. Taylor & Francis, London.

Stejneger, (1925). Chinese amphibians and reptiles in the United States National Museum. *Proceedings of the U.S. National Museum, Washington* **66:** 84.

NOTES ON THE INCUBATION OF THE EGGS OF THE GRASS SNAKE, *NATRIX NATRIX NATRIX*

R. MEEK

561 Coal Road, Leeds LS14, England

INTRODUCTION

The methods employed by herpetologists to artificially incubate reptile eggs are numerous, and many of these appear to be successful. In addition to a variety of incubation materials there is often a diverse approach to the thermal and moisture levels of the incubation medium. During incubation there are many reports of changes in the dimensions and the masses of the eggs (see Packard *et al.*, 1977, for review). Few of these data however have been quantified. This paper reports on a method used to incubate a clutch of grass snake (*Natrix natrix natrix)* eggs based on a regime of fluctuating temperatures. Information is given on the results of this method and also of the changes in mass and dimensions of the eggs as incubation proceeded.

METHOD

On September 23rd 1980, a clutch of ten eggs were deposited by a newly imported female Italian grass snake *Natrix natrix natrix*. These eggs ranged in length from 25-30mm, in width from 16-18mm and in mass from 5.2-6 g. The eggs were incubated in vermiculite to which water was added. The ratio of water to vermiculite was in the region of five parts water to one part vermiculite (in weight). The eggs were sunk into the medium until they were approximately two thirds buried. The container was heated by an incandescant light bulb which was turned on around 0700 hrs each morning until around 2300 hrs each evening. This produced fluctuations in temperature (Fig. 1). Throughout incubation records were taken of the changes in length, width and masses of the eggs at 10, 20, 30 and 40 day intervals. Length and width were straight line measurements across the eggs. Egg mass was determined by triple balance scales.

RESULTS

During incubation, three of the eggs showed signs of collapse. On opening these no sign of embryonic development could be found. Hatching in the remaining eggs began after 40 days; the last egg hatched after 46 days. Complete emergence by the young snakes took place 18-48 hours after first splitting of the shell casings. On inspection one of the young grass snakes was found to have a deformity of the spinal column.

Throughout incubation, changes in length, width and mass were observed. Final lengths just previous to hatching were from 29-33mm, widths from 23-27mm and masses from 14-18 g. The changes in dimensions and mass are highly correlated (length v. mass, $r = 0.87$, $P < 0.001$: width v. mass $r = 0.93$ $P < 0.001$). Growth between these variables can be described by the equation $y = b + m \log X$ where the egg length or width (y) in mm is related to the logarithm (loge) of the mass x in gram by the y intercept b and the slope m. This gives for egg length,

$$y = 16.9 + 5.2 \log x \qquad (1)$$

for egg width,

$$y = 4.09 + 7.64 \log x \qquad (2)$$

It is interesting to note that a slightly higher correlation has been found between egg width and mass. Figure 2 shows the data plotted on semi-logarithmic coordinates with lines taken through the data predicted by the constants in these equations. The data are based on 5 successive measurements on the 7 eggs which reached full term (i.e. $n = 35$).

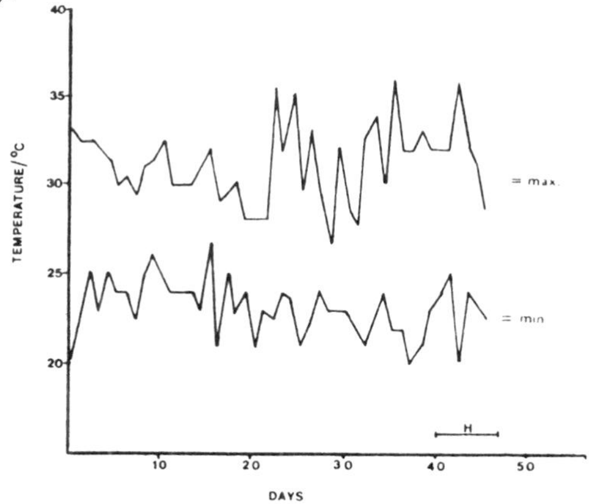

Figure 1. A graph showing the maximum and minimum temperatures recorded to incubate *N. natrix* eggs. Throughout incubation a maximum temperature of 36°C and a minimum temperature of 20°C was recorded. The mean temperature based on all temperature records was 27.1°C ($n = 90$). The hatching period (H) is shown at the lower end of the graph.

Three dimensional growth can be described after transforming the data to logarithms and by the multiple regression,

$$y = o\ x\ \beta_1 m \beta_2$$

where the mass (y) in grams is related to the egg width (m) in mm by the constants o, β_1 and β_2; 95% levels of significance have been attached to β_1 and β_2 using the t distribution (Bailey, 1959). Thus,

$$y = 0.00054\ x\ 1.31 \pm 0.6 m\ 1.75 \pm 0.32 \quad (r^2 = 0.88,\ n = 35) \qquad (3)$$

This equation has slightly higher correlation than equations (1) and (2); i.e. $r = \sqrt{r^2} = 0.94$.

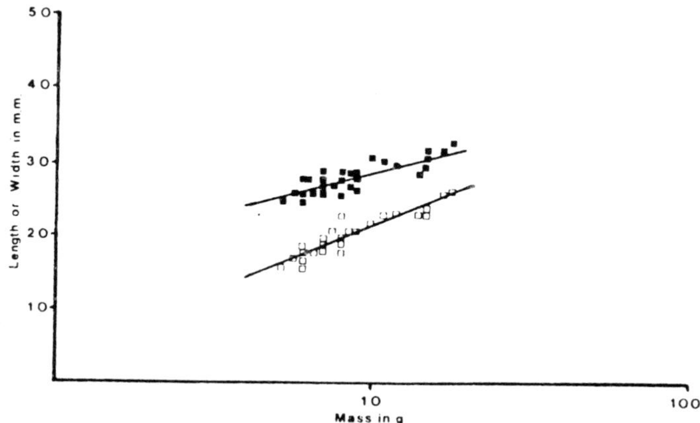

Figure 2. A graph on semi-logarithmic coordinates of egg mass plotted against egg length (■) and egg width (□). The lines taken through the data are based on equations (1) and (2) in the text.

Changes in egg mass are also time dependent. This can be estimated from the quadratic equation,

$$y = 6.273 - 0.062\,X + 0.007\,X^2\;(r^2 = 0.93) \qquad (4)$$

Where the egg mass y in grams is determined from the incubation period x in days. Figure 3 is a graph showing these time dependent changes in mass for *Natrix* eggs with a line taken through the data predicted by the constants in this equation.

After a period of 4 weeks during which the young snakes would accept no food, they were placed in a small container and subjected to a winter cool period. On April 10th 1981, they were housed in a heated vivarium and offered small *Xenopus laevis* and their larvae which they eagerly accepted.

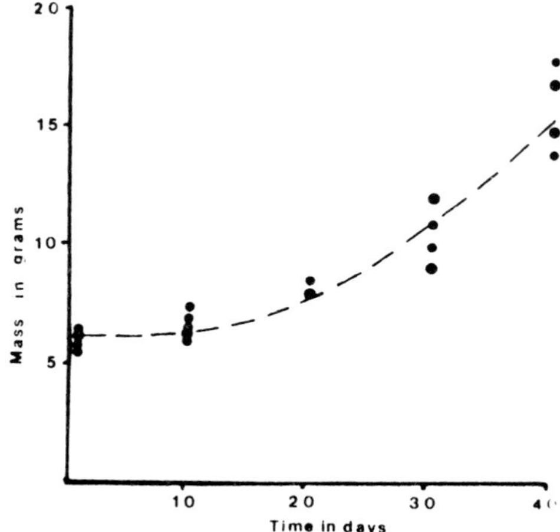

Figure 3. A graph showing time dependent changes in mass of grass snake eggs. The large circles represent more than one data point. The line taken through the data is based on equation (4) in the text.

DISCUSSION

According to Smith (1973) Rollinat recorded a 42 day incubation period for *Natrix* eggs at 20-26°C. This is in approximate agreement with Riches (1976) who states that at 27-29.5°C incubation should take from 40-46 days, but it is marginally longer than a clutch incubated by Swailes (1979). Although it would appear that persistent high or low temperatures are to be avoided (Swailes, 1979; Riches, 1976), the fluctuating temperature regime described in this paper resulted in a normal incubation term of 40-46 days. The growth recorded for these eggs might therefore also be regarded as typical and the mathematical models obtained from the data a useful tool in determining the egg masses at successive stages during incubation. A quantative comparison of growth of the eggs of the lizard *Basiliscus basiliscus* has been described in tabulated form by Claesson (1979) and it is interesting to note that equation (3) agrees well with these data.

ACKNOWLEDGEMENTS

I thank David Hinchcliffe for giving me the grass snake eggs. Alan Jayes and Dr R.S. Thorpe critically read and made helpful suggestions on the manuscript. Helen Meek typed the manuscript.

REFERENCES

Bailey, N.T.J. (1959). *Statistical Methods in Biology.* London; English Universities Press.

Claessen, H. (1979). Reproduction eggs; factors associated with incubation and suggestion for laboratory rearing. *Journal of Herpetology* **13:** 512-515.

Packard, G.C., Tracy, C.R., Roth, J.J. (1977). The physiological ecology of reptilian eggs and embryos and the evolution of viviparity within the class Reptilia. *Biological Review* **52:** 77-105.

Riches, R.J. (1976). *Breeding Snakes in Captivity.* St. Petersburg, Florida: Palmetto Publ. Co.

Smith, M. (1973). *The British Amphibians and Reptiles.* London and Glasgow; Collins.

Swailes, R. (1979). Hatching of grass snake eggs. *A.S.R.A. Journal* **1:** 12-14.

INCUBATION OF GRASS SNAKE *(NATRIX NATRIX HELVETICA)* EGGS

SIMON TOWNSON

96 The Avenue, Highams Park, London E4 9RB

Despite the often repeated account that Grass Snakes mate in April and May, lay their eggs in June or July in compost and dung heaps with hatching taking place 6-10 weeks later, a cursory look at the literature suggests that there remains a great deal to be discovered about the reproductive biology of the Grass Snake. Of particular interest to me is where do they "normally" lay their eggs and under what conditions will they successfully develop? Certainly there is extensive evidence that Grass Snakes do use artificial compost and dung heaps for egglaying, where microbial fermentation may produce an enormous amount of heat with temperatures rising to as much as 40-70^0 C. Stebbings (pers. comm.) has observed that a population of Grass Snakes in Dorset migrated over considerable distances to lay their eggs in piles of saw-dust where he recorded temperatures of over 40^0 C. But where do they lay their eggs when man has not provided a convenient incubation chamber and what extremes of temperature can be tolerated? Perhaps they use natural compost heaps consisting of decaying vegetation at the bottom of a sunny bank, or even occasionally lay their eggs in open patches of sand to be warmed by the sun? Or are the eggs able to develop successfully at relatively cool temperatures, i.e. at ambient shade temperatures; certainly I know of areas with Grass Snake populations where there are no obvious artificial egglaying sites. If eggs are able to hatch successfully under the great thermal range likely to exist under the different situations outlined above, then this species will have developed a great flexibility not seen in many other snakes.

My own, rather limited observations on this subject were made this year when I divided a clutch of eggs and artificially incubated them at three different temperatures. A gravid female snake, approximately 1 m in length was found basking on an old pig-slurry heap on an Essex farm in June. I was informed that several snakes appear at the site at about the same time each year to lay their eggs, despite the fact that the piggery closed some 15 years earlier, which I assume results in the dung-heap no longer being "active". The snake was maintained in captivity for 13 days when it laid a total of 28 good eggs, after which it was fed twice on Common Frogs and released to the wild. The eggs were divided into three groups and placed on vermiculite in small plastic containers, relative humidity approximately 90%. The main group of 17 eggs was maintained at 27-28^{0}C and a smaller group of 4 eggs at 34-35^{0}C in laboratory incubators (Gallenkamp), while a further group of 7 were placed in an unheated room with naturally fluctuating temperature; maximum and minimum temperatures were recorded on a weekly basis. Incubation period and hatching success rate are illustrated in the Table.

Of course we have to be careful about drawing conclusions from only one clutch of eggs. However, the results clearly show that a constant temperature of 27-28°C (which is the temperature at which I usually incubate temperate colubrid eggs) produced a very good hatch rate of 94%, with only one egg failing to hatch. In the group of 4 eggs maintained at 34-35°C, three failed to hatch and when examined were found to have "corkscrew" tails, a deformity associated with high incubation temperatures in other species; this result indicates that 34-35°C is on the limit of their tolerance. The hatch rate in the final group (fluctuating temperature, range 17-30°C) was equally poor (29%); in this situation the eggs were protected from the extremes of temperatures which might be experienced outside if not laid in a heat-generating (i.e. compost heap) site, but more akin to ambient temperatures. There was a noticeable growth of mould on all the eggs in this group during the latter part of the incubation period, but based on experience with other species I do not think this would have affected their viability. This low hatch rate, therefore, is somewhat surprising, although the very small sample size must be considered. Finally, there was an obvious size difference in babies between each of the three groups, with those from the 34-35°C group being quite small, those from the 27-28°C group "medium" size, and those from the fluctuating temperature group the largest.

No. eggs	Incubation temperature	Incubation period	No. hatched (%)	Comments
17	27-28°C	42 days	16 (94)	All hatched babies perfect. One apparently normal baby dead in shell
4	34-35°C	31 days	1 (25))	Hatched baby perfect. Remaining 3 babies dead in shell with "cork-screw" tails.
7	17-30°C Weekly Max. Min 26 24 25 21 30 22 25 21 27 19 24 20 24 17 24 17	62-63 days	2 (29)	Hatched babies perfect. One egg died after 17 days and removed. Remaining eggs contained apparently normal babies dead in shell. All eggs covered in a light mould

Plate 1. Baby Grass Snake feeding on a pre-killed newborn mouse.

All the baby snakes fed voraciously on Common Frog tadpoles placed in approximately 0.5 cm of water in a shallow dish. Thankfully, my somewhat overcrowded garden pond produced a good supply of tadpoles until late September when all but 2 of the babies were released into the wild – a site chosen for its abundance of toadlets, solitude and plenty of cover for hibernation. The remaining two babies are being reared overwinter in a 30 x 15 cm plastic box with a thermal gradient of approximately 24-32°C in the daytime and a night-time temperature between 17 and 22°C. Both are growing rapidly; with the final disappearance of tadpoles in my pond, the two snakes have readily adapted to feeding on pieces of frozen/thawed Plaice, Trout and smoked Salmon which are simply placed in the water dish, with calcium and vitamin supplements ("Reptilin", Sera) added to each feed. More recently they have been offered live baby mice which were refused. However, dead baby mice placed in the water dish which had been 'scented' with fish were readily taken (Plate 1). While it is well known that although the main diet of adult Grass Snakes consists of amphibians, they may also feed on fish, small birds and mammals. Indeed, I know of a snake which, when picked up, promptly regurgitated a bird's wing – presumably the remains of some other predator's kill. However, little is known about the diet of baby Grass Snakes apart from the fact they they will readily accept amphibians. In captivity, I suspect they can be persuaded to eat all kinds of things they would not normally take, particularly if the new food item is 'scented' with acceptable food and the snakes are habituated to a feeding routine. In the excitement at a recent feeding session when Plaice was offered, one of the babies attempted to eat the other and had swallowed more than half of it from the rear end when discovered. However, it is not clear to what extent they prey on other animals such as fish, baby mammals or invertebrates in the wild. According to Malcolm Smith, "the young are often said to eat worms, slugs and insects", but I do not know of any direct observations of this.

It may be assumed that the use of compost/dung heaps as egg incubators is generally an advantage to this species in that its range can be extended further north into cooler climes than would otherwise be possible. But this habit may well have its disadvantages. For example, over the past three years we have had warmer and drier summers than usual. This relatively small increase or fluctuation in high summer temperatures is likely to cause more dramatic effects within the compost heap, with possible deleterious effects for developing eggs. My results indicate that a constant temperature of 34-35^{0}C may cause deformities and death. While compost heap temperatures are likely to be fluctuating rather than constant, it is known that temperatures within compost heaps may far exceed 35^{0}C. Certainly the lower temperatures did not produce a good result with my eggs. Perhaps in cool summers many of the eggs laid outside of suitable heat-generating sites fail to hatch? Malcolm Smith refers to the work of Rollinat in France who reported eggs found in a hole in the earth on the 14th of November which contained living young on the point of hatching, and that "following a cold summer it is not rare to find batches of eggs in the Autumn, in which the young are dead, having been killed by the cold". He also quotes from a letter of Gilbert White, "snakes lay chains of eggs in my melon-beds ...which do not hatch out until the following Spring, as I have often experienced". The possibility that partially developed embryos may be able to hibernate within the egg is of considerable interest and deserves further investigation.

In conclusion, it seems there has been very little systematic research on the Grass Snake in the U.K. either in the field or laboratory, apart from the excellent but unpublished work of Stebbings carried out in Dorset some 20 years ago. Many of the points I have raised in this article have no doubt been studied elsewhere, perhaps in mainland Europe? Nevertheless, I hope other members will be stimulated to contribute articles or letters on Grass Snakes to the *Bulletin.*

CHONDROS – AU NATUREL

R. D. BARTLETT

Director, The Reptilian Breeding and Research Institute, 1421 Olmeda Way, Fort Myers, Florida 33901, U.S.A.

While the breeding biology of the Green Tree Python, *Chondropython viridis,* is now amongst that most thoroughly documented, numerous perplexities yet remain. This is especially true in the area pertaining to the incubation of the eggs. For the edification of husbandrists I wish to here document the programme in effect at the R.B.R.I., which is, because of the area of the country in which we are situated, considerably different from that practised by most other institutions.

During the latter part of 1981, a pair of Green Tree Pythons were acquried to accompany a lone female which had been long in my collection. Additionally, in mid-1982 a second male was acquired. A perusal of the literature indicated that the species should be well able to withstand the vagaries of the weather in south-western Florida with the exception of those few winter days during which the low temperatures associated with passing of cold fronts prevailed. Upon such rare days the temperature may occasionally plummet to the mid-twenties but more frequently it hovers near 40^{0}F. The remaining 10 months of the year, February through November inclusive, should produce a weather pattern not seriously dissimilar to that within the natural range of the species. Considering the portions of the literature which correlated the changes in barometric pressure often associated with the formation of showers to the breeding activities of the snakes, it was decided to house the two pairs out-of-doors under existing conditions in a manner which would fully expose them to the stimuli offered by the changing weather conditions.

Although I seldom use cages of wire construction for the maintenance of any reptile, it was decided to do so in this case. The material chosen as the enclosure was a galvanized welded wire measuring ½ x 1 inch and of this a cage of some 30 x 30 x 36 inches was constructed. It was affixed firmly between the horizontal limbs of a powder-puff *(Calliandra)* bush. Beneath, a tangle of foliage plants, and along the limbs the aroid creeper *Syngonium popdyphyllum,* added to the tropical aspect. Within the cage, limbs were firmly anchored at various levels which would allow the snakes to choose their desired height and positions. Above the front of the cage the foliage of the shrub was thinned, the intent being to allow access of the early morning sunlight, hence providing an area for thermoregulation should the serpents so desire. A large and deep water dish was provided.

Into this, initially, the trio of chondros were introduced. After a day or so of nearly incessant prowling they settled in well, each choosing a different limb as their own. From this day they seldom strayed, returning to what appeared to be the very same spot after each session of movement or basking.

The activity patterns of the trio were similar. Early evening and at dawn they would usually be actively prowling unless digesting a recent meal. They usually coiled upon their chosen perches throughout the hours of full darkness but occasionally remained active long into the night. The earliest rays of the sun drew all to the front of the cage where they would bask in its increasing warmth for varying durations, longer in cool weather, and for correspondingly lesser periods as the temperatures increased. Daylight activity was not uncommon during the summer rainy season. The advent of showers, either real or through the use of a sprinkler system, would bring about an increased degree of alertness. In keeping with the reports of others, it was found that during storm activity defecation and breeding activity were stimulated. Also, drinking usually occurred at this time, the snakes drinking the beads of moisture as they formed upon their coils. Feeding seldom occurred during periods of rain, the snakes preferring to await the coming of darkness for this.

Although I initially worried about feeding or striking chondros engaging their teeth in the wire of the cage, I soon found that such concern was without basis. In the year that they have been so caged, upon but one occasion have I seen a specimen mis-strike when grasping a food animal and these particular specimens are not at all inclined to strike in aggression. Another potential cause for striking, I thought, would be the presence of birds in the scrub. Neither did this problem materialize for as soon as the birds discovered the snakes, with the exception of an occasional scolding bluejay, all vacated the scrub.

While the high temperatures of summer were of no concern whatever, I wondered how low a temperature could be sustained safely by the snakes? By accident, during one unheralded cold front I found that temperatures in the mid to low forties in no way debilitated them. In fact, one female caught, constricted, and consumed a rat soon after sundown on a day when the thermometer never read above the low fifties. It is possible that her body temperature was a few degrees warmer for she had basked in the sunlight until shortly before the food was offered. No longer do I concern myself that the snakes are out on winter evenings when a 30^0 drop from the days high in the 70^0 is possible.

Mating activity was sporadic throughout the spring and early summer prior to the introduction of the second male. After his introduction, moderate aggression between him and the original male became apparent and mating activities became incessant. Although some rather deep lacerations resulted from the hostilities of the males towards each other, it was decided to allow the colony to remain as it was and, luckily, no serious injuries occurred. Eventually their mutual antagonism waned somewhat but mating activity continued unabated throughout the summer.

One of the female snakes seemed more acceptable than the other and usually both males were busily engaged in courtship of her simultaneously. At this time their aggressive attitudes peaked. This particular female, besides sporadic couplings during the daylight hours, was mated by one or other of the males for more than forty consecutive nights during the months of July and August. The second female, while of lesser interest, was also mated on several occasions.

For a period of several weeks at summer's end and as mating activities were waning, both females, which unlike the males had continued to feed regularly, began to fast. After approximately four weeks they, and the males, neither of which had fed for a full three months, began again to feed, easing some of my anxieties.

Although neither looked gravid, I decided in mid-November to place both females indoors so that I might better monitor their conditions. Both they and the males continued to feed ravenously. On 1 December the female that had been mated the most began to actively prowl the floor and perimeters of her cage. Little significance was attributed to this as both had done so before and she certainly did not appear gravid. It was, however, decided to insert a sphagnum tray within a hiding box. On 4 December the prowling female entered the box upon numerous occasions only to emerge moments later. Upon the morning of 6 December I found her coiled in the hiding box, head buried in the centre of her coils. She there remained through the morning of 8 December when she produced 17 eggs all but three of which were clustered. Around these she remained coiled in a tight conical position, exhibiting periodic muscle contractions (brooding behaviour). As temperatures were fluctuating due to the passage of a cold front, it was decided to remove the eggs to an incubator. After removal of the eggs, although the female remained coiled tightly in the box for more than 2 weeks, the brooding contractions ceased.

It was decided that the incubation of the eggs should be attempted in the medium with which I am most familiar: dampened, unmilled sphagnum moss. Along with the benefit of my familiarity it was thought that this medium would offer the best support for the clustered eggs. The sphagnum was prepared in the usual manner, this being to soak it thoroughly and then to wring from it every drop of water. What remained was slightly dampened moss, evenly moist throughout, a medium which I have used over the decades to hatch innumerable reptile eggs. The moss was placed in a warmed (85°F) crockery bowl and upon this were placed both the cluster and the single eggs, all of which were then covered liberally with more moss. Finally a covering of clear plastic was placed over all and affixed securely, rendering the compartment capable of attaining and sustaining a relative humidity of 100%, seemingly a very important consideration in the successful incubation of chondro eggs. The egg compartment was then placed in an incubator which had been preset to maintain a temperature of 85°F (± 1°F).

Ten days later the eggs were checked. All appeared good, having chalky though pliant shells and having become turgid during the day since deposition. On December 22 the heat strip which controlled the temperature of the incubator burned out, allowing temperatures to drop far below the normal level. Repairs were immediate, and incubation continued. On 1 October 1983, a check of the eggs disclosed that one on the outer perimeter of the cluster had died and dehydrated. All others looked well, being chalk white and turgid with minimal windowing.

By 22 January 1983, dimpling was noticeable on several eggs. On the morning of 1 February, after 55 days of incubation, the first hatchling slit the shell and protruded its head. It (as all others subsequently proved to be) was of the yellow colour phase (Plate 1). It was not until the morning of the following day that any additional eggs were slit. At that time nine hatchlings were in evidence. By noontime of 2 February, all remaining eggs had been slit and the first to do so had emerged completely from the shell, to be followed within several hours by its 15 siblings.

It should be noted that the female which deposited the eggs fasted a second time for a substantial period, refusing food the day prior to deposition and not again accepting a meal for an additional 52 days.

Plate 1. Newly hatched *Chondropython*

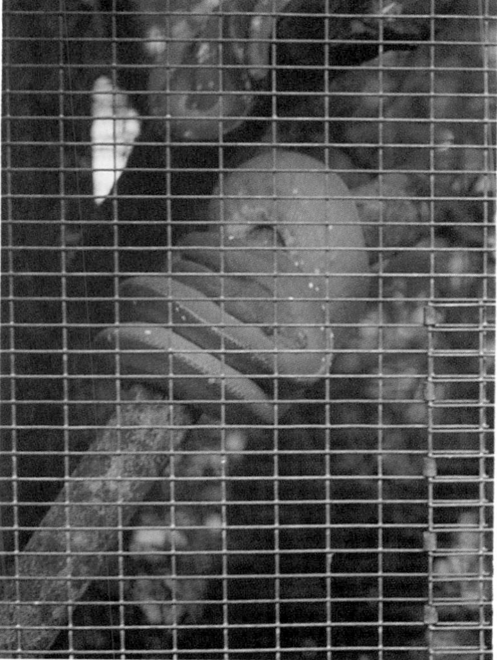

Plate 2. Outside breeding enclosure for adult snakes (photos by Simon Townson)

REPRODUCTION OF THE ROSY BOA, *LICHANURA TRIVIRGATA*

S. NORRIE

14 Newtonwood Road, Ashtead, Surrey

During early 1984 several young Rosy Boas were obtained from California. These were the Mexican Rosy Boa *(L.t. trivirgata)* and two intermediate forms known as 'Intermedia' and 'Myriolepis'. There is however no geographical basis to regard the intermediates as a separate sub-species. (See section on Distribution). The following account of reproduction relates to the form known as 'Intermedia'.

DESCRIPTION

Intermedia is an extremely attractive form of the variable Rosy Boa. The markings consist of 3 even edged broad stripes of pale brown on a buff background. The dorsal stripe being slightly lighter than the stripe on the flanks. The belly markings are off-white with dark brown flecks and spots.

RAISING THE YOUNG

The young snakes were approx. 280mm long and marked as the adult colouration described above. Pelvic spurs were clearly visible on the male but probing proved to be inconclusive.

To encourage consistent growth, the young were housed in plastic boxes in an incubation unit on 15 hours light per day throughout the first summer and winter, the temperature ranging from 24°C to 30°C (75°-85°F). Pink mice were given every 3-4 days.

By the spring of 1985 the female was approx. 440mm, the male slightly larger. The adults were placed in permanent cages with no heating apart from the light source. Minimum temperatures were approx. 13°-16°C (55°-60°F).

REPRODUCTIVE BEHAVIOUR

Feeding became erratic in both the male and female during early June and finally ceased on the 14th June.

The adults had been segregated into respective sex groups until 7th July when the female was introduced to the male. The male followed the female constantly using his spurs to stimulate the female by erecting them and prodding her flanks. Within 20 minutes they were copulating. The pair was left together and during the next 10 days continued to show mating activity. They were seen to mate again on the evening of the 10th July.

Plate 1. *Lichanura trivirgata trivirgata.*

Plate 2. *Lichanura trivirgata* 'intermedia'.

When mating activity ceased in mid July the male resumed feeding heavily, the female however did not feed again until after giving birth.

During the gestation period the female constantly moved to areas of optimum temperature, near the underfloor heater during the night and near the light during the day.

Average temperatures were 23^0-28^0C (74^0-82^0F) although directly under the lamp the temperature would be somewhat higher.

On the 6th October, 91 days from the first mating, the female sloughed. At the end of October she was often observed to be lying out straight as opposed to a more normal coiled or looped posture. By the 6th November (122 days) she was very restless.

BIRTH

During the night of the 124th day of gestation, (based on first mating), 3 young were produced each approx. 270mm in length. Although the female had not fed for 156 days there were no signs of massive weight loss. The overall body shape was still firm and round.

The young sloughed 14 days from birth and began feeding on the 25th day, taking pink mice. It is recorded that they do, however, sometimes feed before sloughing (Van De Pols, 1985), (Granger, 1982). From spur size identification there are 2 females and 1 male.

ROSY BOAS IN GENERAL

There are three widely recognized sub-species of Rosy Boas all originating from California, Baja, California, Arizona and Sonora (Stebbins, 1966), (Townson, 1979).

The 'Mexican' Rosy Boa *(L.t. trivirgata)* is a very attractive sub-species having three dark chocolate stripes on a light cream background.

The Coastal Rosy Boa *(L.t. roseofusca)* has three stripes of pink, reddish brown or dull brown with irregular edges. The background colour is bluish/grey.

The Desert Rosy Boa *(L.t. gracia)* has three stripes of rose, or reddish brown with even edges on a background colour of grey or beige.

A fourth Rosy Boa has been described coming from Cedros Island ajdacent to the Pacific coast of Baja California del Norte, Mexico (Ottley, J.). This has been claimed as a separate sub-species (Ottley, J.) and named *L.t. bostici.*

Other forms of Rosy Boa are generally described as either intergrades or intermediates.

Until recently the Rosy Boa was considered to be difficult to maintain for long periods in captivity often becoming susceptible to respiratory and intestinal ailments and dying in a very short time. However, these observations were made on wild caught animals. The success in keeping captive bred specimens is totally different.

Rosy Boas are easy to keep and require none of the elaborate temperature requirements associated with other boas and pythons.

Despite the relatively small head size they can in fact swallow quite large prey and are extremely powerful and efficient constrictors. Prey consists of small mammals and young birds.

The Rosy Boa has been bred in the U.K. on one previous occasion. This being the Desert Rosy Boa *(L.t. gracia)* (Granger, 1982). From personal communication, experience in the reproduction was very similar to the above account.

REFERENCES

Van De Pols, J. (1985). Personal Communication.
Granger, A. (1985). Personal Communication.
Granger, A. (1982). *Herptile* **7:** (3).
Stebbins, R. (1966). *A Field Guide to Western Reptiles and Amphibians.*
Townson, S. (1979). *British Herpetological Society Newsletter* No. 21.
Ottley, J. (date unknown). *Great Basin Naturalist* **38:** (4).
Ottley, J. Murphey, R., Smith, G. (date unknown). *Great Basin Naturalist* **40:**(1).

British Herpetological Society Bulletin No. 23. 1988

CAPTIVE BREEDING OF THE BRAZILIAN RAINBOW BOA *EPICRATES CENCHRIA CENCHRIA*

RAYMOND A. HINE

P.O. Box 992, Wickford, Essex SS12 9EW

AN INTRODUCTION TO THE GROUP

In 1984 I purchased 6 Brazilian Rainbow Boas. Male No. 1 (M.1) and Female No. 1 (F.1) were unrelated to each other and had been captive bred in California in late 1983. Male No. 2 (M.2) and Females 2, 3 and 4 (F.2, F.3, F.4) were bred in June 1984 by a breeder in Florida.

M.1 was probably the least attractive, being brown rather than orange or red. He did, however, have nice markings, the ‘eyespots’ down his flanks being centred with tangerine.

The four snakes bred in Florida were all a nice shade of orange with grey flanks and strong deep mauve patterning.

The most striking of the six had to be F.1 bred in California. Even at this young age she had a nice red colouration, again with strong mauve markings and a beautiful irridescence to her scales.

As they grow older *E.c. cenchria's* colours became richer and more attractive, unlike other members of the family such as *E.c. maura*. They also grow much larger than these other subspecies, attaining lengths in excess of 2 metres in some cases.

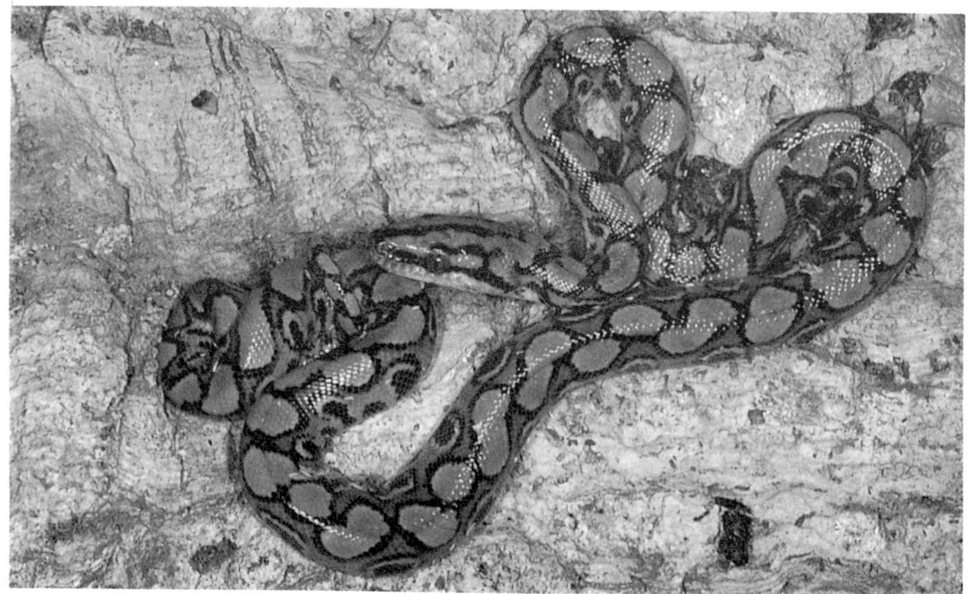

Plate 1. Baby *Epicrates cenchria*. Photo: Chris Mattison

MAINTENANCE

They were originally housed in 12" x 12" plastic freezer tubs with ventilated sides. Newspaper was used as substrate. A clay pipe for hiding and to assist with sloughing and a small clay water dish were the only furnishings. The boxes were placed on shelves in a small thermostatically controlled room with the temperature set at 29°C. A light cycle of 16 hrs day/8 hrs night was maintained by means of a 5 ft fluorescent 'Northlight' connected to a timeswitch.

The young boas grew rapidly on a diet of freshly killed rodents. Within six months they had outgrown their boxes and were transferred to their current cages which are contiplas units with sliding glass fronts. Each unit measures 6 ft x 2 ft x 21 ins high. There is a partition splitting each unit into two 3 ft cages. Each snake has a 3 ft section to itself with a hide box at one end. A shelf was fixed above this and a large water bowl provided for drinking and bathing. The substrate was dust free wood shavings.

For heat and light there was a 60w incandescent light bulb fitted to the ceiling of each cage about 6" from the middle partition. There is a low wattage head pad under the wood shavings below the bulb, giving a hotspot if needed. The cages were designed this way so as to give a temperature gradient, the coolest position being inside the hidebox where it rarely reaches 25°C even on the hottest summer's day. (Although I have no accurate records it seems to hover around the 18°-23°C mark). On the hotspot however it quite often reaches 35°C, and this is hardly ever used by the snakes. In the height of the summer the heat pads are switched off (unless the snake in the cage is gravid).

Needless to say these nocturnal jungle dwellers rarely venture out during the warm daylight hours and can only be seen prowling around their cages in the cool darkness of night. The average night-time low is 22°C and even as youngsters the boas functioned well at these temperatures.

The 16 hr day/8 hr night light cycle was maintained in these permanent cages and it was only changed when the animals were older and being prepared for breeding.

In November 1985 the boas were measured, their approximate lengths being:

M.1 2 years old 4½ ft
F.1 2 years old 5½ ft
M.2)
F.2) 18 months old 4 ft
F.3)
F.4)

PREPARING THE SNAKES FOR BREEDING

Although the snakes had grown considerably in length, they still needed to put on quite a bit of weight before they could be bred.

Walsh and Davis (1983) had breeding success with females weighing 1751-2345 grams. Although my animals were not far off the weight of the lightest of their group, they still did not seem to be heavy enough, considering their length. (I had bred Boa Constrictors on three occasions previously and had found that the females had to be carrying a fair amount of fat prior to mating, in order to recover quickly after parturition).

I do not think adult non-breeding snakes should be over fed but in the case of breeding female boas, which may not eat for 6 to 9 months while gravid, as much food as possible needs to be offered while they will eat it. A heavy feeding regime was introduced with a view to breeding the group in the 1986-87 season.

F.1 and M.1 were the main hope of success; they were just that much older and larger than the others, so I concentrated on these two in particular.

Food was offered every 7-10 days and if refused one day a fresh meal was offered the next and the next until something was eaten. F.1 rarely did refuse and in no time at all she was taking large adult rats, sometimes two per meal.

Over the next 12 months F.1 grew another 12 inches in length and when weighed in November 1986 scaled 2700 grams. The others were not weighed but all except F.4 were thought to be heavy enough to breed.

M.1 although nowhere near as big as F.1 had grown large white pelvic spurs. A year before, these spurs were hardly visible and indeed M.2's spurs were much smaller than those of his older counterpart. This must be, I thought, a good sign of sexual maturity.

Brunner (1977) and Huff (1977), both working with *Epicrates* spp. found that a period of lower temperatures enhanced the breeding results of their snakes. My own experiences with Boa Constrictors showed a short period subjected to lower temperatures worked wonders.

I decided to cool off the group for a period of 6-8 weeks. I did not want to put the snakes through a hibernation, but just to drop the ambient temperature by a few degrees, especially the night-time low.

Firstly I introduced M.1 into F.1's cage and put M.2 in with F.2 and F.3. (F.4 was the lightest of all so she was kept separate and warm and feeding was continued).

I then turned off the heat pads, changed the 60w bulbs for 40w, reversed the light cycle to 8 hrs day/16 hrs night and made the reptile room generally colder by opening vents in the skylights and turning on an extractor fan fitted into an outside wall.

This was all carried out in one go, not as a gradual process. All feeding was stopped, in fact no food had been offered for a few weeks in order to prevent undigested food remaining in the stomachs of the animals during this colder period.

A careful check was kept on the room temperature and on the weather forecasts. If there was likely to be a severe frost or strong winds that night the vents were closed or the extractor turned off.

The cooling period was started on the 14th November 1986 and lasted 52 days in all. In that time the minimum night-time temperature hovered around 18°C. The lowest recorded was 15°C (on several nights). The highest during the day was 26°C with an average nearer to 24°C.

BREEDING

I decided, on the 4th January 1987, to warm the group up. I closed off the skylight vents and the extractor, replaced the 40w bulbs with 60w and turned on the heatpads. The day/night cycle was reversed back to 16 hrs day/8 hrs night. A room heater was connected to a thermostat in case of very low night temperatures (which indeed did happen shortly afterwards with the 1987 big freeze). This heater was set to keep the room temperature above 20°C.

Within 48 hours the cages were back to pre-cooling temperatures and the snakes gradually became more active. After one week they were offered food. The males refused but all three females ate a small rat each.

No mating activity was suspected until the morning of 14th February when the cage housing M.1 and F.1 was found in disarray. On the 17th February copulation was witnessed between these two snakes and lasted for at least 12 hours, this being the only time mating was actually observed.

M.1 and F.1 were kept together for another week but as no more activity took place M.1 was introduced into the cage containing F.2 and F.3. M.2 was transferred to F.1's cage. No action took place with any of these pairings and after about 10 days the males were put back with their original females.

It wasn't until May that M.2 showed any sexual interest at all in the females. He was seen on the 16th copulating with F.2. For several nights after this the cage was in disarray and as F.3 was also in with them it is possible he had mated both females.

Food had been offered occasionally since the start of mating activity but had been refused by all individuals except F.1. She had eaten a small rat on 17th March. This was to be her only meal for 9 months.

THE PREGNANCY

It was obvious by mid May that F.1 was gravid. A large egg-mass had started forming in her mid-body region. It felt, and looked, as if she had just eaten a large rat. Over the following weeks this swelling deflated somewhat and spread tail-wards.

She was given the run of a 6 ft unit at this time with the choice of several hide boxes. She used two of these boxes during pregnancy. A warm styrofoam box filled with damp sphagnum moss was used most nights and when this became too warm during the day she moved into a cooler box containing dry wood shavings. Both boxes were placed partly over the heat pads. The moist box was that much warmer during the day because it was directly under a light bulb. The temperatures in these boxes ranged from 25-30°C in the cool box to 30-35°C in the warm one.

F.2 was examined on the 10th June and she too appeared gravid. She was separated and given the choice of two hideboxes. F.3 was thought to be gravid around this time but later proved not to be. She seemed to have formed the initial egg mass but this disappeared in time and she recommenced normal feeding.

During gestation F.1 spent more and more time inside the warmer moist box. She became very 'pear shaped' with the adipose tissue along her backbone being absorbed into the developing young. Her scales became extremely distended along her flanks and she became very solid to the touch.

She shed twice during pregnancy, once on the 10th June then again on the 4th August. F.2 shed only once, on the 26th September.

On the 10th August F.1 was found inside the nestbox completely upside down. I have witnessed this with gravid Burmese Pythons *(Python molurus hivittatus)* have heard accounts of it happening with Childrens Pythons *(Liasis childreni).* Also the Colombian Boa Constrictors I used to breed would sometimes lay on their side as if in some discomfort. This is probably a way of redistributing the weight of the eggs or developing young inside their bodies. F.1 was always a very placid snake but became quite irritable after her second shed. She did not actually strike but hissed a lot when disturbed. She was left in peace as much as possible.

THE BIRTH AND CARE OF YOUNG

On the 29th September F.1 gave birth to 19 live babies. There were 3 fully formed but dead youngsters and 3 infertile eggs. They were deposited inside the moss filled box at 0700 hrs in the morning. It took her a total of 1 hour 15 minutes from beginning to end. Afterwards she showed no interest in the neonates and crawled into a vacant box.

The birth came 56 days after the last shed which does not corroborate the findings of Walsh and Davis in their 1983 paper. I haven't found the shed to birth gap to be a good indicator of parturition time in live bearing boas. My experiences with *Boa. c. constrictor, Lichanura t. trivirgata* and now *Epicrates c. cenchria* show that shed to birth times can be vastly different between individuals of the same species.

At birth most of the young were active almost immediately, some were still in their fetal membranes and were placed in plastic tubs filled with damp sphagnum moss. The tubs were placed in the environmental room at a temperature of 29°C.

The only youngster measured was a female I decided to keep for future breeding. She was no bigger than the others and measured 450mm.

Most of the brood had their mother's colouring of red, although a few looked like the father. Some had the mother's red colouring and the father's beautiful tangerine centered 'eyespots' along the flanks.

Plate 2. *Epicrates cenchria;* adult breeding stock.

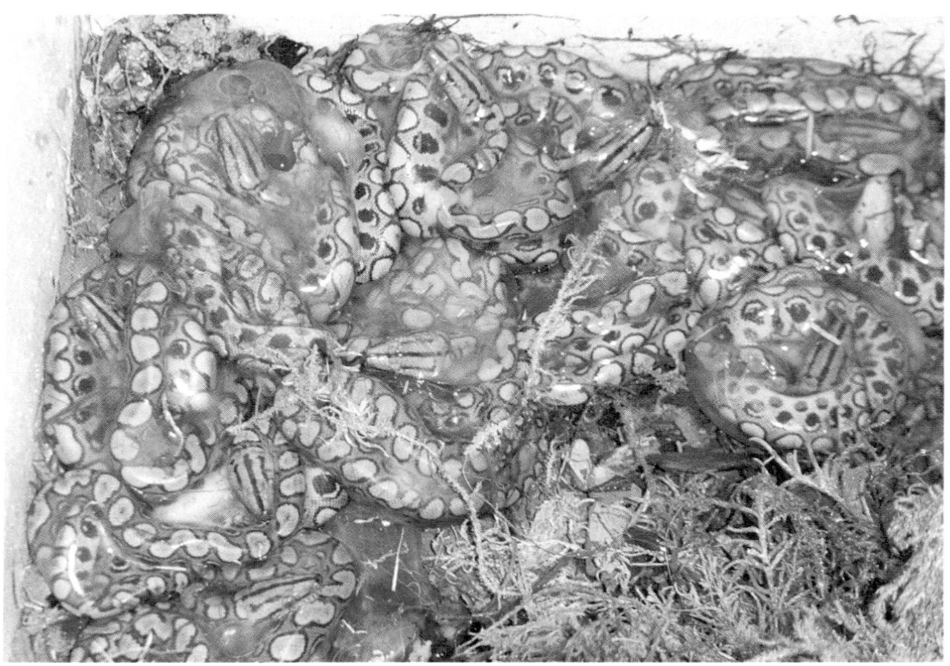

Plate 3. Newborn baby *Epicrates cenchria.*

During the following 14 days all shed, and all had fed before they were 1 month old. The female did not eat until she had shed again, which was on the 16th October.

As mentioned, F.2 shed on the 26th September. All seemed well with her but unfortunately she passed a large quantity of infertile eggs and one partly formed baby on the 21st October.

She was very thin and wasted after this and is only just beginning to put on weight again, 4 months after the birth.

CONCLUSION

I feel the reason for the infertile eggs passed by F.2 was that she was too young. Although their growth is very rapid I think it best not to try pairing *E.c. cenchria* until their 3rd or 4th winter.

The males' pelvic spurs seems to be a good guide to their maturity: they became very noticeable on my two when they were between 2½ and 3 years of age. The possible reason for M.2 not showing any interest in mating until May, when M.1 had mated in February, could be that he just was not fully mature and those extra few months made all the difference.

Brazilian Rainbow Boas make ideal captives, they are extremely attractive and seemingly easy to breed, and for the most part are completely non-aggressive.

ACKNOWLEDGEMENTS

The author wishes to thank Chris Mattison for his excellent photographs which accompany this article.

REFERENCES

Brunner, John C. (1977). Captive breeding of Colombian Rainbow Boas, *Epicrates cenchria crassus. Proc. of the 2nd annual Rep. Symp. on Cap. Prop. and Husb.* (pp. 39-47).

Huff, Thomas A. (1977). Captive propagation and husbandry of *Epicrates* at the Reptile Breeding Foundation. *Proc. of the 2nd Annual Rep. Symp. on Cap. Prop. and Husb.* (pp. 103-112).

Walsh, T. and Davis, B. (1983). Husbandry and breeding of the Brazilian Rainbow Boa *Epicrates cenchria* at the National Zoological Park. *Proc. of the 7th Annual Rep. Symp. on Cap. Prop. and Husb.* (pp. 108-114).

CAPTIVE BREEDING OF THE RHINOCEROS-HORNED VIPER, *BITIS NASICORNIS*

JOHN AKESTER

44 Forbes Avenue, Harare, Zimbabwe

INTRODUCTION

Bitis nasicornis (Shaw), The Rhinoceros-horned Viper, Nose-horned Viper or River Jack, is one of the less well documented members of the African genus *Bitis* and Pitman's comprehensive description of the species is possibly one of the most informative (Pitman, 1974).

Bitis nasicornis inhabits the rain forest areas of tropical West Africa and is found as far east as W. Kenya and N.E. Tanzania. It is a large, stout snake – being one of the 'Big Three' African vipers, *Bitis gabonica gabonica, Bitis arietans* and *Bitis nasicornis)*, reaching an average length of just over one metre. It is just not possible to describe the beautiful markings and colouration of a newly sloughed individual with its complicated geometric pattern in olive, crimson, blue, yellow and rich brown, with a black javelin-shaped marking on the head. However, very soon after sloughing these rich colours start to fade rapidly and within a few weeks the snake has taken on quite a drab look when compared with its former gaudy appearance. It is interesting to note that the Gaboon viper, *B.g. gabonica*, although not being quite as colourful when freshly sloughed, keeps its colouration far longer than *B. nasicornis.* Its most striking characteristics are the cluster of three pairs of horns on the nose which give the snake its popular names, and the very strongly keeled dorsal scales which resemble miniature shark's fins.

Because of the lack of information about this species it was felt that a study should be made of its natural history and, in particular, its breeding habits – closely following the techniques used by us to study its congener, *B.g. gabonica* (Akester, 1979, 1984).

In May 1985 a pair of *B. nasicornis* was received in Harare, Zimbabwe from Ghana, having been in captivity there since September 1984. They were both sub-adults from the Mpraeso district of Ghana (06° 35'N 00° 44W). The immediate problem, once our customary quarantine period had elapsed, was to decide on how to acclimatize them to the conditions in Zimbabwe which are very different from those which they would experience in Ghana. May to September is the dry winter season in Zimbabwe with night temperatures falling to below freezing on occasion with very little moisture in the air at all, as opposed to Ghana where they would seldom experience temperatures below 15°C coupled with a very high humidity. They were therefore housed in heated, glass cages which had a thermostatically controlled minimum temperature of 16°C – the humidity being kept at high level by daily spraying the cages with water.

While they were housed in the glass cages they were fed on mice and small rats and steps were taken to eradicate the high helminth infestation which faecal analysis had indicated that they both had when received. In October 1985 they were transferred to small, outdoor enclosures and remained there until the end of April 1986 when they were returned to the heated, glass cages for the winter. In August 1986 they were again transferred – this time permanently, to a large, outdoor enclosure some $14m^2$ in area planted with thick vegetation and provided with a large pool of water. This enclosure is protected by a security fence which is covered by clear plastic sheeting in the colder months (May to September). At the time of transfer, the minimum night temperature in the enclosure was +9°C but, on clear nights during midwinter, the temperature can drop to as low as +2°C. The enclosure has a built-in sprinkler system which is operated regularly in the dry season and as and when required during dry periods in the summer months.

When gravid the female closely followed the behaviour patterns observed in gravid *Bitis g. gabonica* females (Akester, 1984) and, as the estimated time of parturition approached, the pool was drained and the vegetation thinned out to avoid the neonates drowning in the pool and making it easier to locate them in the enclosure.

Once a parturition had taken place, the neonates were removed from the enclosure as soon as possible and transferred to glass cages similar to the ones used to house the adults and, as they started to feed well and had sloughed for the second time, were transferred again – this time to a small, outdoor enclosure.

OBSERVATIONS

Upon receipt the snakes were weighed and measured – this being repeated at irregular intervals – as and when the opportunity arose as shown in Table 1.

Table 1. Mean mass and length of adult *B. nasicornis*

Date	Male		Female	
	Mass (g)	Length (mm)	Mass (g)	Length (mm)
May 1985	658	800	622	750
October 1985	1042	925	1017	850
November 1986	2050	1000	2450	1000
August 1987	2200	1100	3150	1120
April 1988	2500	1170	–*	1130

*The female was not weighed just prior to parturition to avoid the possibility of stressing her.

B. nasicornis are placid in temperament but can be aggressive when aroused. *B.g. gabonica* are also very placid but when really angered hiss loudly and draw back into a striking coil giving ample warning of their displeasure. However, *B. nasicornis* will strike without any warning whatever and sometimes even without a great deal of provocation. It should be noted that it is not safe to hold them by the tail as it appears to be slightly prehensile and they can, and do, throw themselves upwards and backwards to strike at the hand holding them – this is something that an adult *B.g. gabonica* is not able to accomplish. Possibly because of their partially prehensile tails *B. nasicornis* are able to climb quite well and it is not unusual for us to find the male some distance above the ground in the vegetation. Their afinity to water has often been stressed (Pitman, 1974; Stucki-Stirn; 1979. Ditmars, 1931) hence the name 'River Jack', but we have not found them to be any more fond of water than *B. gabonica*. The enclosure contains a very large pool of water but they are seldom near to it, laying in it or even drinking from it. They do, however, become very active during rainfall or when the sprinklers are turned on – usually taking the opportunity to drink from rocks, vegetation and from off their own bodies. They are, however, powerful swimmers if it becomes necessary for them to take to the water.

The pair tended to keep apart, staying in one place for long periods. However, at 1600h on 21st March 1987 the pair were observed copulating with the male being dragged through the vegetation by the female. The pair broke apart at 1715h.

22nd March: The sprinklers were turned on at 1200h and 1215h the male was observed to be moving up over the female with rapid tongue flicking and head jerking. The female at first moved away from the male but he persisted and at 1310h they were again coupled, with the male being dragged across the enclosure. They remained coupled until 1600h.

28th March: Mating behaviour at 1030h and the pair were coupled at 1130h – separating at 1330h.

11th April: The sprinklers were turned on at 1030h and at 1115h the male was observed to have chased the female to the top of the bunker and, as the female moved off, the male actually fell off in his haste to catch her. At 1130h the pair were coupled – separating at 1430h.

No more activity was observed until 1st June when at 1715h the couple were again in a mating situation with the male being dragged. No more mating activity was noted after this date.

The female continued to feed well until December when she refused food from time to time. She commenced to shuttle between patches of sunlight and shade and in the late afternoons would coil up tightly – remaining like this until the following morning when the sun was again on the enclosure. About this time she began to get very aggressive and continually 'warned-off' with head flashing and hissing.

In late March she began to show signs of sloughing and on 18th April she sloughed very badly – the skin coming away in small pieces. The fragmentation of the skin also takes place in gravid *B. gabonica* females and is one of the indications that parturition is imminent.

At 1700h on 6th May 1988 it was obvious that she had given birth during the day but all that was immediately visible were four stillborn young, three infertile eggs and one very small, live but unsloughed baby. A thorough search was made but, owing to the dense vegetation, only two other neonates were discovered before it began to get too dark to look further.

7th May: As no more neonates were visible, the adults were removed from the enclosure and the sprinklers turned on. Almost immediately numerous babies were observed to be moving around and during the course of the day thirty-seven were collected. During the following day two more were found – making a total of fory-two live young. In both colouration and markings the babies were exact replicas in miniature of the adults – but, of course, as with *B.g. gabonica* no two were exactly alike. The adults were returned to the enclosure and the neonates were sexed, weighed and measured (Table 2).

Table 2
Mean mass and length of 42 neonate *B. nasicornis* born 6th May 1988.
27 males and 15 females

	Mean mass (g)	Mean length (mm)
Males	19.81	243.96
Females	20.00	241.94
Total	19.89	243.09

CARE OF THE YOUNG

With the exception of the small, unsloughed male, all the young were perfect specimens and all had sloughed prior to collection from the enclosure. The unsloughed male was assisted by soaking in warm water with manual removal of the skin, but it never really thrived and eventually died about two weeks later.

The babies were offered new-born mice within a few days of birth and, although a few individuals took them readily, it became apparent that getting the majority to feed was indeed going to be a very difficult task. Over the next few weeks more were induced to eat by putting food in their mouths, but this left a small number which would not take food even if were placed in their mouths, and so it eventually became necessary to force feed them. It is interesting to note that the females fed more readily than the males and all of the ones which eventually had to be force fed were males. At the time of writing (December 1988) most of the young are still having to be hand fed. A number of the young were passed over to the Bulawayo Natural History Museum and I have been informed that a number of reluctant feeders have readily taken small toads (D.G. Broadley, pers. comm.). At this time of the year in Harare small toads are not yet available so we have not had the opportunity to try this for ourselves. In any case, we would like to persevere with the feeding of mice as this will make feeding easier in the future by eliminating the need to wean them back to rodents. It is interesting to note that baby *B. arietans* readily take small toads but change over to rodents as they mature.

Although the individual babies have received approximately the same amount of food, it has become apparent that those which voluntarily took food are doing better and growing faster than those which were induced to feed by putting food in their mouths and these, in turn, are doing better than those which had to be force fed. The former are now, on average, over twice the size of the latter (Table 3).

Table 3.

Mean mass and length of 24 baby *B. nasicornis* as at 5th November 1988.

Group 1. Voluntary feeders
Group 2. Hand fed
Group 3. Force fed

Group	Mean mass (g)	Mean length (mm)	No. males	No. females
Group 1	69.94	340.60	3	5
Group 2	42.79	305.41	6	6
Group 3	33.23	296.25	4	–

We have found that some baby *B.g. gabonica* also give problems with feeding but in the one hundred and fifty or so which we have bred over the past few years, we have never yet had a litter which was as difficult as this litter of *B. nasicornis* is proving to be.

All the babies sloughed immediately after birth and some started to slough for the second time at about three months. This depended on how well they were doing, and some are now undergoing their third slough at seven months, while two are still only just starting their second.

The litter has now been split into five as a precaution against accident or disease, with one batch going to the Bulawayo Natural History Museum, and another batch to another herpetologist. The remaining ones split into good, medium and poor feeders – the good feeders are now in an outside enclosure while the others are still in indoor cages.

DISCUSSION

When the breeding of *B. nasicornis* was first considered it became obvious that, to be reasonably sure of success, the snakes should be given as much space as possible in conditions which were as natural as possible. Space was no problem nor was the provision of thick vegetation, a bunker to hide in and a sprinkler system to provide for watering. However, all this entailed the use of an outdoor enclosure in a climate very different from that which would be experienced by the snakes in Ghana and initially we were very worried by this aspect. However, we need not have concerned oursleves as they acclimatized extremely well to the extent that both the male and the gravid female were left in the enclosure to over-winter, where the minimum night temperatures dropped to as little as +2°C on some occasions. During the day the gravid female basking in the sun could experience temperatures in excess of 30°C. This did not seem to have an adverse effect on her except for perhaps the rather long 'gestation' period of eleven to fourteen months (the first confirmed mating took place on 21st March 1987 and the last on 1st June – the births taking place on 6th May 1988). Although a very close watch was kept after 1st June no further matings were observed and, from the positions of the male and female in the enclosure, no contact took place between them thereafter. Again we are faced with the possibility of sperm retention, delayed fertilization or delayed development of the embryos as with *B.g. gabonica* (Akester, 1979).

B.g. gabonica has a well defined mating and breeding season in Zimbabwe lasting from late March until early June and coinciding with the onset of the colder months and the end of the rainy season (Akester, 1979, 1984). However, in the absence of relevant data it was assumed that the mating season would, in the case of *B. nasicornis*, not be so well defined and it came as a surprise that it coincided exactly with that of our indigenous *B.g. gabonica*. Whether the natural breeding and mating season just happens to fall at the same time as that of *B.g. gabonica* in Zimbabwe, or whether the captive *B. nasicornis* have adapted and adjusted to the conditions in Zimbabwe is a difficult question to answer.

The pre-natal behaviour of *B. nasicornis* shows an interesting parallel with that of *B.g. gabonica*. Both species become very aggressive in the latter stages of pregnancy with head flashing and minatory hissing but usually without actual strikes being made. The final slough before parturition is always fragmentary with the skin breaking up into small pieces leaving bits sticking to the body for several days. Although gravid *B.g. gabonica* females usually take no food at all during the whole period of pregnancy, the *B. nasicornis* female fed well at the beginning and only in the later stages stopped feeding altogether. Gravid females of both species bask in the sunlight but towards evening coil up tightly in places where the heat is retained for example, among the rocks and on the cement surround of the drain in the enclosure.

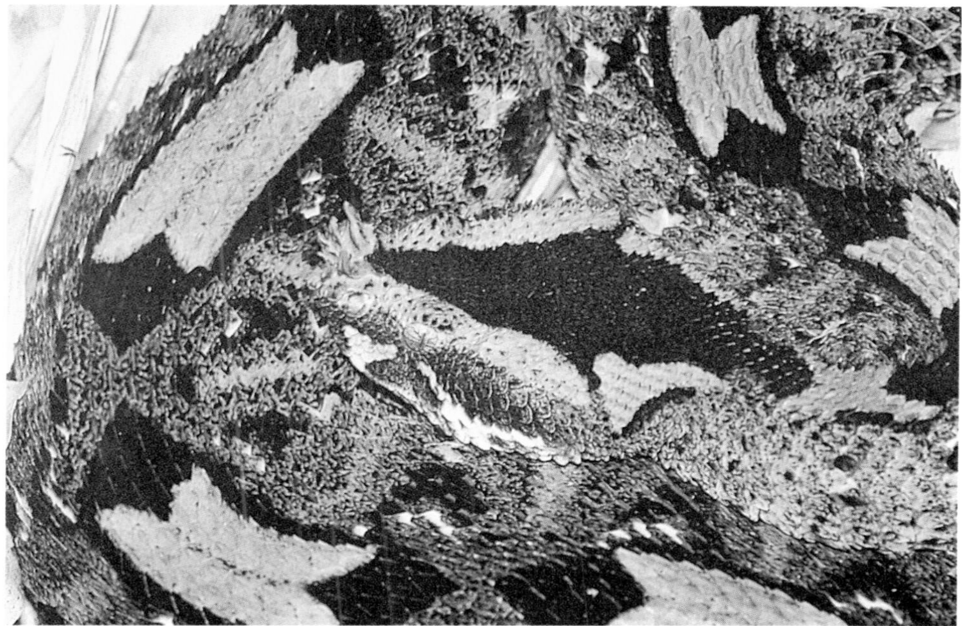

Plate 1. Adult *Bitis nasicornis* showing cluster of three pairs of horns and very strong keeled dorsal scales which resemble a miniature shark's fin.

Plate 2. Head of feeding juvenile *Bitis nasicornis* showing prey being pulled into mouth with fangs.

Although it is not possible to draw accurate conclusions based on the evidence of a single litter of *B. nasicornis*, it would appear that it is more difficult to induce neonate *B. nasicornis* to commence feeding on rodents than it is to start feeding baby *B.g. gabonica* on them.

It is intended that this study will continue to record the growth rate and behaviour patterns of the young *B. nasicornis* and ultimately, when they are mature, extend to the examination of the possibility of male combat occurring in this species.

ACKNOWLEDGEMENTS

This study is supported by a grant from the Zimbabwe National Conservation Trust. I thank Drs. E.V. Cock and D.G. Broadley for their valuable advice on this project and to Dr B. Hughes for his assistance in obtaining the specimens. Special thanks to my wife, Robin, for her continuing assistance which has contributed so much to this study.

REFERENCES

Akester, J. (1979). Successful mating and reproduction by a Gaboon viper, *Bitis gabonica gabonica*, in captivity. *Arnoldia Zimbabwe Rhodesia* **8** (31): 1-5.

Akester, J. (1984). Further observations on the breeding of the Gaboon viper, *(Bitis gabonica gabonica)* in captivity. *Arnoldia Zimbabwe Rhodesia* **13** (9): 217-222.

Ditmars, R.L. (1931). *Snakes of the World.* Macmillan, N. York. 183.

Pitman, C.R.S. (1974). *A Guide to the Snakes of Uganda.* Revised edition. Wheldon & Wesley Ltd. pp 215 & 217.

Stucki-Stirn, M.C. (1979). *Snake Report 721. A Comparative Study of the Herpetological Fauna of the former West Cameroon, Africa.* Herpeto-Verlag: Teuffenthal, Switzerland.

British Herpetological Society Bulletin No. 34. 1990

CAPTIVE BREEDING OF *VIPERA URSINII URSINII* (REPTILIA, VIPERIDAE)

LUCA M. LUISELLI

via Olona 7,00198-ROMA, ITALY

INTRODUCTION

Vipera ursinii, a reptile found, especially in western Europe, in widely separated locations, is now in serious danger of extinction, and for this reason is included in CITES Appendix I (EEC regulation no. 3143/887, Commission of 19 October

1987). The decline of *V. ursinii* can be ascribed to different causes according to the distribution.

Numbers of *V. u. anatolica* are decreasing for reasons which have not yet been established (Honegger, 1978; Dodd, 1987); *V. u. rakosiensis* is in diminution in particular because of the destruction of the habitat and deliberate killing (Honegger, 1978 & 1981; Dodd, 1987); *V. u. renardi* for the progressive alteration or destruction of the habitat (borders of the Steppe and Steppe-forest) (Honegger, 1978 & 1981); Dodd, 1987; Kotenko, 1989); *V. u. ursinii* is affected by various factors (alteration of the habitat, capture and deliberate killing (Honegger, 1978 & 1981; Groombridge 1982; Dodd, 1987); and *V. u. wettsteini* suffers from the same combination of factors as *V. u. ursinii* (Honegger, 1978; Dodd, 1987).

Moreover, the very population structure characteristic of *V. ursinii* renders this reptile more susceptible to a further serious decline in numbers, above all in more western areas, such as the Gran Sasso d'Italia. The same is true for other small populations of European vipers which occupy areas at the borders of their territory, whether in terms of altitude or geographical distribution. For all the reasons given here, the capture of *V. ursinii* where no valid scientific reasons exist, is strongly to be discouraged.

CONDITIONS OF ACCLIMATIZATION

Although the literature on the subject states that the breeding of *V. ursinii* in captivity is extremely difficult (Bruno & Maugeri, 1976; Bruno, 1984), I have been able to show that this species will reproduce habitually in captivity as long as certain precise conditions are fulfilled:

- the specimens must be captured gently, preferably by being lifted by the tail.

- the specimens kept for breeding must be allowed to spend a period of at least 75-80 days in hibernation. It is not necessary to allow the reptiles an enormous amount of space, but it is essential to provide them with a habitat similar to that to which they are used in the wild; one, that is, which offers them a large number of hiding-places in which to take refuge at the first sign of danger.

The soil temperature should vary, according to the sector, from a minimum of 22°C to a maximum of about 30°C. The degree of humidity must be kept at around 78-84% (while I have found it possible to obtain mating and reproduction of *V. berus* with a level of humidity around 80-95%. An incandescent 60 watt lamp, turned on for between four and six hours a day, is sufficient for the heating. As far as lighting is concerned, white fluorescent 30 watt lamps, turned on for at least 8 hours a day, are needed. In my experiments I used conditions of 12 hours of light and 12 of darkness.

Plate 1. Adult *Vipera ursinii ursinii* photographed in sub-alpine sheep pasture, Abruzzo Italy, on 14th May, when much of the surrounding grassland was still covered by extensive patches of snow.

Photo: John Pickett

Plate 2. Adult female *Vipera ursinii ursinii* photographed in the wild basking at the edge of a dwarf Juniper bush *(Juniperus nana)* in montane grassland (approx. 1800m altitude), Abruzzo, Italy.

Photo: John Pickett

Plate 3. General view of sub-alpine habitat of *Vipera ursinii ursinii* in which female shown in Plate 2 was photographed. The vipers are abundant throughout this area of rolling grassland.

Photo: John Pickett

Plate 4. Mountain ridge inhabited by *Vipera u. ursinii* in Abruzzo, Italy. Altitude approx. 1800-2000 m.

Photo: John Pickett

Since *V. ursinii* need a considerable amount of cooling (reflecting the wide diurnal range of temperature in its habitat), it is worth lowering the nocturnal temperature to 12-16^{0}C. In these conditions *V. ursinii* limits its activity to the daylight hours, retiring to its lair during the night. What is more, it exhibits trophically competitive behaviour less frequently, and less intensely, than *V. aspis, V. ammodytes* or *V. berus.*

It was later possible to feed the young vipers with newly metamorphosed frogs, small lizards and even with pieces of beef. The young vipers, like the adults under observation, tend to keep the prey in their mouths for a few minutes, whether it is fed to them alive or dead.

OBSERVATIONS ON THE ADULTS

The adults that I kept in captivity all showed a watchful and irritable pattern of behaviour, even as long as two years after capture.

1 male and 2 females which I have kept since 26 April 1987 have reproduced twice to date (in both cases the same female gave birth, to 4 young on 14 August 1988, and to two, one dead and one alive, on 23 August 1989) while feeding in the meantime on live and dead prey. This consisted or rodents; newborn or recently weaned hamsters: and newborn rats, which proved to be the favourite food of these vipers in captivity (74% of the total food weight swallowed in two years of study). Large apterous Orthoptera were also popular (18%), above all in certain periods. The reasons behind the fluctuations in feeding preference are not clear, given the fact that the experimental conditions in which the vipers were kept did not vary in time. Lizards were occasionally swallowed (7.2%), frogs only on very rare occasions, and never when administered live to the vipers (0.8%).

In general, the females showed more willingness to accept prey of large dimensions than the males; this trait may well be characteristic of the species in the natural state, given that I have often come across cases of females preying on small mammals *(Microtus),* while I have never observed the same phenomenon in males (Luiselli, in prep.).

I have only been able to observe mating on two occasions, first on 27 May 1988, then on 3 June 1989. In each case, both the courtship and the fertilization took place in the day, with behaviour similar to that of *V. berus.*

The growth of the animals was estimated by measuring at average intervals of 7 days, both the total length and the body weight. Figure 2 shows the progress in growth of the male and two females under observation. During the period in which the animals were kept active – from March to November of each year – the snakes each sloughed three times (at the end of May, June and July).

In the natural state, the sloughing cycle seems to be different, and growth on average to be slower (Luiselli, in prep.).

It must be remembered that each individual received an annual supply of food equal to about 300% of its initial body weight, and that in general the largest prey supplied weighed about 15% of the body weight of the snakes.

In the natural state, the yearly growth of this species is probably less.

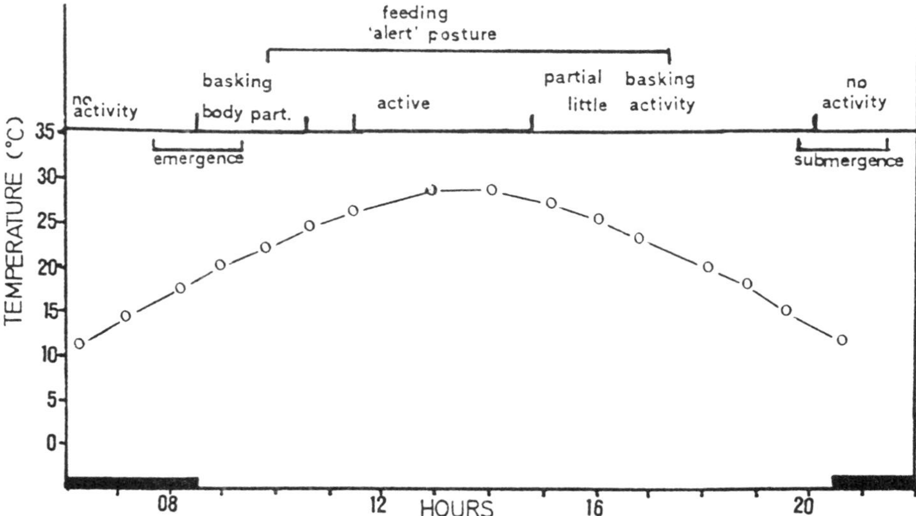

Figure 1. Typical daily behaviour of the adult *V. ursinii* in the laboratory. Behavioural observations in the laboratory (data from 98 days) are shown with ambient air temperatures. Laboratory light period from 08.30 to 20.30. (The symbols of the graph are derived from Spellerberg & Phelps, 1977, though modified).

FEEDING AND GROWTH OF THE YOUNG

Newborn and young of *V. ursinii* in their first two years of life are extremely delicate and difficult to keep.

In the first place, none of the 5 young that I kept (4 born in August 1988 and 1 in the same month of the next year) began to feed spontaneously before the fifth week; two began to do so between the 6th and 7th week, and two more in the tenth week. One young viper, despite force-feeding, never learnt to eat unaided, and died at the age of 96 days.

Moreover, even when the young begin to feed themselves, they will only accept certain types of foods, and stubbornly refuse all others.

In the first year of life, the young vipers would only accept certain kinds of grasshopper, above all those belonging to the Podismidae and Tettigonidae families, and the species belonging to the genera of *Epipodisma, Halopodisma, Tettigoria,*

Phaneroptera, Decticus, Ephippigger and *Troglophilus* were normally accepted without trouble. Members of the Gryllidae, such as *Acheta domesticus,* were normally refused, and accepted by one exceptionally active and voracious individual only.

Individuals of *Grillomorpha dalmatina* were occasionally accepted after the 8th week of life; other Gryllidae were devoured now and then after the 12th week, and with greater regularity between the 16th and 28th weeks. The young vipers particularly appreciated other types of food (pieces of newborn rodents) after the 13th week, but above all from the 30th week on, so that these eventually made up the basic element of the whole diet.

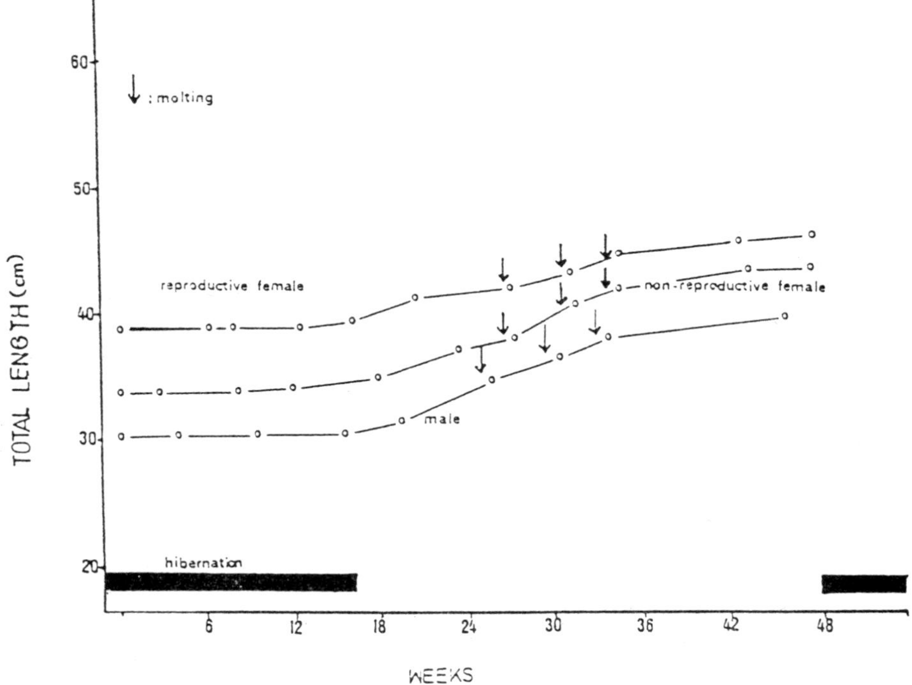

Figure 2. The rate of growth and the sloughing periods of the adult *V. ursinii,* over a period of a year spent in captivity. The period of observation begins on 1 November 1988, and the numbers which follow are in relation to that date.

The graph shows a period of minimal growth (during hibernation) followed by one of maximal growth from the end of hibernation to around the end of July (last sloughing of the year) and one of moderate growth (from August to October).

Plate 5. Detail of spurs of ridge shown in Plate 3 (above). Note the dwarf prostrate Junipers *(Juniperus nana)* characteristic of the habitat of this viper in its high-altitude populations in Europe. Photo: John Pickett

THERMOREGULATORY BEHAVIOUR AND SLOUGHING CYCLE

Three cycles of thermoregulatory behaviour, a daily cycle, a feeding cycle and a sloughing cycle, are observable in the young, as in the young *Coronella austriaca* studied by Spellerberg (1977).

The daily behaviour usually follows the cycle of hours of light and hours of darkness: shortly after the lights are turned on, the young vipers come out of their hiding-places and thermoregulate under the lamp, positioning their bodies according to their thermal requirements. Like the young *V. berus* they are able from birth to flatten their trunks in a dorso-ventral direction, taking up a typically 'ribbon-like' position.

The daily period of basking lasts for a considerably longer time if digestion is taking place in the snake, or during the sloughing cycle. This lasts on average for 7-9 days, from the moment in which the ventral parts begin to become discoloured, to the moment of shedding; the eye usually becomes opaque 3-5 days after the first phase, and remains in this condition for 1-2 days. Finally the eye recovers its normal appearance, and the viper prepares to slough. Though they move very little, and only when disturbed, during the sloughing cycle, the young *V. ursinii,* like the adults, usually continue to feed. This kind of behaviour is fairly exceptional among European vipers, as is that of the females which, both in the natural state and in captivity, feed frequently even in the advanced stages of pregnancy.

Here it is worth mentioning that only 7 days before giving birth, the female in my possession killed and swallowed a hamster weighing 8 g.

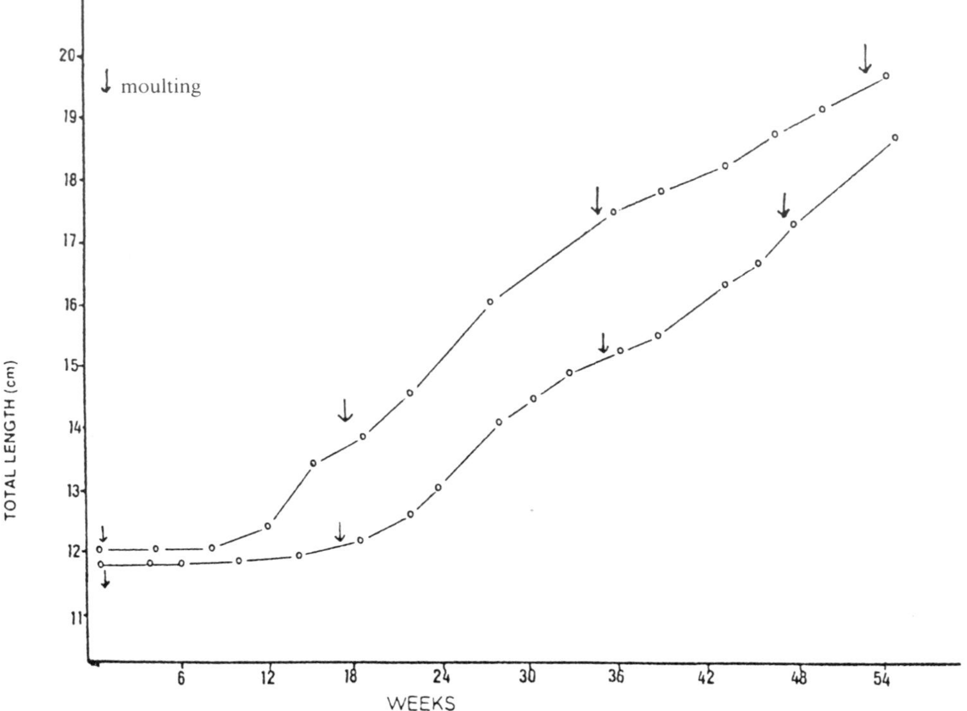

Figure 3. The increase in length and the sloughing periods of two young snakes from birth to the 54th week of life. It can be seen that for the whole year of the study, the young vipers were not allowed to hibernate. The graph shows an initial phase in which the young vipers show only very limited growth, and a later phase characterized by rapid growth.

GROWTH

The growth of the young is characterized by two clearly distinct stages:

a) a first stage (from birth to somewhere around the 6th-10th week) in which no significant increase in length can be noted, while a loss of weight of about 0.2-0.6 g (the original average birth weight of the young is 2.1-2.3 g) can be measured.

b) a second phase in which the vipers begin to gain weight and to increase in length as a result of beginning to feed. In this stage, the speed of their growth depends essentially on the frequency with which they feed.

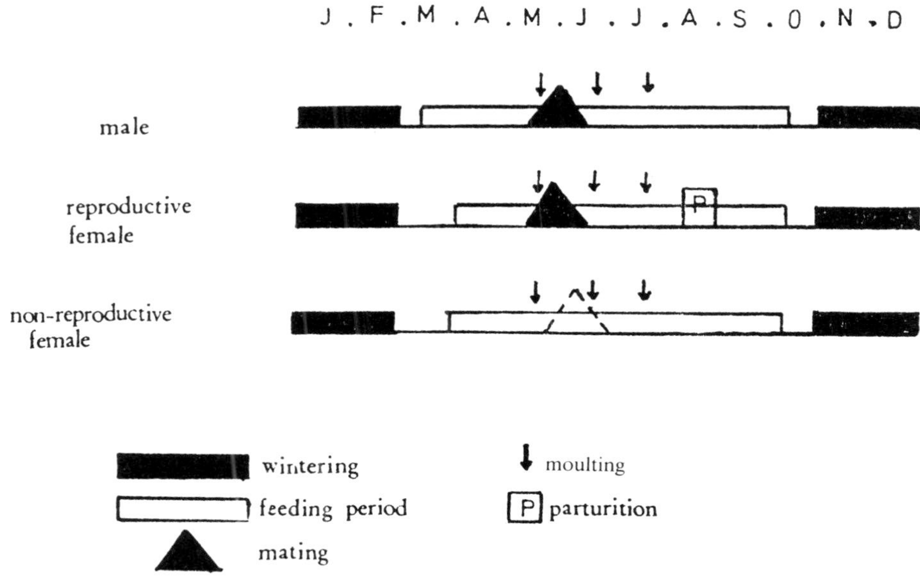

Figure 4. Representation of the annual activity cycle for *Vipera ursinii ursinii* in experimental captive conditions. (The symbols are derived from Saint-Girons *et al.* 1989, though modified).

CONCLUSIONS

It seems, therefore, that *V. ursinii,* though it cannot be compared with species such as *V. ammodytes,* is nevertheless capable of adapting to life in captivity, and can even be bred in captivity as long as a few precise rules are followed which take the animal's particular physiology into account. On the basis of my observations. I believe it would be possible to set up a large-scale plan for the reproduction in captivity of this rare species of viper, with the aim (1) of reintroducing the reptiles into areas in which their population is seriously threatened with extinction, and (2) of studying in more detail the habits and the biology of this extremely interesting snake.

ACKNOWLEDGEMENTS

This study was made possible by the valuable collaboration of my friends C. Anibaldi, C. Bagnoli, M. Capula, M. Picone, L. Rugiero, and above all thanks to the self-sacrifice of U. Agrimi, who for a long time took care of the young vipers born in our laboratory.

REFERENCES

Bruno, S. & Maugeri, S. (1976). *Rettili d'Italia.* Martello, Firenze.

Bruno, S. (1984). *Serpenti d'Italia.* Martello, Firenze.

Dodd, C.K.J. (1987). Status, conservation and management, in: *Snakes, Ecology and Evolutionary Biology,* pp.478-513. Seigel, Collins & Novak (Eds). McGraw Hill, New York.

Groombridge, B. (1982). Threatened snakes of Europe. In: *IUCN/SSC Snake Group, Proceedings of First Meeting, Madras, India, 1982.*

Honegger, R.E. (1978). *Threatened Amphibians and Reptiles in Europe. Council of Europe, Nature & Environment Ser. No 15. Strasbourg.*

Honegger, R.E. (1981). *Threatened Amphibians and Reptiles in Europe. Handbuch der Reptilien and Amphibien Europas.* Akad. Suppl. Vol. Verlag, Wiesbaden.

Kotenko, T. (1989) *Vipera ursinii renardi* in the Ukraine. *First World Congress of Herpetology, Canterbury, 1989.*

Saint-Girons, H., Duguy, R. & Naulleau, G. (1989). Spatio-temporal aspects of the annual cycle of temperate Viperinae. *First World Congress of Herpetology,* Canterbury, 1989.

Spellerberg, I.F. (1977). Behaviour of a young Smooth Snake, *Coronella austriaca* Laurenti. *Biological Journal of Linnean Society* **9:** 323-330.

Spellerberg, I.F. & Phelps, TR.E. (1977). Biology, general ecology and behaviour of the snake, *Coronella austriaca* Laurenti. *Biological Journal of Linnean Society* **9:** 133-164.

CROCODILES, ALLIGATORS, TORTOISES AND TURTLES

British Herpetological Society Bulletin No. 5. 1982

OBSERVATIONS ON *TESTUDO MARGINATA* IN CAPTIVITY

JO JENVEY

Lower Birtley, Grayswood, Haslemere, Surrey

We bought our first two *Testudo marginata,* a male and a female, in 1970, newly imported at a pet shop in Crawley, Sussex. We already owned two small *Testudo graeca* and one *Testudo hermanni* and we were attracted by the appearance of the *marginata.* The female looked very much older than the male as her shell was almost smooth and her splayed margin not as prounced as his, which was beautifully formed and his shell clearly marked with growth rings. The adult *marginata* are readily identified by the elongated carapace, the rear marginals of which are splayed out to form a flat, plate-like area. They are the largest members of the genus in Europe and can exceed a foot in carapace length. Ours were both almost unrelieved black in colour. Both were suffering from an infestation of ticks in their armpits and in a short time their droppings revealed the presence of nematode worms. These problems we dealt with promptly.

The female had been laying eggs in the yard of the shop and indeed we saw evidence of this. *Marginata* eggs are almost complete spheres.

In 1971 we bought another *marginata* male from the same shop. It had been brought to the shop as an unwanted pet, very light in weight for its size although much smaller than the other two. Its colouring also was lighter, having large areas of yellowish colour.

Unfortunately the larger male died during hibernation in the winter of 1972/73 although having appeared perfectly healthy.

To begin with the tortoises were kept in a breeze block enclosure, one and a half bricks high, about 8 x 8 ft with a box for shelter and large stones to climb over, but the large male found escape from this quite easy by choosing a corner where another tortoise was resting, then climbing on its back and levering himself over the edge. We have never seen the female make any attempt to escape, either then or since.

More space was then provided for them and about half the length of one side of the garden was wire netted and bricked off, an area about 20 x 40 ft. A shelter was situated for them in a spot that was sunny in the evening. It was obvious that the larger the area provided for them, the more contented the tortoises are to graze over the whole area and do not spend their time patrolling the perimeter.

On moving house and having many more tortoises, all *graeca* and *hermannii* we were fortunate to be able to provide them with the freedom of the whole garden, which is mainly lawn with shrubby borders, rockeries, concrete and gravel areas, a large compost heap which many love, plus a long open-sided barn for shelter from the sun or rain or to sleep at night if they choose to ignore the house arranged for them. This is a four brick high frame 8ft x 3ft, with a movable corrugated plastic roof projecting over the front for protection from rain. It is kept filled with straw, frequently changed when soiling occurs. This shelter is again situated in a position that is sunny during late afternoon and evening.

The *marginata* eat large amounts of food, although we have noticed that the female appears restless and hardly touches food when she is close to egglaying time. Their diet is composed of cabbage and other brassicas, lettuce, clover, dandelion, plaintain, watercress, milk thistle, cucumber, tomato, apple, pear, banana (including skin occasionally), strawberries, runner bean, courgette, melon, grapes, yellow flowers (dandelion and buttercups) and magnolia flowers. They also like the sedums and sempervivums on the rockery and were last year seen enjoying the petunias. Tinned cat food is appreciated now and again, especially by the babies.

We give them a small feed in the morning when they have warmed up, then they browse over the garden for the rest of the day until about 4 pm when we gather them together for a large feed closer to their sleeping quarters, to which they retire shortly afterwards.

A shallow pool has been cemented into the garden for them to walk into for drinking and bathing. It needs to be very frequently brushed out and refilled as it is nearly always soiled when being used. The tortoises sometimes drink for several minutes at a time (we have recorded twenty minutes) and the young ones drink very often.

The female and her first mate were sexually very active from the time we first had them. In fact the vigorous courtship displayed by the male quite alarmed us at first as, apart from the ritual dance and leg and head biting, he would turn the female over and attack her when she was more vulnerably exposed. Copulation was seen to take place, but she did not attempt to dig a nest for the first few years except on one occasion when they had been moved to another garden while we were on holiday and she tried unsuccessfully to dig at the foot of an apple tree. Each year eggs were dropped at random over the garden, 3 in 1972, 11 in 1973, another 11 on 3 June 1974, but 5 in a nest on the 24 June. All these eggs were unsuccessful as we then had no idea of looking after them properly. In the summer of 1973 our second male took over as the female's mate. Mating takes place daily in fine weather from the time they come out of hibernation to when they go to sleep. Some days repeated mating occurs, often one act immediately following another. The *marginata* males have never shown any interest in other mature female *graeca* or *hermanni,* although smaller *graeca* males have attempted copulation with the female, which always appears unsuccessful as the sizes are so ill-matched and she is generally unco-operative. We have observed our seven year old male (?) attempting to mate with his sister (?), but the courtship display is singularly lacking and the episode brief. We are not certain of the sex of these seven years olds.

In 1975 we decided it was time to obtain some knowledge of the incubation of tortoise eggs and bought the Foyles Handbook by Ivor and Audrey Noel-Hume. So, in preparation for the arrival of eggs, we constructed an incubator from a small Stewarts plastic plant propagator, an aquarium thermostat and a 40 watt blue electric light bulb. This was to be placed in the airing cupboard and connected to a plug there. It was also thought better to provide a more suitable spot for the female to dig as she was seen to try scraping at the lawn without making any impression. A wooden wine bottle box 18" sq was filled with sand and placed near the base of a tree. That summer each time we saw her trying to dig we lifted her onto the sand box. At first she did not care for it, but we persisted and she became used to the feel of the soft, warm sand. A few days later she began in earnest to dig her nest. It was about midday and leaning her front legs on the raised edge of the box she began to scrape with first one hind foot, then the other. Digging took about half an hour until the hole was approximately 4" deep. Seven eggs were laid, taking 23 minutes. When they had been covered and the female had climbed down, apparently quite tired, we uncovered the eggs, pencilled a spot on the top of each to keep them upright and transferred them to margarine pots of sand in the incubator. The temperature was set at around 75°F.

In September, eleven weeks after being laid, our first two babies hatched. We later found that of the remaining five eggs there was one dead baby and four infertile eggs. The babies were transferred to a larger size propagator with a light bulb and thermostat, chicken gravel, stones and newspaper on the floor and small cardboard boxes for shelter. We later dispensed with the gravel as it was difficult to keep clean, using larger flatter stones instead. The second baby started eating chopped lettuce within 10-15 minutes after hatching and only then did the first one take food also, although arriving twenty four hours earlier.

Small plastic lids are ideal for food and water containers, being easily cleaned and renewable. At first we always chopped food for them but now it does not seem necessary: the babies appear quite capable of tearing leafy food and learning to grip it whilst eating. Harder foods like apples we crush or grate. They do seem to like eggshell, especially when very young, and this we provide by pounding chicken eggshells to a fine gritty texture and placing it in small heaps with their food. Water is much appreciated both for drinking and sitting in, especially as it gets warm.

Table 1. Egg laying and incubation

Year	No. Laid	No. Hatching	Place Laid	Date	Time Taken	Date of Hatching
1972	3	0	on garden			
1973	11	0	on garden			
1974 ”	11 5	0 0	on garden nest	3 June 24 June		
1975	7	2	sand box nest	25 June	egg laying time 12.15 – 12.38	1 5 Sept 2 6 Sept (1 baby dead, 4 yolks)
1976	9	6	sand box nest	24 June	digging & laying 12.05 – 13.20	1/2 27 Sept 3 1 Oct 4 2 Oct 5 3 Oct 6 9 Oct
”	9	0	sand box nest	11 July	digging & laying 17.00 – 18.40	
1977	7	7	sand box nest	3 June	digging & laying 12.10 – 13.40	1 12 Aug 2 13 Aug 3/4 14 Aug 5/6 15 Aug 7 18 Aug (opened)
”	10	4	sand box nest	7 July	digging & laying 16.20 – 17.40	1 27 Sept 2 29 Sept 3 1 Oct 4 2 Oct
1978	7	2	rockery nest	8 June	laying time 16.14 – 17.05	1 19 Aug 2 26 Aug
”	10	1	sand box nest	20 Aug	digging & laying 10.45 – 12.30	1 8 Jan ‘79 (opened eggs, several dead)
1979	7	5	sand box nest	23 June	digging & last egg 11.10 – 12.34	1 31 Aug 2 2 Sept 3 7 Sept 4 8 Sept 5 11 Sept
”	9	9	sand box nest	25 July	digging time 15.00 – 16.20 laying time 16.34 – 17.55	1/2 7 Oct 3 9 Oct 4/5 10 Oct 6/7/8 11 Oct 9 12 Oct
1980	11	6	sand box nest	4 June	digging & laying 12.10 – 13.15	1 12 Aug 2/3 14 Aug 4 15 Aug 5/6 23 Aug (eggs opened, 4 yolks)

It was not until a week or two after the hatching when we were trying to find out all we could about the care of the young ones that we had the opportunity of talking to someone who had also been successful but had later suffered disappointment by losing babies with "soft shell". This, we realised, was a serious problem and we then sought advice from a colleague who was warden at the I.L.E.A. Teachers Centre at Regent's Park. He recommended the use of the "Truelite" strip lights and gave us the address to contact. These lights have been very successful and easy to fit, so we use them all the year round, except for the short time we have hibernated the young ones in the last three or four years. Since joining the British Chelonia Group and reading of hibernating very young tortoises, we have for the past two years hibernated all the young over a year old for a period of between six to nine weeks. During the coldest weather the youngest group of babies are put in a shoebox or similar in the airing cupboard for the night.

We have hatched *marginata* now for the last seven years, though unfortunately none last year. The female showed no signs of egglaying although mating took place so we are wondering if perhaps she is now too old. The female has only once been seen to urinate on the nest when digging. We try to dampen the sand slightly when she shows signs of using it, so that the sides do not keep slipping in.

With the warmer weather and sunny days, the babies are put outside in small pens on patches of clover. They are given extra food, water and shelter and stay outside 'til about 5-6 o'clock when the garden becomes too shady and cool, when they are brought inside to their vivarium. If the weather is cold and/or wet they stay inside with their heater and ultra violet, the temperature being around 70°F, and their food is replenished when eaten during the day. We have three vivariums now so that the different year groups can be separated and a stronger one or two seem to develop faster in each group. It also gives the younger ones a chance of feeding without being pushed aside by the voracious older ones. Two of the vivariums are home-made, approximately 2ft 6in square, constructed of glass with wooden bases and removable tops. They are fitted with tubular heaters themostatically controlled, plus a 2ft 40 watt "Truelite" strip. The third vivarium is a "Camplex" plant propagator 18in x 15in with a heated base, also fitted with a smaller "Truelite". The lights are between 4in and 8in from the floor and switched on from 9 am to 4 or 5 pm each day. The 5½ and 6½ year old youngsters live outside freely with the other tortoises. All the remainder are kept in pens when outside, in case they get lost in the garden when there is a particular cold or wet spell.

Experience has shown us that it was unwise to use a fine sand in which to bury the eggs, especially as we dampened it. The result of that was to compact the sand into a hard mass which prevented the movement of the eggs towards the surface at hatching time. We now use a coarse, gritty sand and leave it dry.

From 1975 to date eggs laid	96
Live tortoises hatched	42
Young sold to breeders	15
Deaths since hatching	5
Remaining with us	22

Table 2. Weight chart

Date	Male Simon	Female Victoria	Alpha b: 5.9.75	Beta b: 6.9.75	Gamma b: 27.9.76	Delta b: 27.9.76	Epsilon b: 1.10.76	Zeta b: 2.10.76
19. 3.72	2lb 13 oz	6lb 2 oz						
25. 4.72	3 5½	6 9						
21. 5.72	3 6½	–						
13. 6.72	3 10	6 13						
12. 7.72	3 14	6 10						
19. 9.72	3 15	6 13						
20. 5.73	4 0	6 14						
30. 7.73	4 9	6 14						
26. 5.74	5 0	7 4						
23. 6.74	5 6	6 11						
5. 8.74	5 7	7 6						
5. 4.75	5 0	6 8						
27. 6.75	6 0	7 0						
27. 8.75	6 0	7 1						
13. 4.76	5 10	6 12						
4. 6.76	6 6	7 2						
11. 8.76	6 14	7 2½	0 7	0 5½				
13. 3.77	6 4	6 8	0 10	0 8				
9. 7.77	7 6	7 0	0 14	0 10½				
5. 9.77	7 4	7 1	0 15½	0 11½				
30. 3.78	6 12	6 14½	1 4	0 15½				
9. 5.78	7 6	7 11	1 4½	1 0				
30. 5.78	7 6	7 7	1 5½	1 0				
9. 7.78	8 0	7 8	1 9	0 15½				
20. 8.78	7 12	6 14	1 10	1 1				
11. 4.79	7 4½	6 15	1 10	0 14				
1. 6.79	7 14	7 6	1 12	1 1				
24. 6.79	8 1½	7 4	1 15	1 1½				
21. 8.79	8 5	7 8	2 5½	1 5				
–. 4.80	7 0	6 11	2 3	1 3				
18. 5.80	8 1	7 4	2 8	1 6				
12. 6.80	8 4	7 4	2 8	1 6½	0 12	0 10½	0 8	–
19. 7.80	8 9	7 4½	2 10	1 7	0 11½	0 11½	0 8½	0 7½
26. 8.80	8 1½	7 6½	2 13	1 9	0 14	0 13	0 10	0 9
26.10.80	7 12	7 3	2 12	1 7	–	–	–	–
27. 3.81	7 8½	6 14	2 9	1 7	–	–	–	–
11. 5.81	7 14	7 4	2 12	1 8	0 12	0 13½	0 9½	0 9½
6. 6.81	8 7	7 0	2 15	1 10	0 14½	0 13	0 9½	0 9
11. 7.81	8 13	7 8	3 0	1 12	0 15½	0 14	0 10	0 9½
2. 9.81	8 3	7 5	3 6	1 14	1 1½	0 15	0 10½	0 11
19. 4.82	8 4	7 6	3 4	1 15	1 3	1 0	0 12	0 12
Carapace Length May 1982	12 in	11 in	8 in	6¾ in	5¾ in	5½ in	4¾ in	4⅜ in

Five of the babies have died, showing loss of appetite and general deterioration, in spite of vitamin injections from the vet. The most recent one, a three year old, occurred this year quite suddenly two days after waking from its short hibernation.

For hibernation the babies are put into cardboard boxes, packed with crumpled newspapers and placed in a cold bedroom away from any heating. Regular checks are made to see if they are alright.

The *marginata* do not show any of the aggressive behaviour that our *hermanni* do. They have not succumbed to the runny nose that many of the *graeca* seem to be prone to. The hatchlings' shells have developed more normally than some other captive bred tortoises we have seen. Growth in some of the *marginata* is very rapid. Our second male grew from 2lb 13 oz in May 1972 to 3lb 15oz in September of that year and in five years was 6lb 14 oz. The first two babies, Alpha and Beta, have grown far more quickly than any of the other babies since.

We have found it impossible to sex the young ones, the shells all look alike, similarly their tails.

All the tortoises, with the exception of the smaller babies, are weighed as regularly as we can at one or two monthly intervals throughout their waking period.

British Herpetological Society Bulletin No. 5. 1982

NOTES ON THE MARGINATED TORTOISE *(TESTUDO MARGINATA)* IN GREECE AND IN CAPTIVITY

M.L. HINE

Chelonia Herpetoculture, The Lodge, Normanby, North Yorkshire, YO6 6RH, U.K.

INTRODUCTION

A field trip was planned and conducted in the Peloponnese, at Toloa a small hillside coastal village in south eastern Greece, and Tolon Island, during the months of May and June, 1980. The main objectives of this venture were:

1) To collect a small number of Marginated Tortoises *(Testudo marginata)* for a captive breeding project.

2) To study the natural habitat in order to further the management of this species and its preservation in the wild.

3) To supply captive bred tortoises, in conjunction with the Greek authorities, for reintroduction to the wild if ever the need should occur.

4. To supply captive bred tortoises to other herpetologists and institutions for further study.

After departing from Gatwick airport late in the evening of Wednesday 21st May, 1980, we arrived at Athens airport in the early hours of the following morning. A meeting with the Minister Director General of Agriculture followed and, after a helpful discussion, we proceeded on a 160km journey overland, by coach, to our destination of Tolon, arriving at approximately 14.30. After making a few tentative enquiries in Greek, a local man came to our rescue, bundled us into his car and sped along the dusty village road before depositing us at the door of our future hillside villa apartment, overlooking the sea. As we strolled through the village that evening in search of some local gastronomic delight, we saw three tortoises in private gardens by the sea front. They were, to our great pleasure, *Testudo marginata*. All three were of medium size i.e. 15-20cm carapace length, in good condition and at liberty to roam throughout the gardens.

DESCRIPTION OF HABITAT

It was decided that the main study area would be the middle region of the surrounding hillside, an area of approximately 6km^2 easily accessible from the rear of the villa, and that the secondary study area would be on Tolon Island extending to an area of approximately 1km^2. The island was approximately 1 km from the mainland. The hillside habitat consisted mainly of dry, stony ground with occasional belts of rocky projections, dry grass and low scrub. The secondary habitat was cultivated olive groves, again with stony ground but with the dry grass concentrated around the bases of the trees. The basic habitat of the uncultivated Tolon Island was the same as on the mainland but with the addition of dense, low bush growth. The only evidence of past human activity were the remains of stone terracing and derelict goat pens and shelters.

DESCRIPTION OF TORTOISES

Juvenile: Body colouring is of varying shades of beige with black markings to head and limbs.
Carapace: Round, lacking flare to rear of shell.
Carapace colouring: Centre of costals, vertebrals and marginals is beige with black edging.
Plastron: Round and flat.
Plastron colouring: Basically beige with four pairs of brown to black triangular markings on the pectoral, abdominal, femoral and anal plates.
Head: Small, usually with darker mask-like markings to face and a marking on top of the head between the eyes.
Limbs: Front, black-faced edge. Rear, black-faced edge to feet.

Young Adults: Similar to juveniles. Carapace elongated. Flare visible to rear of shell in males, plus deep concave in plastron. Colouring: Generally a shade darker than juveniles.

Mature Adults: Carapace generally elongated, but not necessarily so in females which only have a slight flare to the rear of the carapace. In the male the carapace is elongated with strongly serrated flare to the rear, deep concave in plastron and hooked jaw. In both sexes, colouring, of body and limbs and carapace is dark brown to black. Plastron colouring: Dark beige with black triangular markings.

FIELDWORK

Fieldwork was conducted daily between the hours of 07.00 and 13.00. On the first morning we sighted a *marginata* on the hillside. It was an adult female of medium size, dark brown to black in colour with a worn, smooth, rounded edge to the carapace and plastron. Later that morning a true pair of adult specimens were sighted in the nearby olive groves, and from then on tortoises were seen frequently.

Table 1. Data collected from wild tortoises during the period 24th May – 1st June 1980

Specimen		Sex	Size CSL	Weight (kg)	Location	Condition
1	*	OMF	24 cm	2.030	Mainland Hills	Carapace worn smooth
2		OMM	24.5 cm	2.030	Mainland Hills	Normal
3		OMF	24.5 cm	2.275	Mainland Hills	Normal
4		YMF	22 cm	1.800	Mainland Hills	Normal
5		OMM	25 cm	2.375	Mainland Hills	Normal
6		OMF	23.5 cm	2.275	Mainland Hills	Damage to carapace
7		YMM	21.5 cm	1.250	Tolon Island	Normal
8		YMM	21.5 cm	1.250	Tolon Island	Normal
9		J	12.5 cm	0.332	Tolon Island	Disfigurement to carapace
10		OMF	25 cm	2.800	Tolon Island	Normal. Largest female (mature)
11		OMF	23.5 cm	1.525	Tolon Island	Normal
12	*	J	7.5 cm	0.070	Tolon Island	Normal
13	*	OMF	25 cm	2.500	Mainland Hills	Disfigurement to carapace
14	*	OMM	29 cm	3.175	Mainland Hills	Normal
15		YMF	21.5 cm	1.575	Mainland Hills	Chip to lamina of carapace
16		OMF	26.5 cm	2.725	Mainland Hills	Rear left leg scarred 1st & 2nd digits fused
17		OMM	24.5 cm	2.150	Mainland Hills	Normal
18		YMF	20.5 cm	1.700	Mainland Hills	Normal
19		OMF	24.5 cm	2.275	Mainland Hills	Normal
20		OMM	27.5 cm	2.600	Mainland Hills	Top front of carapace badly damaged. Old wound
21	*	OMM	27 cm	3.500	Mainland Hills	Normal
22		YMF	22.5 cm	1.800	Mainland Hills	Normal
23	*	OMF	24 cm	2.150	Mainland Hills	Normal
24		YMF	18.5 cm	1.250	Mainland Hills	Normal

J=Juvenile. YMF=Young Mature Female. YMM=Young Mature Male.
OMF=Older Mature Female. OMM=Older Mature Male. CSL=Maximum carapace straight length.
*=Tortoises taken to England.

Information was collected on each tortoise by observing, photographing, numbering, weighing, measuring the maximum carapace straight length, noting the sex and the condition of the specimen, the time of day found and the ground level temperature. A few tortoises were placed in collecting bags and taken back to the villa. There they were washed in an antiseptic solution and de-ticked before being placed in open pens which had been constructed beside the veranda. The tortoises that were not collected were immediately released after the recording procedure.

The weather for most of the time was clear, dry and sunny. The wild tortoises were usually found out and about during the mornings, with the ground surface temperature varying from 18-31°C depending on the time. First thing in the morning most tortoises were observed sunbathing either in or outside their nightly place of retreat in thick, dry grass or low bush growth, before feeding commenced. The main activities observed were walking, sunbathing, and feeding. Tortoises were seen to eat Sowthistle, Chamomile, and a plant called *Medicago orbicularis.* No fighting, attempts at mating, egg-laying or drinking were seen. All the tortoises observed and collected on the mainland were mature adults, whilst those on the island were predominantly younger adults and juveniles, the exception being the largest adult female examined, No. 10, which had a carapace length of 25cm and weighed 2.8kg. (See Table 1).

At the villa the tortoises settled in well together with early morning activity dependent upon temperature and weather conditions. All fed well on a natural diet, but not so well on substitute foods. Males tended to shy away, but attempts at mating were observed. Faeces were inspected for worms resulting in a number of confirmed cases. Of the six tortoises taken back to England, worm infections were cleared within a period of two weeks by chemotherapy.

MAINTENANCE AND BREEDING IN ENGLAND

Housing

Housing consists of an indoor unit of open plan design covering an area of 2.75m^2. Underfloor heating is provided by means of tubular heaters at night with additional overhead heating and lighting by day. This maintains a thermostatically controlled temperature gradient with a range of 20°C to 40°C.

Floor covering consists of hay with a tub of sand set flush to the floor for nest digging if required. During the summer months there is access via a hinged door flap to an outdoor grass covered area of 36m^2.

Feeding

Items of food offered and eatern by tortoises in captivity in England include: dandelion, clover, grass, prickly and smooth sowthistle, parsley, chamomile, thyme, bedding hay, cabbage, lettuce, parsnip, carrot, apple, pear, banana with skin, Winalot dogmeal, vitamin and mineral supplement containing viatmin D3. Prepared food is given twice weekly. Weather permitting, natural food is obtained each day by browsing in outdoor units. Water is available both in outdoor and indoor units.

Hibernation

Table 2. Pre- and post-hibernation 14.5.81 specimens

Specimens	Sex	Placed into hibernation 22.10.80 Weight (kg)	Taken out of hibernation 14.5.81 Weight (kg)	Weight Loss (kg)
1	F	2.062	1.800	0.242
12 not hibernated	J	0.162	0.162	–
13	F	2.012	1.800	0.212
14 not hibernated	M	2.950	2.950	–
21	M	2.725	2.500	0.225
23	F	2.500	2.037	0.463

Juvenile No. 12 was not hibernated because of its size and weight but was allowed to go through a period of torpor brought about by a reduction in temperature and lighting. The adult male, No. 14, was not hibernated because it had not gained a satisfactory weight increase. This, we believe, was because this specimen was rather unsettled and preoccupied with mating attempts rather than feeding.

MATING, EGG-LAYING AND INCUBATION

All tortoises soon settled into their new accommodation after hibernation. The males were no longer so shy and were very active. Aggressive attempts at mating occurred regularly with preliminaries of chasing, butting of shell and biting of the head and limbs of females. When mating, a gutteral noise is made by the male and the female reacts with deliberate head movements from side to side.

On 30.7.81 one of the three female tortoises started to excavate a nest in the soft soil of the outdoor unit during the late, warm afternoon. Using her rear legs alternately a small hole was soon excavated, which was about 10cm deep. After a brief rest the first egg appeared from the cloaca and then dropped into the nest. The use of her rear legs and alternate foot movements resulted in the eggs being pushed inside the nest and packed firmly together. A total of six variably sized, eggs were laid before the nest was finally re-filled and the soil trampled down. By the 13.8.81 all three female tortoises had laid a total of 23 eggs (see Table 3).

All the eggs were collected, washed, measured and weighed before being placed in the incubator.

Plate 1. View of out-door units and access opening's to tortoise house. These units were built after this paper was originally published in 1982.

Plate 2. Inside view, part of tortoise house unit.

Plate 3. Egg laying may start from mid May.

Plate 4. Hatchlings feeding in their indoor rearing units.

HATCHLINGS

Hatchlings were removed from the incubator after the eggsack had been completely reabsorbed and placed in dry, open plan unit with a floor covering of hay. The unit is well lit with a temperature gradient of 18°C to 23°C at night and 23°C to 45°C during the day. Attempts at eating were observed on the first day, and by the second day eating was regular. Water is provided and drinking often observed. To date all 10 hatchlings are doing well.

Table 3. Nesting and egg-laying

Female	Date	Start of Nesting	Start of Egg-laying	Completion of Egg-laying	Ground Temp.	Weather	Soil	No. of Eggs
1	30.7.81	18.00	18.45	19.15	18°C	Warm)	Moist	10
23	2.8.81	10.15	11.15	11.40	21°C	Dry &)	"	6
13	13.8.81	17.15		18.15	20°C	Sunny)	"	7

Eggs varied in weight from 15.07-20.85g, and measured from 3.1-3.7cm in length by 2.7-3.5cm in width.

Table 4. Incubation details

	Specimen	Date of Egg-laying	Days	Temp. Range	Relative Humidity	No. of Eggs	
Batch 1	1	30.7.81	99	26-32°C	65-95%	10	9 eggs infertile 1 egg fertile, dead on inspection. Incubation terminated 6.11.81.
Batch 2	23	2.8.81	70	26-32°C	65-95%	6	6 eggs fertile. All hatched. Incubation terminated 11.10.81.
Batch 3	13	13.8.81	80	26-31°C	65-95%	7	4 eggs fertile, 3 infertile 4 hatchlings. Incubation terminated 1.11.81.

DISCUSSION

Much concern has been voiced about the ill-treatment and death of imported tortoises resulting from collecting methods, conditions of confinement and lack of general provision. However valid these points may be, I feel that these issues should not be generalised to such an extent that the total ban of all tortoise importations is justified.

All the specimens examined during the field trip were in reasonable condition, and despite their confinement and the twenty-one hours spent travelling to England they have settled into their new environment well, and successfully reproduced. This all goes to show that these tortoises are hardy and adaptable creatures that do well in captivity if properly catered for. The availability of tortoises should not be denied to those who can provide suitable facilities, as this will provide valuable knowledge and understandinng of the biology of these animals, and may contribute to their future preservation in the wild.

ACKNOWLEDGEMENTS

I would like to express my gratitude for the assistance given by staff of the Greek Embassy in London, and to the Director-General Minister of Agriculture in Athens, Greece, for his co-operation and support.

Footnote

Since collecting the nucleus of the breeding group, i.e. 2 males, 3 females and 1 juvenile female in 1980, regular breeding has occurred, each year, over the past 11 years.

Approximately 300 eggs have been laid in total and even allowing for nonfertility, death in the shell and a few post-hatchling deaths, the vast majority, i.e. over 250 specimens have been reared successfully.

British Herpetological Society Bulletin No. 21. 1987

OBSERVATIONS ON CAPTIVE JUVENILE SALT-WATER CROCODILES *CROCODYLUS POROSUS*

JOHN DAVENPORT

Animal Biology Group, Marine Science Laboratories, Menai Bridge, Gwynedd LL59 5EH, North Wales

INTRODUCTION

The salt-water or estuarine crocodile, *Crocodylus porosus* Schneider is the largest living crocodilian (perhaps reaching 9 m length in historical times, the largest living specimens are of the order of 6-7 m length). It is the only species known to traverse great distances at sea, which probably explains its very wide geographical distribution (Sri Lanka to northern Australia) (IUCN, 1982). Endangered in most parts of its distribution, the wild populations are generally listed on CITES Appendix I.

However, the species is the mainstay of many crocodile farming operations in the Far East, and some populations (e.g. those of Papua New Guinea and Australia) have been transferred to Appendix II to facilitate managed ranching/farming operations (Luxmore *et al.,* 1985).

In May 1987, 12 hatchling salt-water crocodiles arrived in Menai Bridge from Australia. Their dispatch and export permit documentation in Australia had been arranged by Dr. Graham Webb of the Conservation Commission of the Northern Territories; an appropriate CITES import permit was obtained in the U.K. The funds for the animals' transport and the subsequent scientific work to be performed upon them were provided by a grant from the Nuffield Foundation to the author. The animals were purchased from a crocodile farm (where they would have been reared for their skins and meat) and it was agreed that most would be sacrificed for anatomical/histological studies at the end of the experimental programme, but that any remaining live animals could be transferred to a recognized zoo.

The experimental programme is in progress, being devoted mainly to the gut function of the animals, but with side projects involving studies of locomotory mechanisms and behavioural responses to temperature and salinity. The intention in this report is to describe handling and feeding techniques, and to comment on some aspects of the animals' behaviour.

ACCOMMODATION

The young crocodiles are held in a tank of flowing low salinity water (usually fresh water, but sometimes with added sea water as this is known to promote good skin condition), constantly circulated through a biological filter and header tank. The holding tank (5 m long x 0.4 m wide x 0.6 m deep) is made of epoxy-coated ply with a perspex front for observation. A feeding platform constructed of varnished marine ply may be reached by gently sloping ramps, cross cut to provide purchase for the crocodiles' claws. The whole arrangement is held in a temperature controlled room at 30°C. Given that the species is a "salt-water" crocodile, it might appear strange to keep them in fresh water. However, although wild hatchlings have been seen in full strength sea water (Gregg, pers. comm.), and possess lingual salt glands which secrete a salt-rich fluid to remove a salt load, they do not thrive in captivity in this medium for reasons which are as yet obscure.

FEEDING & HANDLING

For convenience, routine feeding is upon fish or squid available in the laboratories (mackerel, condemned rainbow trout from a trout farm, and squid from the Falklands area have all figured in their diet). Chopped whole food organisms are used to ensure plenty of calcium in the diet (crocodilians are prone to skeletal deformities if fed on filleted fish). Usually, no single food organism is used for more than a week. Experience has shown that daily feeding is wasteful, the animals showing a poor appetite and feeding over a prolonged period. Instead, the animals are fed every second day, which results in rapid and complete consumption of meals. At intervals, the animals have been supplied with large insects, as this elicits interesting feeding behaviour (see below). Cockroaches, locusts and crickets have all been taken readily.

Handling of the animals has so far involved neither gloves nor special apparatus. Although the crocodiles will snap at hands when they are out of the water they do not do so when immersed. The normal capture procedure is to chase each animal into the water and then catch it with two hands, one encircling the throat and immobilizing the head, the other immobilizing the tail.

BEHAVIOUR

For a few weeks the young crocodiles were shy and reacted violently to movements outside their tank. They did not feed in the presence of observers and grew very slowly. Handling was initially kept to a minimum of once per week during weighing sessions. Over a period of 4-5 weeks the animals became progressively tamer and fed more readily. They were handled with increasing frequency as it was intended that they be used in experiments demanding repeated manipulation (e.g. for serial X-radiography). At the time of writing, all animals feed within about 15 minutes of being offered a meal and their sole reaction to handling is to emit loud squawks when first grasped. An initial tendency to urinate when handled has subsided. Initially 50-70 g in weight, the animals have now grown to 110-280 g (5 months' growth).

Feeding behaviour is fairly complex. As soon as regular feeding started, a feeding hierarchy developed, with a few animals growing much more rapidly than the rest as a result of monopolizing (and defending) space on the feeding platform. Initially, attempts were made to counteract this problem by offering more food, but this simply exacerbated the differential growth rate. At present, any animals showing an unusually high rate of weight increase are separated from the others for a few weeks and fed separately until their smaller fellows have "caught up" as far as weight is concerned.

Feeding responses to dead food (fish, squid) are very different from the reactions to live food (insects). At no time have the crocodiles taken dead food placed in their water. Dead food is only taken into the mouth out of water, although the crocodiles often retreat to the water when they have a mouthful of food. In contrast, live insects struggling at the water surface are taken readily and immediately. The crocodiles are also capable of jumping out of the water to catch insects moving on objects above water. To do this, the crocodile first takes up position at the water surface with the snout pointing towards the insect and the eyes focussed upon it. The body is held obliquely or vertically in the water (obliquely if the prey is some distance in front of the crocodile, vertically if the insect is above the predator). The rear feet are drawn forward and their toes parted to deploy the webs between them completely. The crocodile then propels itself upwards and forwards by a powerful downwards and backwards thrust of the hindlegs. As the snout clears the water, the jaws begin to part and are wide open by the time the whole head is above the water line. The jaws snap shut around the insect, which may be as much as a complete body length above the water surface, since the crocodiles are capable of jumping completely out of the water. When on land, the young crocodiles are also able to catch insects, either by side snaps of the jaws if the prey is nearby, or by lunges or jumps if the insects are further away (again, the hinds limbs provide propulsion). Insects which sank below the water surface, even if still alive and showing limb movements, were not eaten.

Whatever the nature of their food, the crocodiles have a problem when swallowing it. Normally, whether on land or immersed in water, the throat of the crocodile is closed by the upper surface of the back of the tongue forming a seal against the palate (air is drawn in through the nostrils). The tongue is not mobile, so cannot be used to move food from the front of the jaws towards the throat. Instead, the crocodile has to throw its head back and use gravity to supply food to the oesophagus (food items are tossed about by head and jaw movements until their longitudinal axes point towards the gullet). This behaviour is effective when the animal is on land, but when a crocodile has taken food into the water, or has captured food at the water surface, the buoyancy of the food items (particularly insects which have a density well below that of water) means that the gravity-based mechanism would become ineffective if the crocodile tried to swallow whilst under water. Instead, the animal adopts a vertical position in the water, with the head projected above the water surface. The crocodile treads water vigorously (by movements of all four limbs), with the jaws pointing skywards, until the food is swallowed.

REFERENCES

IUCN (1982). *The IUCN Amphibia-Reptilia Red Data Book, Part 1.* IUCN, Gland, Switzerland.

Luxmore, R.A., Barzdo, J.G., Broad, S.R. and Jones, D.A. (1985). *A Directory of Crocodilian Farming Operations.* IUCN/CITES, Switzerland and Cambridge.

BREEDING OF THE AMERICAN ALLIGATOR *(ALLIGATOR MISSISSIPPIENSIS)* IN THE SOUTHERN HEMISPHERE

A.E. ERIKSEN

Cango Crocodile Ranch & Cheetahland,
P.O. Box 559, Oudtshoorn 6620, Republic of South Africa

This account covers the successful breeding of the American Alligator *(Alligator mississipiensis)* and is the result of three former attempts. The most recent attempt was detailed in an earlier article (Eriksen, 1987a).

HISTORY

The Alligator breeding population of the Ranch consists of two pairs – the first pair, (hereafter referred to as "Pair A"), consists of a 2.95m male, approximately 22 yrs old, and a 2.2m female approximately 20 yrs old. The second pair, (hereafter referred to as "Pair B"), consists of a 2.9m male, age unknown and a 2m female approximately 16 yrs old.

Pair A and the female from Pair B were imported from America by the Ranch, while the male from Pair B is on breeding loan from another zoological institution. Pair A have been together for approximately 6 years and Pair B for 2 years.

ENCLOSURES

The enclosures for both pairs are virtually identical and are situated adjacent to one another. The dimensions are as follows:- the pens are 10 metres x 10 metres in diameter, the pool being of irregular shape, with a surface area of 45 square metres. The average depth is 1.5m. The pool is of concrete construction and is drained twice a week. Emphasis in the enclosures is to create as natural an environment as possible. At the rear of the enclosure is a small room, which is kept heated in winter; this has a river-sand base, but is not used by the alligators for nest building purposes. The water in the enclosure is not heated.

OUDTSHOORN TEMPERATURE RANGES

	°C	FEB	MAR	APR	MAY	JUN	JUL	AUG	SEP	OCT	NOV	DEC	JAN	YEAR
	MEANMAX	32	30	27	23	20	19	21	23	26	28	30	32	26
1987	MEANMIN	15	14	11	7	3	3	5	7	10	12	14	15	10
	RAIN mm	13	26	21	21	11	19	16	22	21	31	21	10	232 (total)
	MEANMAX	38	35	27	27	18	22	25	25	28	31	33	34	28
1988	MEANMIN	19	17	11	8	5	3	6	8	10	12	13	16	11
	RAIN mm	0	19	22	15	16	3	9	18	1	4	20	0	126 (total)

The water temperatures in summer average 25°C and winter 12°C.

DIET

The diet of the alligators originally consisted entirely of ostrich meat, (readily available in our area), however it was felt that this possibly contained too much calcium, as an ostrich head contains up to 50% bone. It was therefore decided to change the diet to donkey meat, with carcass meal and a vitamin mixture added.

The average feed rates are: 3kg per animal per week during the summer months, i.e. October through to March. The alligators are not fed during the winter months.

BREEDING – 1987/88

The reproduction attempts of Pair A up until and including 1987 were discussed in my previous article (Eriksen, 1987). However, as stated in that paper, success was limited (1 hatchling born in 1987 subsequently died). To summarize, breeding of Pair A began in 1985 with a total of 45 eggs laid on the 14th January 1986. Of these eggs, one was broken and the remaining 44 were placed in an incubator containing no substrate. Five eggs were measured and weighed. These ranged in length from 72.5mm to 69mm, with a diameter of 40.5mm to 39.5mm – the weights averaging 67.5g to 61.9g. Of these eggs, 19 appeared fertile, however banding continued for only 14 days and then ceased. In 1987, 49 eggs were laid – 3 were badly damaged and 2 were cracked. A total of 46 eggs were placed in the incubator once again, with no substrate. Of these, 28 appeared fertile and had begun banding.

After 58 days, on the 26th March, only 5 fertile eggs remained and on day 65 (2nd April), one hatchling broke through the eggshell. As the shell was very tough, the hatchling struggled to free itself requiring assistance after 20 + hours (detailed in previous article). The hatchling appeared to have a problem with its balance and subsequently died 2 months later through drowning, having had to be force fed until this time. At birth the length of the hatchling was 233mm with a weight of 35g.

By day 70, the remaining 4 eggs were opened revealing fully developed dead embryos. The average measurement of the eggs was 71mm long by 39.5mm in diameter, and weight average was 66g.

In 1987 Pair A produced no eggs, however from the 23rd of July 1987 heavy bellowing was heard from both pens, sometimes lasting up to 15 minutes and usually started by the males. This was observed on 18 different days up until the 9th November 1987. Bellowing occurred mostly in the early morning between 7am and 8am, and in the afternoons between 4 and 5pm.

Pair B, which had been introduced to each other and the new enclosure on the 1st July 1987, produced eggs which were discovered on the 22nd January 1988.

On the 8th January 1988, the female started moving the nesting material around and showed signs of aggression, snapping and hissing on approach. However, she made no attempt to attack. On the 17th, she displayed extreme aggression, chasing and lunging at everyone that entered the enclosure. On the 18th she was chased off the nest and a thorough check was made of the nest; however, no eggs were sighted. This was unusual, as her behaviour indicated a lay. Periodical checking of the nest continued until the 22nd January 1988 when it was decided to do a complete check of the whole area. At 9am, 12 eggs were discovered buried under about 5cm of ground, at the back of the nest. No banding had occurred and the eggs proved to be infertile. (It would seem probable that they had been laid on the 17th). Nine of the eggs were completely broken. The average dimensions of the 3 remaining eggs were as follows:– length 70mm, diameter 40mm and weight 63g.

BREEDING 1988/89

In 1988, both pairs produced eggs with pair B producing first.

Vegetation was placed in both pens at the end of October, consisting of a mixture of cut grass (Kikuyu) and leaves of a wild bamboo found in the area. The nests were watered down approximately once a week, to aid in decomposition and to provide moisture. During this period, heavy bellowing was heard from both enclosures. Towards the end of November copulation was twice observed in Pen A, both times occurring at approximately 8am. On the 30th December 1988 at 8am, Female B was observed using her back legs to scrape the nesting material into a mound. This continued for approximately one hour before she re-entered the water. On the 31st December at 8.30am, I entered Pen B. The female lunged off the nest with her mouth open. She was then chased off the nest and the nest was opened. One egg was found near the surface of the nest, with a further 16 found in the centre. One of the eggs had a soft leathery shell and 4 others were cracked. All 17 eggs were placed in a styrofoam box. Holes were punched in the base, with a 5cm deep layer of dampened vermiculite, placed at the bottom (vermiculite was dampened until a drop of water was produced when squeezed). This was followed by a 2cm layer of nesting material. The eggs were then placed one layer deep, on top of the vegetation, which was then covered with another layer of dampened vermiculite.

The styrofoam box was then placed in the incubator which was set at 29°C and a humidity of 94%. A temperature probe was placed in the vermiculite and registered 30°C. This temperature rose in the following week to 32°C, then dropped to 31.5°C where it remained for the incubation period. On the 30th January, the eggs were removed from the incubator, as 7 eggs were infertile and the remaining 10 had ceased banding at approximately day 14. The embryos appeared to have reached stage 12 (Ferguson, 1985).

Egg measurements were on average:– Length 69.2mm, diameter 42.3mm and weight 66g. On the 31st January 1989, one month after Female B's initial lay, one egg was found in the water of her pen, and on the 4th January 1989, 3 more eggs were found in the water. They were placed in the incubator, however, none of them showed any signs of banding and were removed after one week. We therefore had no success with Pair B for the 1988/89 breeding season.

The eggs in Pen A were laid on the 16th January 1989. (Prior to this date, no copulation or nesting behaviour was observed). For 2 weeks prior to this the female spent most of her time in the water, however on the morning of the 16th, she was observed on the nest and at 7.30am we entered the enclosure. The female showed no real signs of aggression, even when approached to within 1 metre. This was completely contrary to her previous protective nesting behaviour, however it was decided to go ahead and check the nest. As soon as wooden barriers were placed against her, she attacked and did not want to leave the nest. The eggs were discovered scattered around the inside of the nest, which contained a lot of sand – obviously scraped up by the female. Most of the eggs were found approximately 1cm from the top of the nest and a lot of them were crushed. A further eight eggs were found approximately 30cm below these eggs and only 1 of these was cracked. The rest were found in clusters scattered around the nest. Some eggs, which were covered in yolk from those that had broken, were first washed in warm water and then rubbed in nesting material, before being placed in the polystyrene container. The minimum and maximum temperatures on the 15th January 1989 were: Min 17°C, Max 35°C, and on the 16th January 1989 the morning temperature was 21°C. Nest temperature measured 27°C. As a point of interest, for one week prior to the 16th January 1989, the female refused to eat. The container and incubator were prepared in exactly the same manner as for Pair B.

On the 22nd March 1989, at 8am, 65 days from date of laying, (the exact no. of days occurring for Pair A's previous successful hatching), pipping was heard coming from the box. However, as it was very weak it was decided to leave the eggs until stronger pipping could be heard. On the 23rd, at 2.30pm, the nest was opened and by this time, 3 hatchlings had already broken through the shells. By 5.30pm, 5 hatchlings had fully emerged – these were washed in warm water and transferred to the hothouse. By 3pm on the 24th March 1989 a total of 10 hatchlings had emerged. Of the remaining eggs, 1 hatchling was found dead in the egg, however it appeared to be under-developed. The remainder were infertile. At birth, the hatchlings measured on average: Length 24cm, weight 40g. 10 healthy hatchlings were produced by Pair B for the 1988/89 breeding season.

HATCHLINGS

For eleven days the hatchlings refused food completely, however, on day 12, one began to eat and this was followed by the rest. The method of feeding was to roll the food mix into a small ball then drop it near the hatchling. This movement seemed to stimulate feeding. Once the hatchlings were eating well, the food was placed around the sides of the pool for the hatchlings to eat in their own time.

They are at present kept in an enclosure, within the hothouse, measuring approximately 5 square metres. The enclosure contains a 2.25 square metre pool with a 40 cm concrete apron bordering it. The pool has a gentle gradient, sloping down to a maximum depth of approximately 16cm. Floor, air and water temperatures are kept constant at 32°C.

HATCHLINGS' FOOD

The food mix for the hatchlings consists of 60% meat, 20% liver, with a vitamin mix added at a rate of 1%. The vitamin mix is based on the "Alligators Premix" (Joanen and McNease, 1981).

The growth rate as at 31 May 1989, was as follows:

Average length: 37cm   Average weight: 128g.

CONCLUSION

Having finally succeeded in breeding Alligators, it would seem from our previous experiences that Alligator eggs do not hatch as successfully when no medium is used. When using a medium, it is my belief that nesting material, or some other form of biotic material, should be used around the eggs. This would seem to promote degradation of the egg shell as stated by Ferguson (1985). A high humidity (i.e. 94 to 98%) is also essential to prevent air spaces and regression of the yolk. Diet of the female alligator is an important consideration and too much calcium in the diet may create too thick an eggshell, thus making gaseous exchange and degradation of the shell more difficult. This is possibly borne out by our successful hatching for the 1988/89 breeding season, as the female was fed a diet of donkey meat with a small amount of calcium added. In previous years she had been fed a diet of ostrich offal, containing nearly 50% calcium.

REFERENCES

Ferguson, W.J. (1985). *Reproductive Biology and Embryology of the Crocodilians.* Biology of the Reptilia, **4** Dev A, Chapt 5.

Joanen, T. and McNease, L. (1981). Incubation of alligator eggs. *Alligator Prod. Conf.* (Gainesville, Florida) **1**: 117-28.

Eriksen, A.E. (1987). Observations on the reproduction of the American Alligator *(Alligator mississipiensis)* in captivity. *British Herp. Soc. Bull.* No. 21 1987.

OBSERVATIONS AND NOTES ON THE CAPTIVE BREEDING OF THE GREEN SEA TURTLE *(CHELONIA MYDAS)* ON GRAND CAYMAN, BRITISH WEST INDIES

SIMON TOWNSON

c/o British Herpetological Society,
Zoological Society of London, Regent's Park, London NW1

INTRODUCTION

The Green Turtle *(Chelonia mydas)* has a worldwide distribution in tropical and subtropical seas, and different races have been recognised throughout this large range. Its colouration is variable, although basically greeny-brown with darker markings, with the flippers and head olive green. This species may reach a weight of several hundred pounds, and Carr (1952) mentions old American records of up to 850lbs. They are found most commonly in shallow areas of continental shelf where there is sufficient food in the form of marine grasses. Diet of the adults consists mainly of vegetation, but they will occasionally take animal material such as jellyfish (Bustard, 1972). During the first year or so of life they are mainly carnivorous. Tagging experiments have shown that Green Turtles migrate thousands of miles between feeding and nesting grounds; for example, experiments by Carr (1968) have suggested that Brazilian Green Turtles travel to Ascension Island in the mid-Atlantic to nest. Little is known about the behaviour and migrations of juvenile turtles.

The Green Turtle is the best known species since it is widely distributed and its flesh has the best flavour. In American and Caribbean waters it was over exploited at a very early date, when they were collected in vast numbers by seamen and settlers as a source of fresh meat, since captured turtles would live for a considerable period. Often the individuals collected were females on the beach about to lay eggs, which no doubt worsened the situation. Because the Green Turtle is so predictable in its breeding and feeding sites it is an easy target for man, who is increasingly moving into previously undisturbed areas.

In different parts of the world the status of this species varies considerably: for example, there are healthy, large colonies on the coasts of Australia (Bustard, 1972), but in some parts of the Caribbean they can no longer be found (Carr, 1968), and on a global scale the Green Turtle is greatly depleted and is listed in the IUCN Red Data book as an endangered species. The world's best known "turtle-ologists", Profesor Archie Carr and Dr Robert Bustard, have talked at great length about the possibilities of farming this species, and have suggested that such a rational exploitation may be the most effective method of conservation.

During February 1979, while studying the herpetology of the Cayman Islands, I was honoured to be a guest of the Cayman Turtle Farm Limited, on Grand Cayman. In this article I will describe the farm and briefly relate some of its history and great success, giving my own impression of this establishment and the importance of the research and achievements carried out there.

DESCRIPTION OF THE FARM

Green Turtle farming on Grand Cayman was started in 1968 by Mariculture Limited, with a small prototype farm at Salt Creek. In 1970 when the turtle population had reached 30,000 the farm was moved to its present site at Goat Rock (Plate 1) and later after financial difficulties, new owners renamed it the Cayman Turtle Farm Limited. Continued expansion has been necessary to accommodate the current turtle population of around 70,000.

Sea water is continuously pumped through all the tanks on the Farm thus ensuring maximum cleanliness and minimum risk of infection. The water is pumped in from the sea at one end of the Farm, circulated and discharged at the other end. Each hour the pumping system circulates 2.6 million gallons through tanks varying in size from 12 to over 75,000 gallons. All the turtles are fed on a pelleted feed, similar in appearance to that used in other livestock farming industries, and is sometimes supplemented with locally mown turtle grass *(Thalassia)*. The pellets float and vary in size according to the age of the turtle, so that they can pick them from the surface. The pellets are high in protein and give an efficient food conversion ratio and rapid growth rate. The amino acids therein are those found to be essential for hatchling Green Turtles by Wood (1974), and are similar to those generally considered essential for mammals.

The Farm is divided into eight distinct areas, which are briefly described below (Plate 1 and Figure 1).

Area One
These eight tanks normally hold turtles between the ages of six and eighteen months, and each tank (depending on size) is capable of holding between one thousand and five thousand turtles (mostly commercial growing stock).

Area Two
These small tanks contain the baby or hatchling turtles, which are all between 3 days and 6 months of age. The baby turtles are brought to these tanks from the hatchery, where the eggs have incubated for approximately 8 weeks at a mean daily temperature of 28°C. The eggs are initially removed from all verified nests on the artificial beach (Area 5, see later), placed in batches of up to 100 in three layers in styrofoam boxes and covered with a muslin cloth and a thin layer of sand. The boxes are then placed in an open-sided hatchery with good ventilation,

temperature fluctuation in the boxes being reduced by the styrofoam. The survival rate of baby turtles on the farm is obviously much higher than in the wild, where the eggs are subject to human and animal predation before they hatch, and after they hatch crabs, birds, and fish kill the majority of the survivors.

Area Three
These two large tanks contain commercial growing stock of a medium size. The length of the carapace can be a rough guide to their age. For example, a 10" carapace indicates a one year old turtle, 15" would indicate 18 months, and 20" about three years. When turtles begin to get sizeable they look incapable of moving anything but slowly; however, they can move surprisingly quickly in bursts of up to 20 miles an hour.

Area Four
These six small round fibreglass tanks came from the first turtle farm site at Salt Creek, where they were floated in the sea attached to cat-walks and contained all the original Green Turtle Stock. Now they contain various species of turtle, including Loggerheads *(Caretta caretta)*, Hawksbills *(Eretmochelys imbricata)* and Ridleys *(Lepidochelys olivacea)*. These are kept purely for observation and research and the Cayman Turtle Farm has no intention of farming these other species on a commercial scale. It is worth mentioning that most other species of sea turtle are carnivorous, which causes their meat to have a strong and less appealing flavour.

Area Five
This large pond (Plate 3) and artificial beach contain the breeding herd. Basically in this area the turtles mate, the females crawl up on the beach to deposit their eggs and return to the water. The pond measures approximately 200 ft (60.5m) by 85 ft (26.5m) giving an area of about 0.4 acres (0.2 ha). It is about 10 ft (3.1m) deep on the north-west side and shelves up to an artificial beach about 35 ft (10m) wide on the south-east side. The capacity of the pool is about 0.75 million gallons, and sea water is pumped through at a rate calculated to give 18 changes daily.

In order to accelerate the Farm breeding programme it was necessary to bring to Cayman mature wild male and female turtles. As the Cayman Turtle farm was not started until 1968 the oldest farm reared turtles are only just reaching maturity. The farm reared turtles can be easily recognised by their far superior shell colours and patterns. In 1973 the first known nestings in captivity occurred in this breeding pond, subsequently eggs were laid on the artificial beach and healthy turtles hatched. This was a major breakthrough and in 1975 the farm achieved its second major step forward when a farm reared female laid 601 eggs and healthy hatchlings emerged.

During the mating and laying seasons farm personnel maintain a 24-hour watch on the pond and artificial beach: all the breeding turtles are tagged so it is therefore easy to keep records of such facts as when and how long each turtle mates, and how many eggs each female lays per nest and per season. In Cayman, mating occurs between April and July each year. Following a complex courting procedure, male and female will mate sometimes for periods of up to 52 hours. The laying season in Cayman is from May until September. During this period and only at night the females crawl up the artificial beach, scoop out a 2 to 3 ft hole with their rear flippers and then deposit their eggs, cover the nest and return to the water. This, of course, is an exact replica of their behaviour out in the wild. Females have laid up to 230 eggs per nest and the Farm has recorded one female which nested 10 times in one season laying over 1,700 eggs in the artificial beach.

Area Six
This double row of tanks holds commercial growing stock from 6 to 18 months. There are also small tanks used for research experiments in feed, stocking density and medication.

Area Seven
These oblong tanks were the last to be constructed at Goat Rock, and water circulation within this particular shape and size tank has proved to be very efficient. Three of these tanks normally hold larger commercial growing stock, whilst three tanks nearest the road are reserved for future breeding stock. As the turtles become older, they spend less time floating on the surface and during non feeding periods can be seen resting on the bottom, occasionally coming up to the surface to breathe.

Area Eight
This large area contains the majority of the growing stock over 18 months of age.

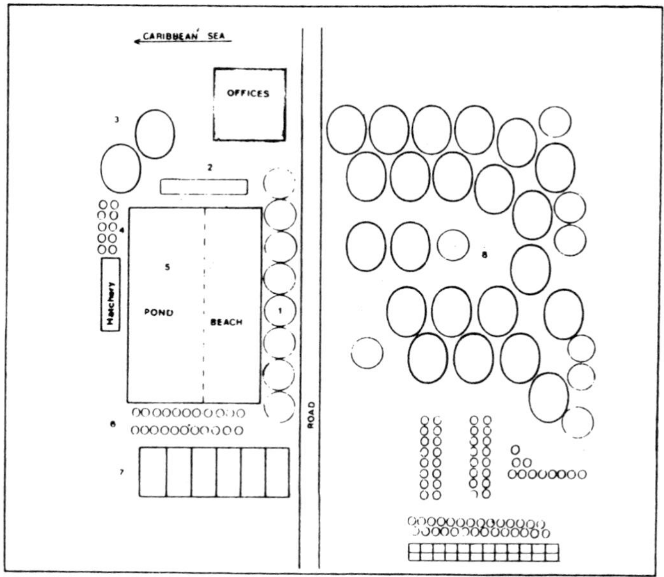

Figure 1. Plan of the Cayman Turtle Farm. See text for explanation of area numbers.

Plate 1. The Cayman Turtle Farm at Goat Rock, Grand Cayman.

Plate 2. Captive bred *Chelonia mydas.* Commercial growing stock over three years old.

Plate 3. The large breeding pond and artificial beach. Turtle tracks can be seen in the sand. Mating pairs of turtles are coaxed into the meshed pens on the right of the picture to prevent displacement of the copulating male by others.

Plate 4. Small tanks used for research and medication purposes in Area 8.

DISCUSSION

I realise that many turtle lovers may not be sympathetic towards the idea of farming turtles for commercial purposes, but I believe that a rational exploitation in this way may be the best approach from the turtle's point of view.

Firstly I would like to make a few points about the way the Cayman Turtle Farm was set up, it's aims and achievements, and the attitudes its owners and employees have towards conservation.

The Farm is a new and unique operation, and in the absence of existing farm stocks to draw on, this pioneer farm had to obtain its foundation material from the wild, but did so with as little disturbance to wild populations as possible (Simon 1975). Up to 1973 the stocking of the rearing tanks at the farm depended entirely on the artificial incubation and hatching of eggs collected from natural beaches, with the permission of the appropriate authorities. During the period 1971-3 almost all of the eggs collected came from nests doomed by tidal washout or volcanic sand, so that loss of hatchlings to the wild was small in comparison with the number of eggs collected, which was 188,568 (Simon 1975).

The Farm is now entirely self-sufficient, since it has taken no eggs from the wild since 1978, and does not intend to do so again (Johnson, personal communication, Cherfas 1979). Representatives of the Department of the Environment and British management authority for CITES (Convention of International Trade in Endangered Species) recently stated that Cayman Turtle Farm meets the criteria for a farm as outlined in CITES, since its products are now derived from a closed operation.

The success of the Farm is heavily dependent on research, and a competent team of zoologists are continually working on more efficient means of turtle husbandry and equally important, a fuller understanding of the Green Turtle's life cycle and biology (Simon 1975; Simon, Ulrich & Parkes 1975; Wood & Wood 1978; Wood 1974; Ulrich & Owens 1974; Ulrich & Parkes 1978). Of particular importance is a complete understanding of its reproductive habits, and considerable progress has also already been made in areas such as nutrition and disease control.

As mentioned previously, the first breakthrough came in 1973 when the first farm laid eggs hatched successfully. Up to this time there had been no reproductive activity in the large breeding pool which contained about 70 ex-wild turtles. However, on April 12th 1973 a burst of mating activity occurred after the introduction of two Surinam males (Ulrich & Owens 1974) at the beginning of the mating season. Not only did the two new males mount females almost immediately after 15 days in transit, but within a few days mating activity was shown by at least two of the previously inactive males. It would appear that turtles kept continuously together all year round do not become sexually active in the mating season, and require some kind of trigger, such as the introduction of the wild Surinam males. Therefore in 1974 the males were segregated from the females except during the mating season, which proved successful: this technique was effective in breeding the Giant tortoises of the Galapagos, and is probably a familiar manipulation to most reptile breeders. The 1974 season provided an interesting example of the importance of the social environment in sexual behaviour (Ulrich & Parkes 1978). A pair of ex-wild turtles, both of which had been sexually active in 1973, were isolated in a large tank from February to June 1974 where in this situation they showed no sexual activity. They were then transferred to the breeding pool, where the male, apparently stimulated by competition, quickly mounted the female, as afterwards did two pool mates.

The table below shows the breeding results for 1973 and 1974 (from Ulrich & Parkes 1978).

	1973	1974
No. of females laying	19	14
No. of clutches	92	80
Average no. of clutches per female	4.8	5.7
No. eggs	11268	9752
Average no. eggs per female	593	697
Average no. eggs per clutch	122	122
Hatch rate %	42.3	44.8

Although the hatch rates are relatively low when compared to eggs collected from wild rookeries (80%) and hatched under the same conditions, these results clearly show that the Green Turtle can be captive bred on a large scale, and with further research and experience these figures should improve dramatically. Whether or not the reproductive cycle from farm bred turtle to farm bred turtle can be completed, is not likely to be answered before the early 1980s, when stock hatched from eggs laid on the farm in 1973 should become sexually mature.

Unlike illegally poached turtles, every part of a farm reared turtle is utilized to make a variety of products, including steak, soup products, shell products (whole shells and jewellery), leather, and oil. Although this exploitation of the Green Turtle may not appeal to many members, I do believe it to be a realistic approach to the problems of conserving the species and satisfying the demand for turtle products. Man has been killing turtles and their eggs in vast numbers for centuries, and passing legislation to protect them has not stopped poaching on a large scale, since many poor people rely on this animal to make a living. However, if there is an alternative to poached material, in the form of superior high quality farm products at acceptable prices, then this can only be a good thing: wild populations will not be threatened by this kind of venture and the control of the distribution and export of farm products should be relatively easy. Strict control by governments should ensure that such products operate within the law, and that pseudo-farms, as with some crocodile farms, do not emerge. Arguments suggesting that selling farm products may stimulate the market and increase demand for wild turtles are not convincing, as there is little evidence for this being true.

The big "spin-off" from this commercial venture is the great deal of knowledge gained, at private expense, about the biology and large scale captive breeding of the Green Turtle. The uses this information could be put to for conservation projects are numerous. For example, Robert Bustard (1972) has shown that releasing pen-reared yearlings to the wild increases overall survival something like 50 to 100 times over the natural situation. Further research has to be completed to determine whether or not pen-reared turtles behave normally when released to the sea, although results so far are encouraging. Alternatively, captive breed hatchlings could be released directly to the sea: survival up to the hatchling stage would be much higher than in the natural situation, where a large percentage of eggs and hatchlings are killed on the beaches. Because the employees and owners of the Farm have been so open and published their methods and techniques developed over many years, we now have the technology and understanding to breed marine turtles on a large scale, which, I am convinced, may prove invaluable to their future conservation.

REFERENCES

Bustard, R. (1972) *Sea Turtles: Their natural history and conservation.* London & Sydney: Collins.

Carr, A. (1952) *Handbook of Turtles.* Comstock, New York.

Carr, A. (1968) *So excellent a Fishe. A natural history of Sea Turtles.* Natural History Press, New York.

Cherfas, J. (1979) The song of the Turtle. *New Scientist* Vol. 84, No. 1185.

Simon, M. (1975) The Green Sea Turtle *(Chelonia mydas);* collection, incubation and hatching of eggs from natural rookeries. *J. Zool., Lond.* 1976: 3948.

Simon, M.H., Ulrich, G.F. and Parkes, A.S. (1975). The Green Sea Turtle *(Chelonia mydas);* mating, nesting and hatching on a farm. *J. Zool., Lond.* 117: 41 1423.

Ulrich, G.F. and Owens, D.W. (1974) Preliminary note on reproduction of *Chelonia mydas* under farm conditions. *Proc. Wld. Maricult. Soc.* 5.

Ulrich, G.F. and Parkes, A.S. (1978) The Green Sea Turtle *(Chelonia mydas):* further observations on breeding in captivity. *J. Zool., Lond.* 185. 237-251.

Wood, J. (1974) Amino acids essential for hatchling Green Sea Turtles. *Proc. Wld. Maricult. Soc.* 5.

Wood, J.R. and Wood, F.E. (1978) Captive Breeding of the Green Sea Turtle *(Chelonia mydas). Proc. Wild. Maricult. Soc.* 7.

ARE SEA TURTLES THREATENED BY SOME CONSERVATIONISTS ?

JOHN PICKETT and SIMON TOWNSON

British Herpetological Society,
c/o Zoological Society of London, Regent's Park, London NW1

In this issue of the Bulletin we have given a large amount of space to the subject of Sea Turtle farming and conservation. This is because there have been recent developments of a political nature which are of unusual importance for sea turtle conservation and farming: developments which may have far reaching consequences not only for the future of sea turtles but for the future integrity of the conservation movement and for the principles of the breeding of any wild animal for any purpose in captivity.

Certain individuals and conservation organisations have been actively and vociferously campaigning against the existence of the Cayman Island Turtle Farm; few measures have been spared in the attempt to ensure the commercial failure and eventual closure of the farm. An account of the Farm and its political problems was given in the last issue of the Bulletin (No. 1, June 1980: *Observations and Notes on the Captive Breeding of the Green Sea Turtle,* Chelonia mydas, *on Grand Cayman, British West Indies,* by Simon Townson and *Political Problems for the Cayman Turtle Farm: Which Way Conservation?* by John Pickett and Simon Townson). More substantial detail is given in two papers in this issue: *Cayman Turtle Farm Ltd., the Crock of Gold* by W.A. Johnson and *Turtle Farms and Ranching* by Professor L.D. Brongersma.

The arguments used against turtle farming are hard to understand, and very disturbing; their nature is wholly negative and their effect, it seems to us, will be to do grievous harm to turtle populations by making impossible the application of rational conservation measures. The articles in this issue give ample illustration of the critical problems facing turtle conservation, and indicate the sensible balance of measures which would achieve success. They show well that a constructive and positive line can be taken. However, the people who propose these constructive measures are in a minority, and because at present the more negative ideas prevail, and obtain most publicity, their chances of application are slim. Influential bodies such as the Fauna and Flora Preservation Society, Friends of the Earth, and TRAFFIC wish to see a moratorium on all trade in turtle products, to include those produced in genuine farms. This would be most inappropriate, because existing international controls allow for trade in farmed or ranched products and the governments and people of the countries concerned have a real vested interest in the survival of sea turtles; there is incentive for effective protection and conservation of remaining populations, as exemplified by the ranching operation in Surinam and the Cayman Turtle Farm. This has been shown to work. If such operations are not permitted to exist, then the future for sea turtles is plain. Real incentives for national protection would be removed, thereafter conservation would depend only on ethics or moral principle. In the difficult human circumstances current in the areas in question – political instability, weakness of government control and law enforcement, pressure for commercial development of beach areas, general impoverishment – reliance on human virtue alone is extremely unlikely to work. The strongest protection that can be given by the most exceptionally determined governments it that of armed soldiers patrolling nesting beaches. The only instance when such a measure has been taken is in Mexico. This has been ineffective. Archie Carr, in a report in the Marine Turtle Newsletter *(Encounter at Escobilla,* Marine Turtle Newsletter No. 13., Nov., 1979) states that the armed protection by marines of the laying beaches of the Olive Ridley in Oaxaca has become lax, and in some cases the marines assigned to the work had not been effective. It can be expected that this most extreme form of protection will be given to turtles only in rare instances. Local predation will effectively be unchecked: nominal conservation laws in countries where people have little motivation for obeying them, and national controls are weak, have little chance of success. Most of the countries concerned will be preoccupied with other more pressing affairs. Finance is lacking. The international conservation organisations, both voluntary and official, are unlikely themselves to be able to fund the measures which would be necessary on such an extensive a scale. An international trade moratorium, stringently and effectively enforced by the Customs authorities of the rich importing nations would not be sufficient: local consumption in the countries of origin, so difficult to prevent, is enough alone to bring extinction. So how will the turtles then be saved?

Farming and ranching seems, plainly, the best hope of encouraging real and meaningful protection of turtles and, if given the chance, will grow to dominate trade because of the predictability of supply and the quality and standardised nature of its products. As Professor Brongersma points out, we are here dealing with a domesticated animal. Probably, never in all history could the domestication of an animal have met with such opposition. Fortunately, on the subject of farming we are not working in the dark. Besides the remarkable achievement of Cayman Turtle Farm in the establishment of a self-sustaining captive breeding colony of the Green Turtle, we have the example of crocodile farming: within a period of a few years it has become phenomenally successful, and shows what can be done when constructive policies are applied. Young crocodilians have been produced in abundance for restocking programmes (the Gharial has been brought back from the edge of extinction), leather is produced for the demands of trade, employment is created, and the public is educated. The farming of **crocodiles** has shown that it can be done without indirectly harming wild populations by stimulating an increased trade in illicit crocodile products, which is one of the chief fears and strongest arguments of the opponents of turtle farming. The breeding of turtles is in a broad way not dissimilar to breeding crocodiles; both are long lived and prolific, both are critically endangered, crocodiles perhaps the more immediately so; both are important in trade, and both have shown themselves to be amenable to management in captivity. However, crocodile farms have been able to establish themselves without the intense opposition which has done so much harm to the Cayman Turtle Farm and which, if continued, will retard progress, or worse, in the conservatin of marine turtles.

An argument repeatedly used by the opponents of turtle farming is that there is no hope of farms meeting the world demand for turtle products in the forseeable future, and that by the time they could do so some species may be beyond recall. They say that as the farms cannot achieve the point of supplying 100% of world demand soon enough, and that their continued existence would make it difficult to control illegitimate trade, they should be outlawed. In fact, the Cayman Turtle Farm supplies 10% of world demand – a significant proportion for a single farm. It would seem quite possible, in view of this, if a concentrated effort is made, to establish new farms modelled on Cayman Turtle Farm to reach the desired level of supply. As it is an emergency for the turtles, the Convention on International Trade on Endangered Species could make special exception, for a limited time, to the new definition of "captive bred", to allow new farms to sell first generation stock (CITES at present only allows trading of captive bred stock of a population shown to be capable of producing second generation offspring).

These new enterprises could be overseered by international conservation bodies to avoid any risk of false accusation, or of abuse. Because of Cayman Turtle Farm's success in developing the technology of breeding turtles in captivity, the time needed for the establishment of new farms would be much shorter than that taken by itself. It surely cannot be too difficult for means to be found to correctly identify farm produce at international posts, and ensure that illegal wild-caught turtle products are not smuggled, or at least reduce illegal produce to an insignificant fraction, as with all contraband in international commerce. An influential section of the conservation movement has lost much time and consumed a great deal of energy in its illogical harassment of Cayman Turtle Farm. This energy could have been applied, and can be still, to the encouragement and enlargement of farming and other rational conservation measures. The issue is urgent; boldness and imagination are required. If this line is taken, there is a certain future for marine turtles, and it may yet bring back "the fleets which Columbus found", a return which Archie Carr so eloquently longed for in his book "The Windward Road".

It seems to us that the alternative to this policy is hopeless, such a long shot as to be beyond consideration by sensible men. The broader implications for conservation are also bad. In the sad story of the campaign against the Cayman Turtle Farm we have seen the wilful suppression of facts and distortion of truth: this is a disgrace to science and puts in danger the integrity of conservationists in general. This is not the path of progress. Also, if the same irrational principles are applied to other conservation fields, are we to see the dismantling of farms for all kinds of other animals? Will the captive breeding of any wild animal be steadily outlawed? This may, now, seem incredible, but the logical extension of the principles now prevailing would be so. This is a bad omen for the future.

British Herpetological Society Bulletin No. 2. 1980

TURTLE FARMING AND RANCHING

L. D. BRONGERSMA

Rijks Museum Van Natuurlijke Historie, Postbus 9517, 2300RA Leiden, Netherlands

From of old, marine turtles have been exploited by man. Probably, wherever man reached coasts where turtles were abundant, and where these came to lay eggs, man will have used the meat and/or eggs as food. Diodorus of Sicily (Oldfather, 1935: 140-145) and Pliny (Plinius (died A.D. 79), 1561: 256) refer to the tribe of the Chelonophagi, the turtle eaters, who lived in Carmania, a region bordering on the Strait of Hormuz (forming part of the Iran of today); besides eating the meat of the turtles, they used the carapaces to cover their huts. According to Schenkl (1897: 34), the Greeks and Romans of antiquity did not eat turtle meat, although they may have used parts of turtles for medicinal purposes. However, they did use tortoise-shell. Pliny (Plinius, 1560: 13; Schenkl, 1897: 10) mentions Carvillius Pollio as having introduced the use of tortoise-shell to embellish beds, sofas and cabinets. In later centuries the Loggerhead served as a food animal in the central and western Mediterranean. Schoepff (1793: 79) states that in Italy the monks were very partial to Loggerhead meat. In more recent times, Vella (in Davidson, 1976: 387), and Kouki (n.d.: 187, 193) give recipes for preparing turtle meat and turtle stew.

The seafarers that crossed to the Caribbean, and those that went to the East Indies, learned to know and appreciate marine turtles as a source of good and wholesome food. In the first place this concerned the Green Turtle *(Chelonia mydas* (L.)*)*. They found turtles to be hardy animals, which one could keep alive on board for extended periods, and which thus could serve as a supply of fresh meat during long voyages. As the fame of the Green Turtle reached Europe, live turtles began to be shipped from the Antilles and from the island of Ascension to England. In the middle of the 18th century the arrival in London of Green Turtles was still a fact worthy of notice (Gentlemen's Magazine, 1753: 441, 489). These shipments often sustained heavy losses. Alexander (1837: 300) refers to a shipment of 200 turtles, of which but four survived, and Hornell (1927: 46) considered a loss of fifty per cent not infrequent. Of course, steamships reduced the duration of the ocean crossings, and hence lowered the risks of having to jettison large numbers of turtles during the voyage. After World War II, ships with freezing plants made it possible to import, without any loss, dead and eviscerated turtles, not only from American Atlantic and Caribbean waters, but also from countries bordering on the Gulf of Aden, the Persian Gulf, and from the Indian Ocean. In the past, real turtle soup may have ranked as an article of luxury; gradually it became a product that came within the reach of people of most moderate means. The high standard of living of the last decennia resulted in a greater demand, and this gave a boost to trade. In the USA not only real turtle soup but also turtle steak and turtle burgers came into demand, and these products became available in many supermarkets.

It is not the exploitation for food alone that threatens the survivial of marine turtles. There are several other factors that form as great a danger, if not an even stronger threat. In many areas, the sandy beaches suitable for nesting are now lost to recreation, building, construction of highways, etc. (e.g. E coast of Southern Florida; the Mediterranean). It is by now a well-established fact that beach erosion may account for a considerable loss in eggs (Fowler, 1979: 948, tables 1, 3: Tortuguero, Costa Rica; Fretley & Lescure, 1979: 30: French Guiana; Schulz, 1975: 127, tables XXV, XXVI: Surinam). The surf may wash out the eggs and the contact with salt water prevents their further development. Schulz (1975, table XXV) states that in Surinam within a four year period (1970-1973) some 1,387,000 Green Turtle eggs and (table XXVI) in the years 1971-1973 about 55,000 eggs of the Leathery Turtle *(Dermochelys coriacea* (L.) *)* and 47,500 eggs of the Olive Ridley *(Lepidochelys olivacea* (Eschscholtz)*)* were "doomed" eggs (doomed not to develop). Part of these could be used locally for human consumption, part could be transferred to a hatchery where they are protected from predators, and part could be used for supplying eggs to turtle ranches and turtle farms. A turtle ranch is an enterprise wholly dependent on obtaining eggs from natural beaches, which are hatched on the ranch to be raised until they are of a sufficient size for slaughtering. Such an enterprise is to be found in Surinam, where a number of raised turtles are released into the sea. Another ranch is to be found on the island of Reunion in the Indian Ocean; it obtains its eggs from Europa Island (in the Mozambique Channel) and from Tromelin Island (North of Mauritius). A turtle farm is an enterprise keeping turtles in captivity and where these turtles breed. At the start such a farm will have to import adult turtles and/or eggs to build up a breeding stock, but in due course the farm becomes independent from the populations living in the wild.

Attempts to keep Green Turtles and have them breed in captivity have been made already in the beginning of the present century, but without success, on Great Inagua Island in the Bahamas in 1903-1906 (Churchill, 1904: 12; 1905: 14; Bennet, 1906: 14; Boeke, 1907: 126-127) and in Curaçao, Netherlands Antilles in 1905-1907, 1908-1915 (Fock, 1906: 22; 1907: 25; Boeke, 1907: 125-133; Van Breemen, 1910-1914; Pleyte, 1915: 4-5). Creeks or parts of bays were fenced off in such a way that circulation of the water remained possible. It was assumed that in these fenced-off creeks there would be an ample supply of food (sea-grass, algae, etc.). After some years, it proved in Curaçao (1913) that in a fenced-off part of the "Spaanse Water", the not very numerous turtles had become emaciated, there was no tendency to reproduction at all, and the experiment ended in 1915 (Pleyte, 1915: 4-5).

At one time Professor A. F. Carr (Gainesville, Florida) pleaded for the farming of turtles (inter alia: Carr, 1967, 1968: 238; 1973: 255), and in this connection he also thought of fencing-off creeks. He ends the chapter dedicated to this subject with the following sentences: "Turtle ranchers of the future will have to get their hatchlings from nests on artificial beaches. The nests will be made by female turtles that have mated with males living behind fences", and "A technology of green turtle husbandry will have to be developed. Once that is worked out it will be a double blessing: people will be fed and species will be saved". In 1968 a turtle farm was founded on Grand Cayman Island (B.W.I.), and although Professor Carr was not its founder, it may be said that he stood at its cradle, and his writings on farming will certainly have stimulated the founders of Mariculture Ltd. One was faced with great problems, for there were many unknown factors, e.g. the age at which a turtle becomes mature, etc. After some years Mariculture Ltd. came into financial difficulties; the farm was taken over by a new company, Cayman Turtle Farm Ltd. (CTF). Mariculture was an enterprise that in the first place aimed at making profits as speedily as possible. Of course, CTF also aims at a situation in which the costs will be covered, a situation that has not yet been reached. In 1974 a task force of the Survival Service Commission met at Miami, and some of its members went to Cayman for discussion with Mariculture Ltd., and this resulted in the adopting by IUCN of the "Principles and Recommendations" with regard to turtle farms and ranches. CTF has proceeded strictly along the lines of these Principles and Recommendations.

The farm had to acquire adult turtles to serve as a breeding stock, and these came from various sources: Ascension Is., Surinam, Costa Rica, Nicaragua, and Mexico. They also purchased eggs (inter alia from Surinam). In 1973 the first eggs were laid on the farm, and in 1978 the stage was reached that so many eggs were laid on the farm's artificial beaches that there was no further necessity for importing eggs from natural beaches. Besides, in 1978, females that had hatched on the farm had started laying. Thus CTF became self-sufficient. It has been shown that a long migration to and from the nesting beaches with intervals of two or three years, such as occurs in nature, is not necessary. In captivity females may lay in consecutive years, and in various parts of the year. Thus, in fact the turtles on the farm have become domesticated.

In March 1979, the countries that signed and ratified the Washington Convention on the International Trade in Endangered animal and plant Species (CITES) accepted a definition of "bred in captivity"; only those animals meet this definition that have originated from parents that themselves have been generated and born in captivity, i.e. they must belong to a second generation born in captivity. Only when agreeing with this new definition, permits for the import and transit of, and for the trade in such animals, may be obtained. Such a definition does not cause much trouble with regard to species of which the generations rapidly succeed one another, and which allow production within one or two years. In the case of marine turtles matters are different. In these animals a period of more than 10 years may elapse between the hatchling from the egg to the reaching of maturity. CTF (and its predecessor Mariculture Ltd.) came into existence at a time when completely different rules were in force, and the company, having always kept to the Principles and Recommendations of 1975, might expect that no drastic changes would be made, without at least establishing an ample period of transition. The demand of "bred in captivity", as now defined, may be made for the offspring of the first farm-bred generation, but one cannot make such a demand for animals that years ago were hatched from legally imported eggs and which have been raised at the farm. In so far as such animals are not used for breeding, there must be a possibility to slaughter them and to trade the products, to give the farm some income. The number of this group of animals will decrease rapidly, for eggs are no longer imported.

The new definition of "bred in captivity" will be disastrous to the project in Surinam, where eggs are collected from the natural nesting beaches, watched in a protected hatchery, and raised in captivity, a method by which meat is produced without having the heavy expense of a farm. The restricted level of exploitation which has been taking place in Surinam for years already, is financially favourable to conservation, as the proceeds are used in part for the protection of marine turtles. By making existence impossible for bonafide farms and ranches, one will not save the turtles.

Sometimes it is said that the marketing of turtle products by CTF will stimulate the demand, and this will lead to an increase of poaching, but this is merely an allegation without any factual foundation. The demand for turtle products existed long before the farm was founded, and the capture of marine turtles, allowed in a number of countries, also existed already for a long time. In 1974 the question was put to Mariculture Ltd. whether it felt that it could satisfy the world demand for turtle products. This was an unreasonable question. A farm just started will need time to arrive at full production and one farm alone will not be able to supply the whole world with turtle products; it is just as unreasonable to expect that with his live-stock a single farmer could provide all the meat for a whole country. When the technology of turtle farming has been fully developed and mastered by CTF, and this is the case at present, it will be possible to establish turtle farms (and ranches) in other parts of the world, each to use breeding stock (or eggs) from the population naturally occurring in the region. Then, a product of a good and stable quality can be supplied in sufficient quantities; the demand for turtle products obtained from poachers, which products will be of less table quality, will decrease and eventually it will cease.

In the past many parts of turtles taken in the wild, for preparing turtle soup, were thrown away. At the farm everything is used: meat, liver, skin (leather), oil, scutes, etc. Thus, besides being a source of good quality meat (with little fat), the farmed turtles are a source of numerous other products. A process has been developed by CTF to use the scutes of the Green Turtles in arts and crafts, and this may well help to decrease the demand for tortoise-shell from the Hawksbill *(Eretmochelys imbricata* (L.) *).* The production of turtle products by turtle farms (and well-controlled turtle ranches) may lessen the pressure on the populations in the wild. It is worth mentioning that two renowned specialists on turtle conservation, Dr. G. R. Hughes (Natal) and Dr. J. P. Schulz (Surinam), realize fully the importance of CTF. When developing the technology of turtle breeding one must be aware that one is working with living materials, of which much is still unknown. One must give such projects time to develop the desired techniques and to put them to the test, but one must not try and make the development of turtle farming impossible on the basis of slight grounds and unfounded suppositions. The possibility should not be excluded that in the long run farms will be the only place where one can watch turtles in abundance.

Besides lessening the pressure on natural populations CTF is also beneficial to conservation by the research done at the farm by Drs. Jim and Fern Wood, as well as by the opportunities it offers to other scientists. The farm disposes of an almost unlimited supply of materials for research. Being a taxonomist and anatomist, the present author in the first place thinks of the possibilities for research in these fields. The question as to how many subspecies can be recognized within the species *Chelonia mydas* (L.) has not yet been answered. A first attempt at studying the difference between the various populations could be made at CTF where adult turtles from various populations are available. There, one could make a detailed comparison, e.g., of turtles from Surinam as compared to those from Ascension Is., from Costa Rica, Nicaragua, and from Mexico. The results of such a study may show in what direction further studies in other parts of the world may be undertaken. Much is still to be learned about the processes taking place in the living turtle, and here again the farm could assist. Of course, some of the results may have to be checked by research on specimens in natural populations, but working with the turtles in the farm may be a welcome opportunity to develop methods and techniques.

It is to be hoped that the authorities in various countries (and in the first place in the USA) may soon come to the conclusion that CTF does a good job, that the ban on turtle products from this farm should be lifted, and that in fact at the farm one has to deal with domestic animals to which the CITES limitations should not be applied.

REFERENCES

Alexander, Sir James E. (1937) *Narrative of a Voyage of observation among the Colonies of Western Africa in the Flag Ship Thalia.* London, XXIV + 428 pp., ill.

Bennet, W. Hart (1906) *Colonial Reports – Annual No. 496, Bahamas, Report for 1905-6,* 38 pp.

Boeke, J. (1907) *Rapport betreffende een voorloopig onderzoek naar den toestand van de Industrie van Zeeproducten in de Kolonie Curaçao, pt. 1.* The Hague, Belinfante, (4) + 201 pp., pls., charts, plans.

Breemen, P. J. van (1910-1914) *Verslag van den toestand van de Visscherij in de kolonie Curacao.* Annexe (Bijlage) to the colonial Report on Curaçao, which in itself is an annexe to the minutes of the meetings of the Second Chamber of the States General. Year 1909: Bijlage U1910; year 1910: Bijlage V, 1911; year 1911: Bijlage IJ, 1912; year 1912: Bijlage AA, 1913; year 1913: Bijlage EE, 1914. Handel. Tweede Kamer, Sessions 1910/1911-1913/1914.

Brongersma, L.D. (1979a) Schildpaddenfarms. *Versl.gew. Verg. Afd. Natk., Kon.Ned.Ak. Wet.Amst.,* 87, 1978, no. 10: 136-140.

Brongersma (1979b) Schildpaddenfarms. *Panda,* 15, no. 10: 137-140.

Carr, A. (1967, 1973) *So excellent a Fishe, A Natural History of Turtles,* Garden City, N.Y., Nat. Hist. Press, xii + 249 pp., ill.; 2nd. ed., 1973.

Carr, A. (1968) *The Turtle, A Natural History of Turtles.* London, Cassell, xvi + 248 pp., ill.

Churchill, J. Spencer (1904, 1905) *Colonial Reports – Annual – No. 428, Bahamas Report for 1903-4,* 41 pp. (1904); id., no. 471, for 1904-5, 34 pp. (1905).

Davidson, A. (1972, 1976) *Mediterranean Seafood.* Hammondsworth, Middlesex, Penguin Books, 425 pp., ill. (repr. 1976).

Fock, D. (1906, 1907) *Koloniaal Verslag van 1906. -Ill. Curaçao.* Annex C to Handel. Tweede Kamer, Session 1906-1907; id., year 1907, Session 1907-1908.

Fowler, L.E. (1979) Hatching Success and Nest Predation in the Green Sea Turtle, *Chelonia mydas,* at Tortuguero, Costa Rica. *Ecology,* 60, no. 5: 946-955.

Fretey, J. and J. Lescure (1979) *Rapport sur l'étude de la protection des Tortues marines en Guyane française. Notes sur le projet de réserve naturelle de Basse Mana.* Paris, Lab. Zool. (Rept. Amph.). Mus. nat. Hist. nat., 56 pp., charts.

Hornell, J. (1927) *The Turtle Fisheries of the Seychelles Islands,* London, H.M. Stationery Office, 55 pp.

Kouki, M. (n.d.) *Poissons Méditerrañens, Cuisine et Valeur Natritionelle.* Tunis, (4) + 254 pp.

Oldfather, C.H. (1935) *Diodorus of Sicily, with an English Translation, II.* London, Heinemann.
Pleyte, Th.B. (1915) Overzicht, aangevend in hoeverre in de kolonie Curaçao sinds het jaar 1903 vegolg is verleend aan verschillende wenken op landbouwkundig en economisch gebied, etc. Bijlage (Annexe) D, *Koloniaal Verslag 1915-III Curacao,* annexe to: Handel. Tweede Kamer, Session 1915-1916.
Plinius Secondus, C. (1560) *Historiae Mundi, vol. II. Lugdunum, J. Junta,* 526 pp + index.
Plinius Secundus (1561) *Historiae Mundi, vol. I,* 409 pp. + index.
Schenkl, K. (1897) *Die Schildrote im Alterthum.* Prag.Wiss.Ver.Volksk. Linguistik, 14 pp.
Schoepff, J.D. (1979) *Naturgeschichte der Schildkroeten mit Abbildungen erlautert,* Fasc. III-IV: 33-88, pls.
Schulz, J.P. (1975) Sea Turtles nesting in Surinam. *Zool. Verh. Leiden,* no. 143, 145 pp., 28 pls.
Schulz, J.P. (1980) *Zeeschildpadden, die in Suriname leggen.* Natuugids, serie B, no. 5, Paramaribo, Stichting Natuurbehoud Suriname, 114 pp., ill.

NEWTS, SALAMANDERS, TOADS AND FROGS

British Herpetological Society Bulletin No. 17. 1986

TEN YEARS OF GARDEN PONDS

TREVOR BEEBEE

434 Falmer Road, Woodingdean, Brighton

INTRODUCTION

It's become well-known that garden ponds can be excellent breeding sites for most of Britain's native amphibians provided they are made and maintained in suitable fashion. Having now spent 10 breeding seasons at our current abode, with the first pond installed a month or so after our arrival, it seemed like a good time to review the various successes and failures. This article reports the results of deliberately introducing 7 species of amphibians, 5 native and 2 alien, over the past 10 breeding seasons.

THE SITE

The garden dimensions are some 13 x 25 metres, set on a west-facing slope of the South Downs. The first pond installed (pond 1) is in a relatively cool area of the garden, though it receives sun for a good part of the day. It was made in February 1977, with overall dimensions c.3x4x0.6 (max) metres. It has multiple-depth shelves and a greater variety of plant life than the other 2 pools; these include an ornamental lily, yellow flag iris, king cup, water soldier, water parsnip, Canadian pondweed, hornwort, groenlandia, curly potamogeton, square St John's Wort, tubular water dropwort and (sometimes) water crowfoot. Pond 2 was first made in 1978 but has been modified on many occasions; since 1983 it has been about 0.7x1.5x0.4m, with uniform depth and a glass side-window. It is in a warm and sunny position, but has relatively few plants (mostly notably water plantain and arrowhead, with some hornwort and Canadian pondweed). For much of the year it remains green and soupy with single-celled algae. Pond 3 is the largest (3x5.5x0.6 (max) metres), made in January 1979 in the sunniest part of the garden. It has only 2 depths; 80% is at the maximum, and 20% forms a uniformly shallow (7-8cm) shelf. Plants include blue iris, hornwort, Canadian pondweed, frogbit, water soldier, lesser yellow lily and greater duckweed as the most abundant.

Ponds 1 and 3 are made from butyl, pond 2 is concrete. Fish are absent from all, though I have tried (unsuccessfully) to introduce 3 and 10-spined sticklebacks to pond 2. These have perished in the recent severe winters. I have stocked the ponds as richly as possible with invertebrates; pond 1 has water scorpions *(Nepa),* lesser and greater water boatmen, water spiders, horse leeches, damsel and dragonfly *(Libellula* and *Aeshna* type) nymphs, flatworms, *Limnaea* and ramshorn type snails and various small water beetles. Pond 3 is also rich; it has smaller leech species (not horse leeches), otherwise as in pond 1 but with healthy populations of great diving beetles and saucer bugs. Water lice and shrimps are common in all ponds, as are large blooms of daphnia in spring and early summer. Differences in the temperatures attained at different depths in pond 1, and at the same depth in ponds 1 and 3 are summarized in Table 1, the results of some max/min thermometer measurements in 1985 and 1986. As expected, temperature variation was greatest in shallow areas which can get up to blood heat in summer. Pond 1 seemed to stay slightly warmer than pond 3 in winter (though the differences were not significant); in spring minimum temperatures in the shallows stayed higher in pond 3, and in summer pond 3 was certainly the warmer of the two.

Table 1. Pond temperature

		Depth variation (Pond 1)			Variation between ponds (at 40mm depth)	
Season	Temp. measured	40mm	200mm	450mm	Pond 1	Pond 3
Winter	Minimum	2	4.5	5.5	4.1	3.3
	Maximum	9	7.5	5.5	9.1	8.2
Spring	Minimum	1	3	11	2*	4.3*
	Maximum	24	19.5	14.5	10.1	10.1
Summer	Minimum	15.5	15.5	14	10.9	12.3
	Maximum	37	26	21	20.7**	22.8**

Seasons for depth variation measurement were in fact single months (Jan, Apr & Jul) in which thermometers were left in place for 2-3 weeks before taking single (cumulative) readings. Seasons for variation between ponds were: Dec-Feb, Feb-Mar & Apr-Jun (all inclusive). In these cases measurements were taken at weekly intervals and the figures are the averages of these measurements. *, ** = pairs singificantly different by t-test.

METHODS

For the most part I have simply observed events (numbers of spawn clumps etc) and noted them; amphibians were however introduced to the ponds deliberately in the first instance (see below) either as spawn or adults, so colonisation was not natural. I made a conscious choice that the ponds would be for pleasure rather than science, a rule I broke only once in 1986 with mark/recapture exercise to estimate newt numbers. For this I did the following, over one 24 hour period at the end of April: (a) I went around the ponds 5 consecutive times after dark one evening, with a powerful torch and hand clicker-counter, registering the numbers of crested, alpine, male palmate, male smooth, and total "small" female newts in turn and separately for each pond. (b) I set Llysdinam-type newt traps (5 each in ponds 1 and 3, 2 in pond 2) late in the evening, and collected newts from them early next morning. All caught newts were toe-clipped, returned to the pond they came from, and left for 6 hours. (c) Later in the day, the ponds were netted vigorously for 15 minutes each and animals caught and counted (together of course with noting the numbers of marked individuals of each species in each pond). Population size for each species in each pond was calculated from the formula:

$$P=a(n+1)/(r+1)$$

Where P=estimated number; a = number toe-clipped initially; n = number caught in second round (netting); r = number netted bearing mark. Standard deviation was calculated as:

$$SD = a^2 (n+1) (n-r)/(r+1)^2 (r+2)$$

These formulae are appropriate for single exercises involving less than 20 recaptures (as these did).

Table 2. Breeding activities of frogs and toads in the garden ponds

YEAR	SPECIES								
	COMMON FROG							COMMON TOAD	EDIBLE FROG
	First Spawn Laid	Last Spawn Laid	Spawn Period (Days)	No. Clumps	No. Frogs Killed M	F	Total	No. Strings in Pond	First Spawn Laid
1978	–	–	–	1(4)	–	–	–	(1)	June 17
1979	March 14	April 21	38	32	0	0	0	(3)	None laid
1980	Feb 21	March 24	33	56	0	0	0	(20)	None laid
1981	Feb 16	March 11	25	56	6	4	10	(1)	May 25
1982	March 4	March 21	17	130	2	1	3	1(2)	May 29
1983	Feb 23	March 19	24	110	23	12	35	2	June 9
1984	March 4	March 23	19	92	20	9	29	1(2)	June 9
1985	March 5	March 31	26	86	6	2	8	(5)	May 25
1986	March 16	March 31	15	105	22	9	31	1	June 17
Average	March 2	March 25	23	83*					June 6

*Excludes 1978. M=Male, F=Female

THE AMPHIBIAN STORY

The fate of frog and toad introductions is outlined in Table 2. Common frog introduction actually began in 1977, with 11 clumps of spawn. This may not have been necessary, as there were certainly "native" frogs in the garden and 1 pair of these spawned in pond 1 in 1978. After a small booster of more spawn in 1978 I have added none since. The first progeny (from 1977) seem to have returned in numbers in 1979, where most still spawned in pond 1 though a few latecomers used the new pond 3. Since 1980 pond 1 has been completely abandoned for spawning, though it is still popular as an overwintering site, and all frog breeding (with occasional exceptions of odd clumps in pond 2) has subsequently been in the warmer pond 3. Numbers seemed to increase to a peak in 1982, fall off somewhat and most recently (after the severe winter of 1985/6) resurge again. Pond 3 teems with frogs in March, and breeding has been successful – with froglets emerging – every year so far. This success has not been without cost to the frogs, however. The breeding activity attracts predators, and in the peak years of 1983-4 considerable numbers, mainly males, were killed and left near the ponds. The cause turned out to be a vixen which had taken up residence at the end of the garden; she was caught in a live-trap and moved, since which time mortality rates from predation have apparently dropped sharply. However, this may be deceptive because foxes kill wastefully; sometimes only the head was eaten, often nothing at all (the frog just being bitten through). Other predators eat the lot and leave no trace and in the last 3 years I have watched a pair of crows visiting the pond and doing just that. These figures also do not include frogs dying from no obvious cause – presumably exhaustion – during or shortly after spawning. There are always a few of these, say 2 or 3 visible each year on average, but murky water and weed growth has prevented serious estimation. They seem to be mainly females. In the last 2 winters deaths from suffocation under ice have been significant, dramatically so in 1986. Almost all the visible mortality this year (see Table 2) was from this cause, again selecting for females. Interestingly, no dead frogs were seen in pond 3 after the ice melted but 16 in the small pond 2 (including 6 immatures not listed in Table 2) and 21 in pond 1.

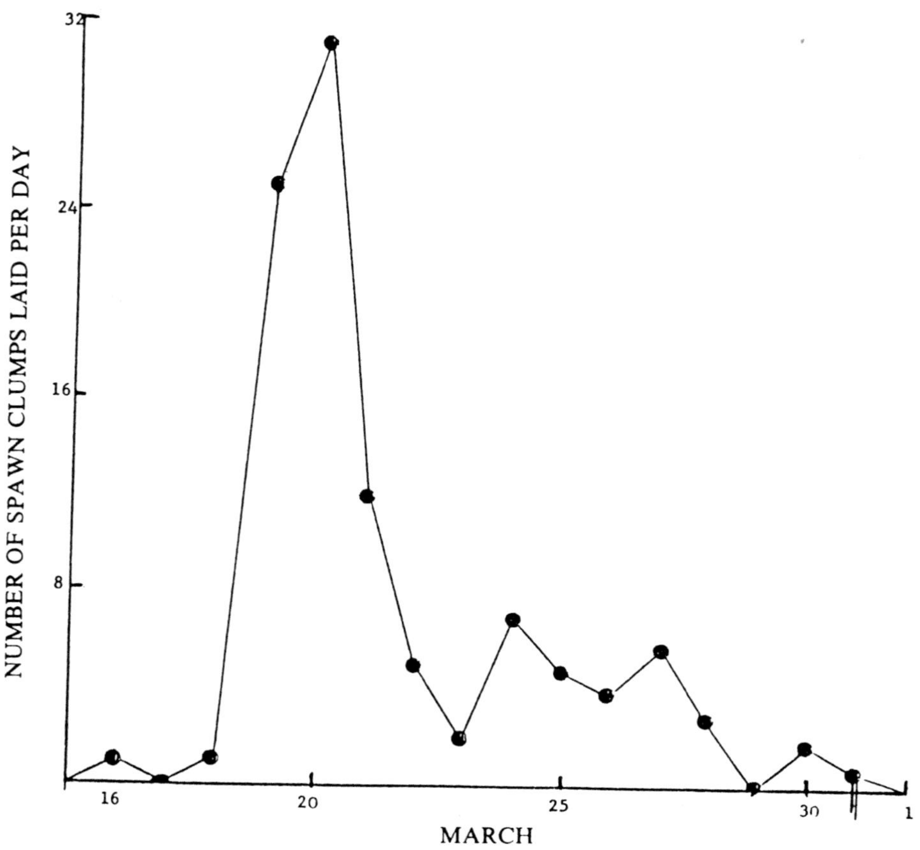

Figure 1. Frog spawning pattern in 1986.

The starting date for spawning has varied by a full month, from mid-February to mid-March, over the past decade. The duration of spawning has also varied, from about 2 weeks (after the late thaw of 1986) to more than a month. Delays are of course often caused by intervening cold spells, but the pattern of 1986, a sharp peak with 2-4 nights of frantic activity, followed by a series of stragglers, is quite typical (figure 1). Usually 1/2 to 2/3 of the spawn is laid during the peak, which in turn usually comes within 4-5 days of the first spawn clump sighting. 1981 was unusual in this respect, with a gap of more than a fortnight between first spawn and the main activity.

The situation with common toads could scarcely be more different or less satisfactory. Despite persistent attempts, sometimes with substantial amounts of spawn (e.g. in 1980, when many toads were rescued from a cracked pond and spawned in captivity) there are no signs of a colony establishing. Odd pairs and males do turn up, and in recent years I have had 1 or 2 spawn strings laid; interestingly the toads always use pond 1 and avoid pond 3 completely, perhaps because there are so many frogs there. The spawn, however, has never given rise to toadlets. Sometimes it just dies (as this year), other times it develops slowly, tadpoles grow very slowly and disappear when about half-grown.

I first released edible frogs back in 1977 (8 adults from France); these bred in 1978 and then disappeared. In 1980 I introduced about 20 adults and juveniles caught in a Surrey claypit and these have spawned every year subsequently (always in pond 3). This too, however, has never come to anything. I suspect hatchlings are eaten or inhibited by the high density of common frog taddies, but even spawn put in tanks has fared poorly with slow growth rates and only once did I produce (tiny) froglets indoors. The colony is thus slowly diminishing, with only 6 adults in 1986. Their behaviour is interesting; males dominate pond 3 but females migrate to ponds 1 and 2 before and during the breeding season, except for a brief visit to pond 3 to mate. When the males calm down (usually by July) the females return to pond 3 until late summer; then there is a general move to pond 2, which receives a lot of afternoon sun in autumn, before disappearing into hibernation. Some females certainly overwinter in pond 3, because every spring I rescue at least 1 from amplexus by male common frogs.

Newts have, on the whole, fared better than anurans in my ponds. These have always been introduced as adults rather than spawn or tadpoles; in Spring 1977 I released about 20 smooth newts, 10 palmates, 5 great crested and 5 alpines into the newly-created pond 1. This was supplemented in 1978 with another 5 crested newts, and in 1981 with about 20 or more palmates. There were conspicuous increases in numbers of smooths, palmates and cresteds coming to the ponds in the spring of 1979, suggesting that these species can become mature (both sexes) within 2 years. Alpines, on the other hand, took off a year later implying a longer growth period for this newt in Sussex. Table 3 shows the first dates each year when I observed individuals of each species in my ponds. Careful observation, along with extensive netting and weed removal in November and December every year, has convinced me that there is essentially no overwintering by newts in my ponds; I have never seen a single adult of any species at this time, though a few larvae do remain. There were no significant differences between the 3 British species on this basis, but I am sure this measure is not really sufficient to describe what is going on. It has long been my impression that the bulk of the palmate population arrives earlier than the other 2 natives, and the mortality figures this year tend to confirm this notion. When the ice melted in March, there were 8 palmate newt corpses (4 of each sex) but only 2 male smooths (and no cresteds or alpines). These undoubtedly migrated in January before the severe weather descended. Alpine newts always arrive much later than the other 3, usually well into March. In the mildest winters of the decade (1983 and 1984) I watched female crested newts laying eggs in pond 1 well before the end of January.

I refrained from any serious attempts to estimate the size of my newt populations until this last year. The results of the mark/recapture exercise are shown in table 4. Since this was a single attempt, the numbers reflect only the newts present at one partiuclar time in Spring (albeit when I judged numbers were near their peak, at the end of April) and should therefore be thought of as minimum figures. Smooth newts are obviously the commonest type, with several hundred present spread across all 3 ponds but especially abundant in warm pond 3. Alpine newts have done extraordinarily well, with at least 100 again using all 3 ponds. Palmates are outnumbered by smooth newts by at least 10:1, but seem to maintain a viable population at this low level. None were trapped in pond 2 but 5 subsequently netted there. Crested newts seem to have stablised at low 10s of adults and, interestingly, seem to select slightly for the original pond 1. Adults are rarely seen in the small pond 2, and never stay there long. Certainly it is noticeable that

Table 3. Dates of first newt sightings

YEAR	SPECIES			
	Smooth	Great Crested	Palmate	Alpine
1978	Feb 26	Feb 26	Feb 26	April 9
1979	Feb 11	March 1	March 4	March 25
1980	Feb 3	Feb 4	Feb 5	March 2
1981	Jan 16	Jan 22	Jan 25	March 6
1982	Jan 23	Jan 30	Jan 30	March 9
1983	Jan 3	Jan 5	Jan 3	March 14
1984	Jan 2	Jan 2	Jan 2	No recorded
1985	Jan 28	Feb 2	Jan 28	March 4
1986	Jan 18	March 15	March 17	March 10
AVERAGE	Jan 25	Feb 4	Feb 4	March 14

far more large crested newt larvae are seen every year in pond 1 than in pond 3, and I believe that for some unknown reason most crested newt recruitment is still from this pond. It may be that newt eggs in pond 3 are prepared by the large number of frog tadpoles and smooth newts present there.

Table 4. Newt population estimates **A**

SPECIES	POND 1 No (SD)	1 % of Total	2 No (SD)	2 % of Total	3 No (SD)	3 % of Total
Smooth	115 (32)	22	48 (15)	9	364(111)	69
Palmate	8 (3)	31	(5)	(19)	13 (4)	50
Great Crested	12 (4)	63	0	0	7 (2)	37
Alpine	43 (12)	44	16 (8)	16	39 (21)	40

B

SPECIES	M:F Sex Ratio Estimate In Traps	M:F Sex Ratio Estimate By Net	Mark/Torching Estimates Ratio*	Numbers Counted Ratios** By Trap	By Net	By Torch
Smooth	1.3	1.2	1.89	1	3.4	4
Palmate	–	1.8	2.00	1	17	13
Great Crested	3.0	0.8	0.95	1	0.75	2.5
Alpine	3.5	1.3	2.00	1	1.2	1.8

*= Ratio of total numbers estimated to be present (in all ponds) by mark-recapture to the highest count of the species by torching (all ponds) on a single occasion.

** = Ratios of animals caught or seen by the 3 methods (totals for all ponds) during the mark-recapture study, setting the usual lowest (trap figure) at 1. This assumes torching counts of females can be divided into smooth: palmate at the proportion estimated by mark-recapture.

It was interesting to compare the population sizes calculated from mark/recapture with those measured directly by netting, torch counting and trapping. Torching stands out as a powerful and simple method for these small pools; essentially all of the large great crested newts can be seen directly, and probably about half of the smaller species. Trapping also produces a sex ratio which is probably inaccurate (biased towards males) for all 4 species.

DISCUSSION

It has been fascinating to see the enormous population densities that can build up, at least for some species, in the garden environment. Frogs are so abundant that many individuals show signs of poor health; those seen foraging in summer are often skinny and look in poor condition, and limb mutilations are frequent, suggesting pressure of food supply and predation. It is easy on a warm summer evening to find 30-35 adult frogs trying to scratch a living in a garden (to which they are not of course confined) of less than 1/6 acre. Interesting questions have also risen, such as why do toads and edible frogs fail to breed, and what determines the relative numbers of the newt species? Only 7 houses up the road is a large pond with a thriving toad colony, probably assisted by pond size and the presence of fish (which predate competing frog tadpoles). But I suspect there are also more subtle problems, difficult to address, of water chemistry and suchlike. It is notable that pond 1 has become a miniature dewpond in terms of the amphibians using it (no anurans, lots of smooth newts, some cresteds and palmates). Frog and toad spawn simply will not survive in this pond now, though pressure from newts is less than in pond 3. It has proved possible to crop the amphibians doing well for the benefit of others wanting specimens; I have lost track of how many clumps of frog spawn, alpine and crested newts I have supplied over the years. I reckon that the ponds can withstand the abstraction of at least a couple of pairs of cresteds and a dozen or so alpines each season. Certainly the pleasure derived from these pools has been out of all proportion from the work involved installing and stocking them.

British Herpetological Society Bulletin No. 6. 1983

A NOTE ON THE BREEDING OF THE RED-SPOTTED NEWT IN CAPTIVITY

PAUL A. VERRELL

Department of Biology, The Open University, Walton Hall, Milton Keynes, MK7 6AA

In a previous note (Verrell, 1982), I described a regimen for maintaining adult red-spotted newts (*Notophthalmus viridescens*) in breeding condition in the laboratory. I here describe a method for rearing juvenile newts, or efts, from eggs deposited in captivity.

This method was employed in the spring breeding season of 1982 as part of a larger investigation of the reproductive biology of this species. All of the adults used were derived from the same source and maintained under the same conditions as described previously (Verrell, 1982). Thirteen adult females were paired with adult males, and each was allowed to become inseminated with a single spermatophore. These females were then isolated in transparent plastic boxes measuring 20 x 12 x 12cm, and containing unaerated, aged tap-water at a temperature of about 20°C and fragments of a variety of water weeds. The females were fed daily with chopped up earthworms, and all eggs deposited in the weed removed and placed in an opaque plastic trough measuring 27 x 24 x 15cm; this contained aerated, aged tap-water at about 20°C. Details of the breeding efforts of the 13 females are presented in Table 1. Although all were inseminated, three of the 13 females failed to lay any eggs. For the 10 females which did lay, the interval from the time of insemination to the onset of oviposition ranged from one to five days. There was a positive correlation between the number of eggs laid and female snout-vent length (r = 0.7, P < 0.05).

Table 1. The breeding efforts of the thirteen inseminated female newts

Female	**Snout-vent length/mm**	**Number of eggs laid**
1	43	None
2	44	20
3	45	56
4	46	21
5	46	23
6	46	48
7	47	52
8	48	34
9	49	None
10	49	58
11	49	101
12	50	78
13	51	None

A total of 491 eggs were produced by the 10 females. These eggs were checked daily and any tadpoles found were removed and placed in one of several plastic troughs as described above. These were filled with aerated, aged tap-water at about 20°C, and contained fragments of water weeds and small piles of stones which broke the surface of the water. The tadpoles, which appeared to be wholly carnivorous, were given a liberal diet of zooplankton collected from local ponds.

The onset of metamorphosis was marked by a reduction in the size of the tadpoles' external gills. Metamorphosis took place between 24 to 73 days after hatching. Newly metamorphosed newts, juveniles known as efts, left the water and climbed onto the piles of stones provided. These efts were removed and placed in a transparent plastic container measuring 24 x 12 x 12cm, floored with damp tissue paper and kept at a temperature of about 10°C. They were given a liberal diet of live fruit flies.

Although 491 eggs were laid, only 26 efts were produced; 25 of these are still alive at the time of writing. Ninety two per cent of the total mortality observed occurred during the tadpole stage of development. For instance, on one occasion, there was mass mortality in one of the 'tadpole troughs', apparently caused by rapid fouling of water. It is hoped that, with more careful management, future attempts at breeding red-spotted newts will be more successful.

REFERENCES

Verrell, P.A. (1982). A note on the maintenance of the red-spotted newt in captivity. *British Herpetological Society Bulletin* **5**: 28.

REPRODUCTION OF THE SMOOTH NEWT, *TRITURUS VULGARIS*

PAUL A. VERRELL*

Animal Behaviour Research Group, The Open University, Milton Keynes MK7 6AA
** Address as from August 1986: Allee Laboratory of Animal Behavior, Department of Biology, The University of Chicago, 940 East 57th Street, Chicago, Illinois 60637, U.S.A.*

As anyone who has tried will know, it is very difficult to obtain information on the way in which male mating success is determined in newts and salamanders (Order Caudata), mainly because it is almost impossible to observe the activities of individual animals in the natural environment. Consequently, we are forced to rely on rather indirect data to provide us with the information we need. The approach that I favour is one which combines field- and laboratory-based observations and experiments. Field data on the dynamics of breeding populations can tell us much about how a male's mating success is constrained by factors external to him, such as the availability of sexually responsive females bearing eggs for fertilization. Laboratory studies can reveal details of the behavioural strategies a male can enjoy in order to inseminate such females. And finally, behavioural experiments coupled with more physiological investigations can indicate how a male's mating success is constrained by events occurring within his own body, such as the process of sperm formation. Needless to say, all of these factors must surely interact in complex ways in order to produce the patterns of individual male mating success which occur in natural populations.

Over the last six years, I have been investigating the way in which male mating success is determined in our most common tailed amphibian, the Smooth Newt *(Triturus vulgaris).* This work has adopted the multidisciplinary approach outlined above. Here I can only present a brief summary of the major results of this work. Before I start, I have great pleasure in acknowledging a number of other biologists with whom I have collaborated: Tim Halliday, Dave Sever, Helene Fancilon, Norah McCabe and Miriam Griffiths.

Male Smooth Newts exhibit two behavioural strategies which enable them to inseminate females. The first is for the male actively to court the female, he stimulates her with his courtship display, and then inseminates her by transferring at least one spermatophore. The second strategy is for the male to interfere in an ongoing courtship, and quite literally 'steal' an insemination by behaving in a sneaky way.

This second, competitive strategy should be most frequently adopted by males in natural populations at those times in the breeding season when responsive females bearing eggs for fertilization are least frequently encountered. Such a time is when females are busy laying their eggs on the leaves of water plants and are not responsive to male courtship.

In a study of the dynamics of a Smooth Newt breeding population, we found that, in mid-summer, females tend to lay their eggs in a very synchronized manner, en masse. This observation led us to predict that competition between males for responsive females should be particularly intense during this period. We are now testing this prediction by observing male sexual behaviour in a natural population; our preliminary results suggest that, during the egg-laying period, many of the sexual encounters we see involve males adopting the sneaky, competitive strategy described above. In this way, they obtain opportunities to inseminate the few responsive females which are available.

However, it does not matter how many responsive females are available to a male if he has insufficient sperm to fertilize their eggs. After all, it is the fathering of offspring, not simply the transfer of sperm, that is the goal of reproduction in male animals. As part of a larger study of the annual reproductive cycle of the Smooth Newt, we investigated the issue of sperm availability by examining the structure of the testes of males collected at different times of the year. The picture which emerges is one which is typical of amphibian species which live in temperate regions. Within any one breeding season, males seem to have a limited amount of sperm in their testes and associated ducts. This is a consequence of the way in which sperm are made; sperm for use within any one breeding season are found in the previous year. Incidentally, female Smooth Newts yolk their eggs in a similar manner. What is more, this long-term limitation in overall sperm supply appears to be accompanied by a shorter-term limitation in spermatophore availability. This is indicated by the observation that an interval of more than one day is required between two courtship encounters if the male is to deposit the same number of spermatophores during each encounter. We think that this is due to a temporary depletion of the materials necessary to produce spermatophores; these materials are secreted by at least two clusters of glands situated in the male's cloaca.

All of this information can be integrated to provide a general picture of the determination of mating success in male Smooth Newts. During the breeding season, the availability of both eggs for fertilization and sperm to fertilize them vary over time. At the beginning of the season, responsive females bearing such eggs are relatively abundant and sperm are freely available. However, as the season progresses such females become harder to find and males compete amongst one another for opportunities to inseminate them; at the same time, the males' sperm supply becomes depleted, and their testes make sperm for use in the next, not the current, breeding season.

As is usually the case when one does research, the work that led to the conclusion discussed above has also led us to ask many other questions about the reproductive biology of Smooth Newts. For example, we know that the size of a male's testes, and thus the number of sperm he can produce, depends on his body size, this depends on his growth rate. One area we are now pursuing concerns the relationships between an individual's size, his age and the amount of effort he invests in reproduction. It is certainly clear that much remains to be done.

British Herpetological Society Bulletin No. 25. 1988

MAINTENANCE AND BREEDING OF *TRITURUS KARELINI*

JOHN BAKER

Department of Biology, The Open University, Walton Hall, Milton Keynes, MK7 6AA

INTRODUCTION

There is little available information concerning the care and captive breeding of any urodele, with the exception of the Axolotl (e.g. Nace *et al.*, 1974), under laboratory conditions (but see Verhoeff-de Fremery *et al.*, 1987 for details relevant to *T. cristatus).* Today, however, with increasing pressures on natural populations and a corresponding increase in legislation dealing with the collection of animals from the wild, there is perhaps a greater need for laboratories and private individuals to breed and rear their own animals.

The following notes were made during the breeding and maintenance of *Triturus karelini* in a laboratory.

T. karelini has been recognised as a full species within the *T. cristatus* group (Bucci-Innocenti *et al.*, 1983). It occurs throughout northern Turkey and across to the south of the Caspian Sea, the Crimea and East Balkans (Engelmann *et al.*, 1986).

METHOD

Adult newts were captured in 1987 at two sites, Karacabey and Adapazari, in north-west Turkey by Chris Raxworthy as part of a comparative study of the courtship of *Triturus* species. At the time of capture (early April) adult males were in courtship dress and females were already ovipositing.

On arrival in the laboratory newts were housed in a 90 x 45cm tank, water depth of 15cm. Large numbers of ova were deposited in a short period of time, during the first two weeks of April. The females preferred to oviposit on bunches of polythene strips (15 x 1cm) rather than on *Ceratophyllum demersum,* the only weed in the tank.

Care of Larvae. Larvae were reared in shallow water in plastic containers (30 x 24cm) filled to a depth of 6cm. They were initially fed on zooplankton netted from a local pond and strained through a small hand net. As soon as the larvae had grown large enough, *Tubifex* was added to the diet. They also ate the larvae of *Triturus vittatus* that were housed in the same containers. The water in the containers was changed as necessary and replaced with unconditioned tap water with no apparent ill effects to the newt larvae.

Ten larvae were reared to metamorphosis. As each one attained this stage of development, it was anaesthetized in MS-222 (Sandoz) and measured to the nearest 0.5mm. Sizes of the metamorphs (mm) were as follows:

	Mean	Range
Total length	61	47-72
Snout-vent length	33	26-38

Care of Juveniles. After metamorphosis the juvenile newts were housed in plastic tanks (39 x 25 x 21cm) filled to depth of about 10cm. A piece of expanded polystyrene was floated on the water surface to allow the newts to leave the water. However, the animals remained aquatic for most of the time. Occasionally an individual would leave the water during the night but would usually return during the course of the following day. The tanks were kept in a warm laboratory, so that water temperature fluctuated around 20°C.

The newts were fed on earthworms, pieces of beef heart, maggots (as sold to anglers) and a food pellet ('ReptoMin', a Tetra product). Food items were offered roughly five days a week, only feeding quantities that would be eaten at once.

'Wintering' Period. On 11.12.87 each newt was placed in an individual margarine tub with some damp tissue paper. They were given a period of cooling by placing in an incubator cabinet at 12°C for a week. They were then transferred to a refrigerator where they were kept for a further 60 days at a temperature of 4°C. During the wintering period no food was offered, but the containers were checked every week or so to ensure that the paper did not dry out. Mean weight loss during the wintering period was 3%.

On emergence from 'wintering' the newts were placed in a 60 x 30cm aquarium filled to a depth of approximately 15cm, placed in an unheated shed. Thus the newts were exposed to a natural photoperiod and temperature fluctuations. Males developed fully grown crests in less than a week and these showed no signs of regression until 15.5.88, i.e. the males were in breeding dress for about three months. Ova were first seen on 23.4.88, 67 days after emergence from wintering.

Sizes of five animals (total and snouth-vent length) at one year old were as follows:

Sex	Total Length	Snout-Vent Length	Breeding
Male	104	58	Yes
Male	104	58	Yes
Male	100	55.5	No
Female	120	63.5	Yes
Female	107	59.5	No

DISCUSSION

There are two points of note. Firstly, under laboratory conditions this species can be grown to sexual maturity in one year. Secondly, the animals reared in the laboratory behaved differently (see below) to wild caught animals that are temporarily maintained in the laboratory for observational work. There are implications to both of these points.

Minimum age at first breeding *Triturus* species in a field situation is probably two years (Beebee, 1980). Growth under the captive conditions described is much faster than growth rates inferred from the field. Trendelenburg is reported to have reared *T. cristatus* to maturity in nine months, also under laboratory conditions. (Verhoeff-de-Fremery *et al.,* 1987). The speed with which these animals grew to sexual maturity would suggest that sexual maturity is not age limited, but more subject to growth rate and body size.

The behavioural differences observed are manifest by the length of time the males retained their secondary sexual characteristics. Usually workers capture newts during the aquatic phase and transfer them to aquaria releasing them again after the breeding season. However this suffers from the drawback that most species rapidly lose condition. Verrell (1982) described a technique for maintaining *Notophthalmus viridescens* in breeding condition, but this regimen does not work for some other species. One problem encountered when trying to observe the courtship of *Triturus cristatus* at the Open University is the fact that, after capture, males' crests rapidly regress and the animals are very unwilling to court. The same was true of the original stock of adult *T. karelini.* Use of laboratory-reared stock could circumvent the problem of certain species not performing sexual behaviour in the laboratory.

ACKNOWLEDGEMENTS

Thanks to Dave Billings and Chris Raxworthy for freely given advice.

REFERENCES

Beebee, T.J.C. (1980). Amphibian growth rates. *British Journal of Herpetology* **6:** 107.

Bucci-Innocenti, S., Ragghianti, M. and Mancino, G. (1983). Investigations of karyology with hybrids in *Triturus boscai* and *T. vittatus,* with a reinterpretation of the species groups within *Triturus* (Caudata: Salamandridae). *Copeia,* 1983 **3:** 662-672.

Engelmann, W. Von, Fritzsche, J., Günther, R. and Obst, F.J. (1986). *Lurche und Kriechtiere Europas.* Enke.

Nace, G.W., Culley, D.D., Emmons, M.B., Gibbs, E.L., Hutchinson, V.H. and McKinnel, R.G. (1974). *Amphibians. Guidelines for the Breeding, Care and Management of Laboratory Animals.* National Academy of Science.

Verhoeff-de Fremery, R., Griffin, J. and Macgregor, H.C. (1987) *The UFAW Handbook on the Care and Management of Laboratory Animals.* 6th Ed. (Ed. Poole, T.) Longman Scientific and Technical.

Verrell, P.A. (1982). A note on the maintenance of the red-spotted newt in captivity. *British Herpetological Society Bulletin* **5:** 28.

British Herpetological Society Bulletin No. 30. 1989

REPRODUCTION TWICE A YEAR OF THE CRESTED NEWT IN CAPTIVITY

COGALNICEANU DAN

str.Cr.Manolescu 2, sc.A, ap.13, 78176-Bucharest, Romania

As with most temperate amphibians, the Crested Newt *(Triturus cristatus)* undergoes brief, annual periods of mating. Mating always takes place in spring and is accompanied by great morphological changes. During the breeding season the male developes a high dorsal crest and its colours become more vivid. The crest begins to grow, and the tail-stripe to intensify in colour just before the males go into hibernation, complete development taking place rapidly when the males enter the water in spring (Steward, 1969).

The gametogenetic cycles in newts are controlled by endogenus (hormonal) and environmental (temperature, moisture and photoperiod) factors. Temperature seems to be the major factor controlling gametogenesis in many salamanders, including newts (Duellman & Trueb, 1986).

In nature newts reproduce only once a year, during springtime when courtship, mating and oviposition take place. Simms (1968) reports a captive female of *Triturus cristatus* that mated twice (that is, during two different periods) and laid two clutches of eggs in one season.

There are two possible ways of stimulating the reproduction of newts outside their normal breeding season. One is by inducing breeding with pituitary extracts or human chorionic gonadotropin; the other one uses a low-temperature treatment (mentioned by Astier, 1975).

I succeeded in inducing captive newts to breed twice a year by maintaining them during the summer period at low temperatures (4-8°C). After the normal spring mating, the appetite of the newts starts decreasing and they begin to manifest their desire to quit the water. This is correlated with the increasing temperatures at the beginning of summer. Normally the newts will pass to their terrestrial phase of life and will return to water only next spring (or sometimes in autumn for hibernation). By taking the newts at this moment and placing them in a clean plastic box filled with pieces of moist sponge, a box that can be easily kept in a refrigerator, one can speed up their normal life cycle. The box will be provided with sufficient holes so as to ensure good ventilation. Two major points are to be considered when placing the newts in the refrigerator, i.e. in choosing the shelf that offers a temperature around 6°C and in providing good ventilation. Death of animals might occur at this stage due to excessive moisture, because of a too low temperature, or because of a deficit in aeration. It is therefore advisable to check the box every week, and remove any dead animals.

It is necessary for the newts to be healthy and well fed. Very good results are obtained when 2-3 weeks before placing them in the refrigerator they are fed every other day with whiteworms and earthworms *ad libitum.* During the last 4-5 days feeding must be stopped, thus allowing the newts to eliminate the faeces.

It is quite difficult to establish the period required for keeping the newts at low temperature. The most important factor to be considered is the outside temperature. To remove the newts at outside temperatures of about 30°C will just spoil things, since the temperature needed for their reproduction is around 15-20°C. Anyway, the minimum period of time needed for keeping them in the refrigerator is about 30-40 days.

After taking the newts out from the refrigerator, care must be taken, as some newts might refuse to enter the water. A good method is to place them in shallow water and then raise the water level little by little; or, to place a small raft in the aquarium and release the newts on it; in less than an hour most of them will enter the water. If everything goes well the newts will start feeding the next day. At this stage any kind of live food will do. By now the animals will start developing sexual characters and in about a month from the induced hibernation courtship will start. It is not possible to obtain the same degree of fecundity and of courtship display in autumn as in spring. The first eggs deposited may be infertile but the rest will develop well. If the females are kept without males they will deposit less than a dozen unfertilized eggs.

The last important point to be remembered is to ensure a temperature of about 20°C for the developing eggs and the hatched larvae.

This method may be applied to other species of newts as well. It can be applied all year long: for example, we can "store" the newts in October and take them out in January, so that by springtime we can have fully developed larvae.

The amount of eggs deposited by a female will not exceed one third of the number of eggs it deposited in the previous spring period of reproduction. This might be due to the so-called post-nuptial spermatogenesis, that results in the male having a limited sperm supply (Verrell, 1986), and, of course, to a limited amount of eggs available by the female.

It seems necessary to mention that if after the induced reproduction the newts are allowed to hibernate normally (outdoors or in a cold room), the forthcoming spring they will reproduce normally.

The method is easy to do and will provide you with year-long satisfaction in breeding newts.

REFERENCES

Astier, D. (1975). Contribution a l'etude du triton. These, *Eccle Nationale Veterinaire de Toulouse.* No. **28.** pp. 100-101.

Duellman, W. & Trueb, L. (1986). *Biology of Amphibians.* McGraw-Hill Book Co. pp. 13-20.

Simms, C. (1968). Crested newt. *Triturus cristatus* L., double brooded in an indoor aquarium. *British Journal of Herpetology* **4:** 43.

Steward, J.W. (1969). *The Tailed Amphibians of Europe.* David & Charles: Newton Abbot. pp. 103-105.

Verrell, P. (1986). Male discrimination of larger, more fecund females in the Smooth Newt, *Triturus vulgaris. Journal of Herpetology* **20:** 416-423.

British Herpetological Society Bulletin No. 6. 1983

A NOTE ON THE CAPTIVE MAINTENANCE AND BREEDING OF THE PYRENEAN MOUNTAIN SALAMANDER *(EUPROCTUS ASPER ASPER)* [DUGÈS]

P. J. WISNIEWSKI and L. M. PAULL

Glamorgan Nature Centre, Tondu, Bridgend, Mid Glamorgan

The nominate subspecies of the Pyrenean Mountain Salamander is an inhabitant of rocky, montane streams at an altitude of 600m or more in the Pyrenees of Spain, Andorra and southwest France, where it spends much of its life in water or beneath waterside stones. Several authors (e.g. Steward, 1969) have considered this and other montane urodeles impossible to maintain under captive conditions because of their low temperature and high oxygen requirements.

Two pairs of *E. a. asper* were obtained in November 1981 and housed in 30 x 20 x 20cm plastic tanks, one pair per tank. Each tank was fitted with a polystyrene and glass lid, the layer of polystyrene allowing the entry of an air-line but preventing the escape of the salamanders. A thin layer of coarse gravel was used as a substrate and each aquarium was filled to a depth of 8cm with well-matured tap water. Several small, sloping pieces of slate and plant pot were placed on each tank bottom to serve as retreats whilst land areas were provided by supporting large flat slates upon rocks. Vigorous aeration was provided and the tanks placed at floor level in a cool, dark corridor. Temperature varied with the ambient temperature, between a minimum of 0°C (aeration prevented freezing) and a maximum of 18°C (mean temperature 9.5°C). The salamanders, although sluggish at all times, remained active throughout the year. Tank cleaning was kept to a minimum, the water being changed once a month and each animal was fed individually once a week, thus avoiding undue disturbance.

All specimens accepted food readily, taking small pieces of earthworm (always rejecting pieces larger than about 2cm) and ox-heart enriched with Vionate. Various small aquatic invertebrates, i.e. *Chironomus riparius* larvae, *Asellus aquaticus* and Ephemeroptera spp. were also taken. Feeding occurred only in the water and these specimens have been observed to spend very little time on land.

Mating behaviour, as described by Ahrenfeldt (1960) has occurred in every month of the year and is prolonged, pairs often feeding whilst coupled. On 10.6.82, three, creamy white eggs were found attached to the underside of a submerged piece of slate, although one egg had unfortunately been crushed. In addition, two clear jelly masses were found close to the eggs. On 23.6.82, the same pair produced a further five eggs. Mean temperature during the month of June was 15°C. All eggs were moved to a well aerated bowl of matured water. The first two eggs hatched on 11.7.82, approximately one month after laying. Of the second batch, one egg hatched on 17.8.82, one egg disappeared and was presumably eaten by one of the tadpoles and the other three were infertile and were attacked by fungus (*Saprolegnia* sp.).

The tadpoles were fed upon *Paramecium* and *Cyclops*, these having been cultured in 'green' water enriched with "Liquifry No. 2". As they grew, they also accepted small *Culex* sp. larvae and chironomids. Three months after hatching, the largest tadpole attacked the two smaller tadpoles, killing one individual and mutilating the other, such that it died of its injuries three days later. Clearly, youngsters will have to be separated in future, although similar species, e.g. *Salamandra s. salamandra*, have not proven to be so aggressive towards their peers (Wisniewski and Paull, in prep.).

The remaining youngster, a male, now measures 4cm at the age of six months and is feeding well upon whiteworms (Enchytraeidae).

Both adults and tadpoles have proved to be reasonably hardy, even when their aeration system failed during hot weather. Under conditions of minimal disturbance, cool temperatures and high humidity it should be possible to breed this species regularly.

REFERENCES

Ahrenfeldt, R.H. (1960). Mating behaviour of *Euproctus asper* in captivity. *British Journal of Herpetology* **2:** 11.

Steward, J.W. (1969). *The Tailed Amphibians of Europe.* David & Charles: Newton Abbot.

British Herpetological Society Bulletin No. 10. 1984

CAPTIVE REARING AND BREEDING OF NORFOLK NATTERJACKS, *BUFO CALAMITA*

MARK JONES

6 Brookside Cottage, The Street, Brampton, Beccles, Suffolk NR34 8DZ

During 1980 I became interested in the possibility of rearing and breeding native Natterjacks, with a view to setting up or assisting with future conservation projects involving this species. Accordingly I applied for and was granted a licence from the Nature Conservancy Council and, armed with some preliminary advice from Trevor Beebee, in June 1981 I collected a dozen tadpoles from a duneland site on the Norfolk coast.

The survival rate was high and, at the beginning of December, I put nine well-grown toadlets into hibernation in a tank half full of sand, placed in my garden shed. At this point my luck ran out as I had failed to appreciate just how cold the winter of 1981/82 was going to become. The toadlets had dug into the sand which was about five inches deep, and which was overlaid by layers of slightly damp moss. However, the cold penetrated through the sides of the aquarium before it occurred to me to "lag" it, and the entire contents were frozen. The result was eight dead toadlets, and another which never really recovered, and which died shortly after emerging from hibernation the following March. It may be signficiant that this was the largest of the batch, and so may have been more resistant to cold.

In May 1982 I collected another batch of Natterjack tadpoles, 25 in all, which had just reached the free swimming stage. These came from the same site as the first batch and were collected a few from each dune-slack to minimize the chances of future inbreeding. My present breeding stock originates from this batch, as does Roger Gouldby's.

Natterjack Toad *(Bufo calamita)*, resident in a B.H.S. Conservation Committee vivarium for captive breeding purposes

So far I have achieved a 100% survival rate with these toads and I have retained 15, having passed on 10 to Roger Gouldby (5 in 1983 and 5 in 1984).

The method of raising tadpoles and toadlets, which we have both adhered to, and which seems to work well, is as follows. The tadpoles, which can be reared from spawn quite easily, can either be kept in a large tank with a sandy bottom and an inch or two of water, or in a shallow p.v.c. "slack". In each case they need a good deal of sun and are happy in quite tepid water, as long as they are not overcrowded. Water plants are not necessary and, if present, should be kept sparse.

The tadpoles will feed on rabbit-pellets, which seem to provide a fully balanced diet. However, if crickets or earthworms fall into the water these will also be devoured.

It is a well known fact that Natterjack tadpoles develop rapidly and the spawn to toadlet cycle can be as little as five or six weeks. In my experience, the most crucial time in rearing Natterjacks is during the transition stage from tadpole to toadlet. One cause of fatality is drowning; if the developing toadlets cannot leave the water with ease they will become exhausted very quickly and will go under. Therefore it is essential that a pond or slack has very gently sloping sides so that the toadlets can walk out of the water with the minimum of effort. A saucer-shaped profile is ideal. It is during metamorphosis that many of the weaker animals seem to succumb. The survivors do not attempt to feed until their tails have been completely reabsorbed. At this time they are capable of feeding on only the smallest of invertebrates, and getting this sort of food for them can be tricky. A method which I have found to be successful is to take a bucket and hold it under a hedge or nettle-patch whilst beating the vegetation with a coal-shovel. This will result in a larger number of invertebrates of varying sizes, ranging from mites to hoverflies, all mixed in with dead leaves and twigs. These hedge-beatings can be tipped into a corner of the toadlets' tank, and the litter removed much later, when the toadlets have been through it and have selected the most manageable food-items. If one is not careful one can easily remove small toadlets when removing the litter, and it is also wise to keep an insect-proof lid on the tank during feeding to prevent the "beatings" from escaping all over the house. Hedge-beatings will be available until November, but they are difficult to collect from wet vegetation and this is important to remember, as the small toadlets need to be fed daily.

Natterjack toadlets can grow rapidly when provided with a plentiful food supply and by the beginning of their first hibernation the average length of this batch was just under 3cm. One specimen reared by Roger Gouldby in 1983 measured 42mm prior to being hibernated, which must be a record for a Natterjack less than six months old. The average length of my toads at the end of the second year was just over 51mm.

It is best to rear toadlets in an indoor tank for at least the first year of their lives, and to get the best results it is vital not to keep too many. As they grow so do their appetites and, on two occasions I have found it necessary to pass on small numbers of rapidly-growing toads because I was having trouble in finding enough food to go round.

The newly-metamorphosed toadlets should be kept in a well-ventilated tank with an inch or two of sand on the bottom. Some loose moss should be provided at one end, and this should be kept damp, but not sodden. I consider that a water-tray is not necessary and may even be a hazard, and so I keep the tank interior slightly damp by judicious application of a plant-sprayer or atomizer. The interior of the tank should not be allowed to become humid but some sunshine can and should be allowed in. The toadlets should be kept in damper conditions for the first few days after metamorphosis than subsequently, as at first their skin is damper and more delicate. However, after this time, the skin becomes lighter in colour and drier in texture and the toadlets then become more lively and mobile.

Hibernation is the next obstacle for the young toads, and their survival rate will largely be dependent on the provision of suitable quarters, and on their size and health. For their first two winters my Natterjacks have mostly been hibernated in tanks in one of my sheds. These tanks were furnished as previously described, and were placed on old kitchen units close to the single shed-window, where they received little direct sunlight. One batch spent the first winter in a coldroom at the University of East Anglia where they hibernated successfully at a constant low temperature, in a similarly furnished tank. Under these circumstances I have tended to put toads into hibernation at the end of October and I have dug them out again in early to mid-March, as soon as the first animals have begun to emerge. The tanks have then been placed in a conservatory which receives afternoon sunshine.

Feeding Natterjacks seems to present no problems except that of finding enough food, as they have voracious appetites whatever age or size they are, and will feed readily as long as their body temperature is high enough. The adults will eat spiders, grasshoppers, crickets, mealworms, earthworms, caterpillars and moths, and I feel that it is important to provide Natterjacks with as varied a diet as possible at all times.

As for breeding Natterjacks in captivity, this has been reasonably straightforward, and seems to be dependent on:–

a) Rearing robust healthy animals
b) Providing conditions for breeding and living which are as similar to those of the toads' natural environment as possible.

Following emergence from their second hibernation in mid-April, my Natterjacks were kept in a large tank for about two weeks, and then transferred, a few at a time, into the outdoor enclosure which I had previously adapted to suit their needs. This enclosure, which forms part of a complex which includes two other larger ones, measures 6' x 7' with a two foot high wall and is placed to receive sunlight for the greater part of the day. The toads had previously spent several months in it during the previous summer, and had done well.

Interior landscaping has been designed to resemble a section of dune or heathland and the enclosure had to be filled to a depth of up to one foot in places with sand, to enable typical heathland plants to become established (our local soil is heavy and clayey, and quite unsuitable for such a flora). The raising of the interior level of the enclosure also countered the shading effect of the walls, increasing the amount of sunshine within. This is an important factor, as it is known that Natterjacks need sunlight and like to bask (Beebee, 1983). Plants chosen for the enclosure included *Festuca glauca; Erica carnea;* and cultivars of *Erica tetralix* and *Calluna vulgaris.* The sandy areas between the plants have been kept largely clear of weeds to enable the toads to dig freely, as they would in their natural environment, and there are a number of pieces of old gorse-wood and small logs scattered about, also for cover. A shallow p.v.c. liner "slack" approximately 2'6' x 3'6", and 4" maximum depth occupies a dip in the centre of the enclosure.

Following their re-introduction into the enclosure, the male toads soon began to congregate in the slack and to call. This occurred mainly during the evenings and at night, but sometimes during the morning as well. The noise from over-flying jet aircraft seemed to act as a stimulant and would usually start off a spate of croaking. Probably no more than two or three males were ever calling at any one time, but even so, the noise was audible in the house even with the television on! Roger Gouldby experienced similar behaviour from his colony which were kept in a similarly landscaped but larger (9' x 11') enclosure. Females which ventured into the slack were quickly grasped by the males, which would maintain the amplex even if the female subsequently left the water. The sex ratio amongst my Natterjacks appears to be 9:6 in favour of the females, and Roger Gouldby also has a greater number of females than males.

Although a large proportion of the males appeared to be sexually mature and in breeding condition, the females seemed not to be so well developed, and the breeding activity resulted in only two spawn strings for my colony, and three for Roger's. The spawn strings laid in my enclosure were both largely fertile and were deposited at night on the 26th May and 26th June. The strings laid by Roger Gouldby's toads were laid on the 14th June, 26th June and 10th July. The first and third strings were mainly infertile but the second string was almost completely fertile.

The tadpoles which resulted from these spawnings were reared, both in the enclosure slacks and in aquariums, to a stage where they were about to develop back legs and were then collected up and released at an introduction site in north-west Norfolk. Roger and I estimate that we released at least 6000 well grown tadpoles, but this is a conservative guess. In addition, I have passed on 55 toadlets to persons who expressed a desire to rear and hopefully breed from them. I originally kept back 100 tadpoles for rearing to toadlets, but following metamorphosis, I lost nearly half of these, simply because however much food was supplied, the smaller ones could not seem to compete with their larger brethren. As I passed on toadlets and reduced numbers in the tank so the smaller specimens received more intensive care and the survival rate increased accordingly. Once I got down to 20 or so, there were no more fatalities.

One observation of breeding Natterjacks, which was made by Roger one night when he was watching his toads by torchlight in the company of a photographer, may be of particular interest. A male was seen to be calling on the edge of the p.v.c. "slack". It would call for a few seconds and then swivel round a few degrees and commence to call again. Eventually the toad had completed a full circle in this way having called to all points of the compass.

At the time of writing my Natterjack colony is preparing to spend its first winter outdoors in the enclosure, and most individuals have now dug burrows into the sand or else have graduated towards the brickbuilt hibernation chamber located in one corner. It will be interesting to find out if they can succeed in breeding again, perhaps more successfully, in 1985.

REFERENCE

Beebee, T.J.C. (1983). *The Natterjack Toad.* Oxford University Press.

British Herpetological Society Bulletin No. 13. 1985

FURTHER NOTES ON THE CAPTIVE BREEDING OF NATTERJACKS *BUFO CALAMITA*

MARK JONES

6 Brookside Cottage, The Street, Brampton, Beccles, Suffolk NR34 8DZ

Following my article detailing the successful captive-breeding of Natterjack toads of Norfolk origin (BHS Bulletin No. 10, December 1984), members may be interested to learn of further developments during 1985 in relation to outdoor colonies maintained by myself and by Lowestoft-based BHS member Roger Gouldby.

Of the 15 individuals which went into hibernation in my enclosure during the late autumn of last year, most, if not all, have survived. My uncertainty on this point is due to my not being able to gather together more than 14 at any one time; a conclusive count would involve removing the entire contents of the enclosure including all the sand therein, which would be a gargantuan and destructive task.

Most of the toads dug down into the sandy interior of the enclosure to overwinter, and several congregated around the roots of a particularly large *Erica carnea* for this purpose. Only one used the purpose-built hibernation chamber, the floor of which was also lined with sand, with a layer of dry moss above it.

On 31st March several toads were seen to have emerged from hibernation, and the rest appeared in ones and twos during the next ten days or so. They gathered in the hibernation chamber and sat under the asbestos roof, out of sight but absorbing the heat of the sun conducted through that material during the daytime.

No breeding behaviour was noted amongst my colony until mid-May, when some pairing off took place. However, there was no sign of the males calling and no spawn resulted from these liaisons. In contrast, a pair of Roger's toads produced a spawn string on 6th May. This seemed to be fertile but, possibly due to very cold weather, only around 100 tadpoles eventually hatched out and Roger's toads did not subsequently produce any more spawn, although further breeding behaviour continued during the next few weeks.

On 8th June one or more of my male toads was heard calling during the day, for the first time since emergence from hibernation. On the 10th, following persistent calling and pairing off amongst various individuals, a string of spawn was found in the enclosure "slack". I should point out that the "slack" remained very cloudy throughout this time and did not clear until some time after all the spawn had hatched, so I had to locate new strings by "dragging" the bottom with my fingers every day for about two weeks, and memorizing their locations. Not an easy job, to say the least! The following day there was another string, and the third (and final) string came to light on the 13th June. All three strings appeared to have been laid during the preceding nights. Males were heard calling at all times of the day and night. Regular checks indicated that these strings were mainly or wholly fertile, but the unseasonally cold weather which followed may have had a damaging effect, as I never saw the large numbers of tadpoles in the slack that I expected from this quantity of spawn. Despite the removal of some sections of spawn to two aquariums in order to ease possible overcrowding in the pool, the total number of tadpoles raised was less than 1000. This was despite a low mortality rate following hatching. Observation of the tadpoles during their early stages in the pool was badly hampered by the cloudy water.

Most of my tadpoles were released at an advanced stage of development, at an introduction site on heathland on the Suffolk coast. They were released during July, in two batches of 500 and 450, respectively and, it is hoped, will form the basis of a new colony; the first Natterjacks to be found wild in Suffolk for over 20 years, since the species finally became extinct in the county.

Of the 100 or so tadpoles reared by Roger Gouldby, most did well until metamorphosis, but the toadlets were reluctant to feed in the majority of cases, and only about 15 have survived at the time of writing.

It is worth mentioning that Natterjacks have cannibalistic tendencies and, as Roger and I can both verify, they will eat their own toadlets if there is enough of a size difference for this to be possible.

As I mentioned in my previous article, I have more female Natterjacks than males, and I had expected seven or eight spawn strings this year, especially as all the females appeared to be well-grown and mature. The reason for such low productivity is hard to pinpoint, but could be due to a number, or a combination, of reasons such as overcrowding, stress, unseasonal weather or lack of competition amongst males. Roger Gouldby considers that his females were gravid but that the males were not particularly interested. The season was of short duration this year, with breeding and courtship behaviour in my enclosure mainly confined to the second and third weeks in June, apart from a brief spell during the first half of May.

The measurements (snout to vent) of the 14 Natterjacks located in my enclosure on 11th August and therefore just over three years old, ranged from 68mm down to 52mm with the majority measuring around 60mm.

REFERENCE

Jones, M. (1984) Captive breeding and rearing of Norfolk Natterjacks *(Bufo Calamita). British Herpetological Society Bulletin* **10:** 43-45.

British Herpetological Society Bulletin No. 13. 1985

NATTERJACK *(BUFO CALAMITA)* TADPOLE BEHAVIOUR IN CAPTIVITY

TREVOR J.C. BEEBEE

434 Falmer Road, Woodingdean, Brighton, Sussex

INTRODUCTION

There has been an increasing realization over the past 20 years or so that tadpoles are more complicated in their behaviour patterns than was once supposed. For example, anyone with more than a passing acquaintance with common frog and toad tadpoles can scarcely fail to have noticed how secretive the former become as they grow up, while in comparison, common toad tadpoles are often to be seen swimming conspicuously in open water. In fact, tadpoles of the *Bufo*-type toads sometimes demonstrate a dramatic shoaling behaviour that has been witnessed in both North American and European species. It has been much argued as to whether this shoaling serves to stir up food particles from the pond bottom, constitutes a defence against predators or is for some as yet unknown purpose. Natterjack tadpoles are usually easy to see, though unlike those of the common toad they have not been reported to form proper shoals. Searching for natterjack tadpoles and trying to assess their numbers in a pond has become a widely applied practice among conservationists monitoring the various colonies in Britain, since it is one way of assessing breeding success over a period of years. However, this approach does presuppose that the tadpoles always behave in much the same way (i.e. are equally "seeable") whatever the weather or their stage of development, and some observations in the field have indicated that this assumption might be wrong. In particular there have been cases where whole cohorts have apparently disappeared within a week or so of expected metamorphosis, to be followed a while later by reports of toadlets around the ponds. To try and clarify what might be going on in the breeding ponds, I set up a simple observation tank to record how natterjack tadpoles behave under conditions intended to simulate the edge of a breeding pool.

METHODS

Natterjack spawn was obtained (under licence) for captive rearing as part of a general research and conservation programme. Soon after hatch, 16 tadpoles were transferred to a container with about 5 litres of water arranged as shown in Figure 1. A fibre mat was used to support a layer of sand the full length of the angled slope and thus prevent it accumulating at the deepest point. This sand and suitably arranged flat stones provided potential refugia for the tadpoles, which also had available to them water varying from 0 to 12 cm in depth. The tank was set up in a position receiving direct sunshine from at least 0700 to 1900 hours, and the water kept clear of algae etc. for easy observation by gentle periodic flushing with a hosepipe. Food, in the form of rabbit pellets, was added periodically as required and always after the final observations of the day.

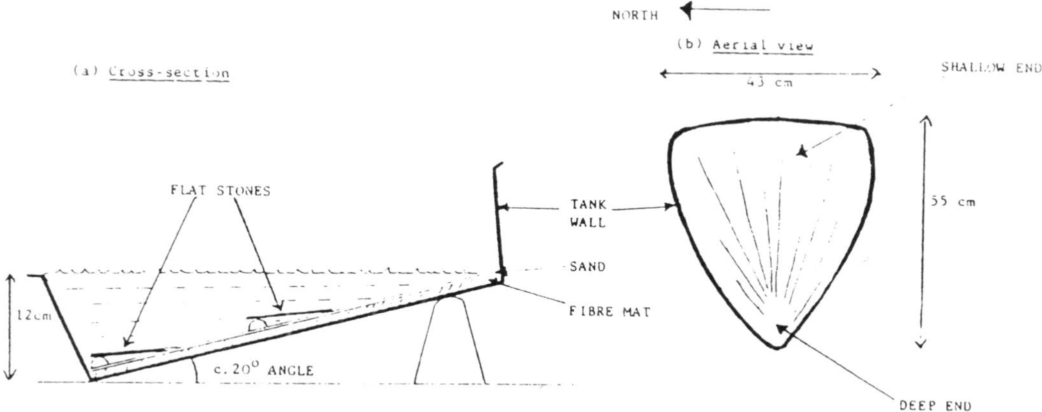

Figure 1. The observation tank.

Observations were made up to 3 times each day, at 0800, 1300 and 1900 hours. Record was made of: (a) the number of tadpoles visible (i.e. not concealed in sand or under stones); (b) number actively swimming, as opposed to resting on the bottom. Occasional tail-wiggling was not recorded as active swimming, the whole tadpole had to be moving through the water. (c) numbers of tadpoles visible in the top (shallow) and bottom (deep) halves of the tank (d) % cloud cover; (e) water temperatures at the shallow and deep ends (1cm and 12cm depths), using a thermoprobe digital thermometer.

After metamorphosis, the toadlets were released at the site from which the spawn was taken.

RESULTS

For most of their lives in the tank, the natterjack tadpoles were easily visible and did not hide in silt, under stones or in the small pieces of weed also available to them. From the start of the observations (shortly after hatch) until full grown at 25mm or so some 3 weeks later, it was unusual to see less than 70% of them at some time each day; on average more than 80% were visible (Figure 2a). However, during the final stages of development there was a dramatic decrease in observability coinciding with elongation of the back legs until, during forelimb emergence, all the animals remained hidden (mainly under the submerged stones) at all times of day irrespective of weather.

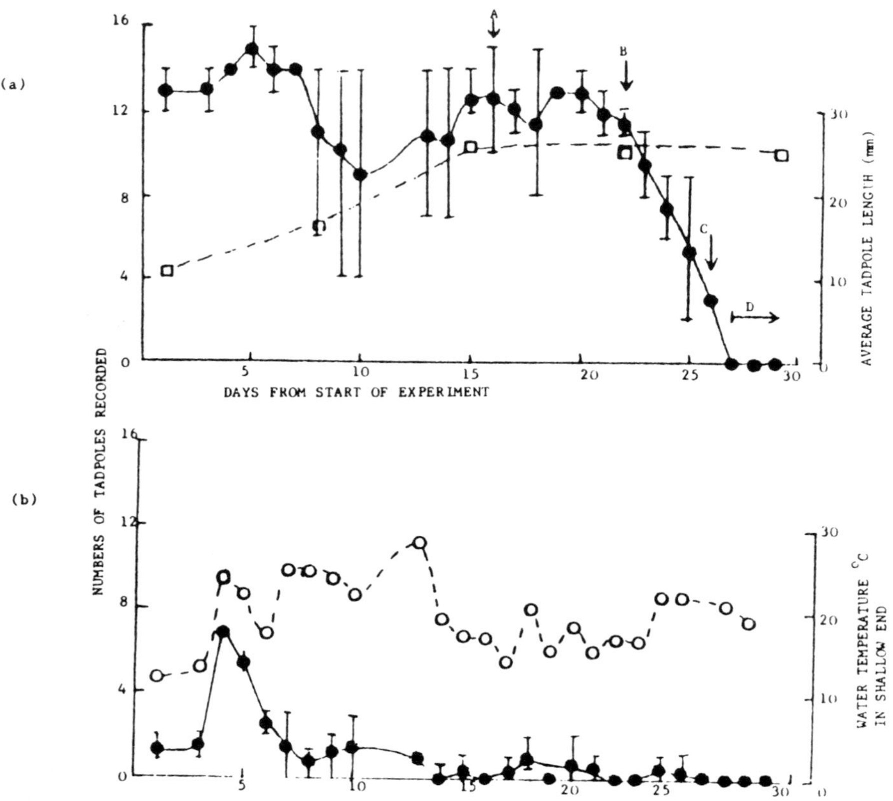

Figure 2. Tadpole behaviour during development.

• – Numbers of tadpoles visible (average, with range of values for 1-3 records of each day); □ average size of tadpoles; o water temperature (average of 1300 and 1900 hour measurements in shallow end); in (a), tadpole numbers represent total visible; in (b) they represent the numbers actively swimming (in this case the average and range of just 1300 and 1900 hour records). A = Hind limb buds appear; B = Elongation of hind limbs; C = Forelimbs appear; D = Metamorphic climax.

Although readily visible, natterjack tadpoles were singularly inactive for most of the time. As shown in figure 2b, apart from a brief burst of activity early in life (at 12-14mm long) where up to 50% of them could be seen actively swimming at any one time for just 2-3 days, more than 90% were usually resting virtually motionless on the sandy tank bottom. Although the early peak of activity coincided with warming weather conditions, equally high temperatures later on did not have this activating effect. It appeared that natterjack tadpoles became more sedentary as they grew larger.

Table 1. Daily patterns of tadpole behaviour.

Time of day	Average no. tadpoles visible			Average no. tadpoles actively swimming	
	Total	Tank top (shallow end)	Tank bottom (deep end)	Days 2-6	Days 6-20
0800	9.1 (4.0)	3.2 (3.5)	5.3 (2.6)	0.5 (0.7)	0.2 (0.4)
1300	13.2 (1.6)	8.7 (3.0)	4.3 (2.8)	3.0 (1.4)	1.2 (1.0)
1900	11.8 (3.0)	4.9 (4.1)	6.7 (4.0)	4.5 (2.4)	0.5 (0.7)

Standard deviations are given in brackets.

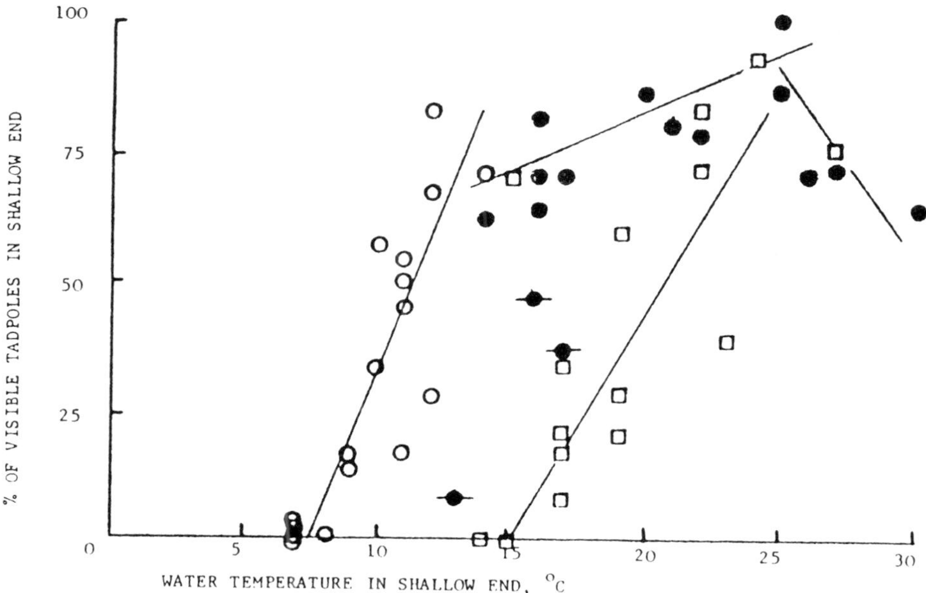

Figure 3. Tadpole behaviour and water temperature.

—●— records taken at 0800 hours; ● records taken at 1300 hours; ● 13 hour records in which the deep water was warmer than the shallow end; □ records taken at 1900 hours.

There were tendencies to select different water depths at different times of day (Table 1). The usual situation was for the fewest tadpoles to be visible early in the day, and these would generally be inactive in the deeper part of the tank. By mid-day most had moved into the shallows, swimming activity was greater and the highest proportion of animals visible. In the early evening a move back towards deeper water and/or concealment was detectable, though small tadpoles could be very active at this time (1900 hours).

There were clear correlations between water temperature and the part of the tank selected by the tadpoles (Figure 3). At 0800 hours, cloud cover was poorly (insignificantly) related to water temperature (data not shown) but the warmer the water, the more tadpoles accumulated in the shallow end ($r = 0.857$, $p = 0.001$) indicating a response to warmth rather than light intensity. All this despite the fact that the temperature gradient across the tank was never more than 1° (data not shown). By 1300 hours the water was approaching its daily maximum temperature and up to about 25° there was still a significant (but different) correlation between numbers of tadpoles in the shallow end and water temperature there ($r = 0.735$, $p = 0.01$). Above 25° the situation seemed to change, selection for shallow water dropping off markedly. Observations at 1900 hours indicated yet another significant but different correlation between tadpole positioning and water temperatures ($r = 0.680$, $p = 0.01$); at this time of day tadpoles accumulated in the deeper water at temperatures which, at 0800 hours, would have enticed them all into the shallows (i.e. 14-17°). At both 1300 and 1900 hours there were strong inverse correlations between cloud cover and water temperature, making it impossible to distinguish between the effects of temperature and light intensity on the behaviour of the tadpoles.

DISCUSSION

These observations were made under conditions which neither completely mimicked a pond (there was a very restricted range of water depths, for example) nor permitted separate control of factors such as light and temperature. It is important to realise these limitations, and what was seen cannot be taken to reflect the full repertoire of natterjack tadpole behaviour by any means. Nevertheless, I think the results are of some interest and seem to relate to aspects of behaviour noticed in the field. The relative activity of natterjack tadpoles, and their tendency to live on the pond bottom, contrast with the more active and mid-water existence of common toad tadpoles to the extent that behaviour might even assist with identification in the field. Telling common and natterjack toad tadpoles apart by appearance alone is notoriously difficult.

It looks as if we should expect natterjack tadpoles to be readily visible (i.e. not hidden in silt, etc., or in deep water) for most of their development, except perhaps on very hot days when water temperature exceeds 30° in the shallows. This can certainly happen, I once recorded 38° (warmer than blood heat!) in a shallow natterjack pond on a sunny day in June. Observers should expect to see few, if any tadpoles under such conditions since the lethal limit is 30-33° and the animals are likely to be seeking cooler surroundings at the pond bottom. The above observations also appear to explain why whole populations of tadpoles sometimes seem to disappear just before metamorphosis. They become very secretive at this time, and not seeing any cannot be taken to mean that they are not there. At early stages of development, up to the appearance of distinct hind limb buds, the middle of the day (except when very hot, as above) is probably the best time to look for natterjack tadpoles around the pond margins. It looks as if there may be a basic diurnal rhythm, with tadpoles retiring to deeper water at night but preferring shallow pond edges by day, subject to modification by environmental factors the most important of which is probably water temperature. There is obviously scope here for more systematic study under controlled conditions.

Finally, it is tempting to use these observations to help explain the different responses of common and natterjack tadpoles to food shortage. Food stress causes early mortality of common toad tadpoles leaving the survivors to grow normally (i.e. there is intense competition) whereas natterjack tadpoles respond by a general reduction in growth rates and little or no mortality. The greater activity of common toad tadpoles perhaps leads to a rapid utilisation of metabolic reserves, thus putting weaker animals at high risk of mortality quite quickly if food runs short. The more leisurely natterjack tadpoles should use up their reserves more slowly, and thus be more likely to survive in a situation where encounters with food are infrequent.

British Herpetological Society Bulletin No. 2. 1980

KEEPING AND BREEDING THE EUROPEAN GREEN TOAD *(BUFO VIRIDIS)*

DAVID BILLINGS

Red House Farm, Brakefield Green, Yaxham, East Dereham, Norfolk

INTRODUCTION

The three Green Toads I orginally obtained several years ago shared an (unheated) greenhouse with three pairs of Edible Frogs *(Rana esculenta)*, two pairs of Common Toads *(Bufo bufo)* and a pair of Green Lizards *(Lacerta viridis)*. Last year I purchased three more male Green Toads and another female, so I now have four males and three females of this species.

The floor covering of the greenhouse consisted of a mixture of clay, sand and peat in which various rockery plants and ferns were planted to provide cover for the inmates and for decorative effect. Rocks, pieces of cork bark and other bark were also placed in various positions as hiding and basking places for the toads and lizards. The plants grew and spread among the rocks producing a pleasing overall appearance. A small area of bare soil was left into which the toads could burrow. This proved very popular with the Green Toads which would bury themselves for long periods, with only their eyes and nostrils exposed. I have found that Green Toads, unlike many other amphibians, tend to avoid very thick, dense vegetation.

In one corner of the greenhouse, a moulded fibreglass tank was sunk, the dimensions of which were 75cm x 45cm. It was 15cm at its deepest, one end containing a shallow ledge about 6cm deep. More rocks were placed around the perimeter of the pond in order to conceal the rim, and I planted some marginal plants such as Japanese Striped Rush *(Acrous calamus variegatus)* and Water Forget-me-not *(Myosotis palustris)* in pots at the "shallow end" of the pond.

GENERAL CARE

Green Toads inhabit the warmer regions of Europe and Asia, those usually offered for sale by dealers originating from countries bordering the Mediterranean, where winters are of much shorter duration than those experienced in the U.K. I would therefore hesitate to recommend over-wintering them in an open air outdoor vivarium, particularly if situated in Northern England or Scotland.

Green Toads can be over-wintered far more successfully if allowed to hibernate naturally in a greenhouse or cold frame. I have over-wintered all my own Green Toads without any losses in such accommodation for several years, including the severe winter of 1978-79. It is, of course, essential to allow them to hibernate if an attempt is to be made at breeding them. If the above points are borne in mind, the Green Toad is an excellent inmate for a "community" vivarium, being hardy, long-lived and neither aggressive towards other inmates nor unduly timid.

Feeding presents no problems; Green Toads will accept anything that moves and is small enough to swallow. Mine are fed on as varied a diet as possible, which includes earthworms, crickets, leatherjackets, slugs, moths, caterpillars and mealworms (by far their favourite food).

BREEDING

I could never induce my Green Toads to spawn in the set-up mentioned above, and one reason was probably the small size of the pond. However, earlier this year we moved house, and on the evening of 13th June all my reptiles and amphibians were moved to a bigger greenhouse (260cm x 260cm) at the new house. The layout of this greenhouse was along similar lines to those of the old one, but the pond provided was much larger and deeper. It consisted of plastic sheeting 155cm x 95cm, and was 60cm at its deepest, having a shallow margin one end about 5 cm deep, sloping gently to the deeper end. I had filled the pond with ordinary tap-water a week previously.

The weather the following day was appreciably warmer, and during the early evening my attention was directed to a strange melodic "trill" which at first I took to be the call of a bird, possibly a warbler. On closer investigation I found the sound was emanating from the direction of the greenhouse, and on approaching it I could see the largest of the male Green Toads sitting, half submerged in the water at the margin of the pond calling vigorously. The note produced lasted for about five or six seconds, being repeated after a pause of about the same duration. It continued calling throughout the night and early morning of the next day.

Later that morning it was attempting amplexus with one of the females in the pond. The female however, seemingly bored with these attentions, left the pond with the male still attached and proceeded to wander around, walking into as many obstacles as possible apparently attempting to dislodge the stubbornly-resisting male. I did not have the opportunity to observe them again until the early evening when the pair were back in the pond and still in amplexus. The other three males were also in the pond but were showing no signs of sexual behaviour, merely sitting passively at the water's edge. These three are not yet fully grown however, and may not be sexually mature as their nuptial pads are not very conspicuous yet.

When I entered the greenhouse later in the evening (about 9.00 p.m.) the pair had separated and I was delighted to find several strings of spawn, wound around the submerged water plants (Canadian Pondweed and Hornwort). I removed all the spawn I could find and placed it in a 90cm x 38cm aquarium tank heated to around 75^{0}F and placed so as to receive maximum sunlight to encourage a good growth of algae. A layer of gravel had been placed on the floor of the tank.

REARING THE TADPOLES

I subsequently found that providing heating for the tadpoles was unnecessary since several dozen were later discovered swimming around in the greenhouse pond and these were growing well. The spawn in the heated tank took about three days to hatch and within another two days the tadpoles were free-swimming, feeding actively on the algae growing on the sides and bottom of the tank. I soon found it necessary to drastically reduce the many hundreds of tadpoles in this tank, the surplus being removed to alternative accommodation (in the form of old kitchen sinks). In addition to the naturally growing algae, I supplemented the tadpoles' diet with goldfish flake-food and pond-pellets; they grew rapidly and only two weeks after hatching, those tadpoles in the heated tank had visible rear legs.

The main difficulties will, no doubt, arise when metamorphosis is complete and I am faced with the prospect of finding enough aphids and other tiny insects on which to feed the toadlets. I will obviously attempt to hand-rear only a small number and will report on my success (or otherwise) in a later issue of the *Bulletin.*

CONCLUSION

It would appear that the breeding of my Green Toads was stimulated by one (or a combination of) the following factors:-

a) a change of environment
b) the provision of a more suitable pond
c) a fairly rapid change in weather conditions.

It is an established fact that goldfish and other pond-fish can often be induced to spawn after being transferred from one pond to another. They will also often commence spawning after a sudden change in the weather.

I would welcome any comments from other members of their own observations on amphibian breeding successes particularly as a result of any of the above factors.

British Herpetological Society Bulletin No. 10. 1984

HUSBANDRY AND CAPTIVE SPAWNING OF THE COMMON SPADEFOOT TOAD (*PELOBATES FUSCUS INSUBRICUS* CORNALIA)

FRANCO ANDREONE

Via Borgnuovo 17, 10040 Valdellatorre, Torino, Italy

INTRODUCTION

Pelobates fuscus insubricus is a subspecies of *Pelobates fuscus,* which has a distribution extending from France to the Urals and North Balkans. *P. f. insubricus* is an endemic race of the Po Plain; recent research indicates that it is extinct in its former range in southern Switzerland. In Italy its area of distribution includes Piedmont, Lombardy, Venetia and Emilia. The Common Spadefoot is a specialized amphibian; it is nocturnal, hiding itself underground during the day. It therefore prefers environments with a sandy soil rather than dry. Such an ambient is heath, and in Italy this habitat was born after the destruction of ancient forests. In recent years *P. f. insubricus* has disappeared from many places where at one time it was common, a process generated by continuous human pollution. Because of this it was decided to start a programme of captive breeding and subsequent reintroduction, using tadpoles and adult animals, in a locality where it is certain that the species was at one time widespread.

CAPTURE

The specimens were found near Novara (north-west Italy) in May. I decided to search for the animals in this place after having been told of their presence by a friend. The entire area is subject to a gradual but continuous process of drainage which will, in the near future, kill all amphibian populations. The taking of specimens from this place has no contra-indication, I being careful also to capture only a few of them. The hunt was conducted during a cold night, as Spadefoots are totally nocturnal and fossorial, and only in the breeding period is it possible to find them in sunlight. I used a powerful torch to light up the little brooks running alongside the country roads.

The first Spadefoot to be found was a male trying to mate with a Green Frog *(Rana esculenta).* I think that the male didn't hear the right answer from the frog and so it "thought" that this was a female of its own species. Similar behaviour is common in the males of several other anurans like, for example, the Common Toad *(Bufo bufo)*, often seen embracing any kind of object, from submerged roots to the hands of a man touching it.

The other Spadefoots were picked up along a fence surrounding a little artificial pool. The animals, three males and five females, were attracted by the presence of the water. Capture is relatively simple since these anurans don't try to escape when exposed under torch light, and so it is possible to easily pick them up by hand. When caught several Spadefoots released a sharp smell, very similar to that of garlic. In fact the German name of *Pelobates* is Knocker Krote, Garlic Toad.

All nine animals were put into a plastic box with moss and fresh leaves.

GENERAL CARE

Husbandry of the Common Spadefoot is relatively simple. I put the animals in an all glass terrarium with a surface of 60cm x 40cm and a height of 30cm, but this last dimension is not too important for breeding success since they are fossorial amphibians and don't climb. The floor of the terrarium was covered with a mixture of sand and clay to a depth of 10cm to allow the animals to cover themselves with sand. On one side of the terrarium I put a little basin full of water. Then I tried to feed the animals with living insects which they immediately accepted, eating them with a quick movement of the head.

SPAWNING

The Spadefoots, obviously in breeding condition, went immediately into the water and started to mate. Males, like Common Toads, tried to embrace the females but, since they outnumbered the females (6/3), there were some bachelors which wanted to dislodge a couple of males. All the males emitted a plaintive call, similar to "clock-clock"; the females also emitted a similar sound, but more acute. Amplexus in Pelobatidae is lumbar, as in other primitive anurans, unlike the families Ranidae and Bufonidae which have an axillar amplexus. The function of the strange humeral gland, distinctive in males, is unknown, but it may be useful in copulation. Coupled males defended themselves by kicking out with strength, but, since their hind legs have a hornlike spur, they often wound the "bachelors", or the embraced female.

Two females, obviously with eggs, accepted embrace, while the third one refused to mate. The two pairs, in order to avoid injury and tiresome interference, were separated and put in an aquarium 120 x 40 x 50 cm, one third full of water with some stones to provide the animals with a dry retreat. The water temperature was about 16°C. After being in amplexus for 24 hours the animals laid short strings of spawn, wound around submerged objects. The two couples spawned at different times; one pair at 9 a.m., the other at 12 noon.

The spawn strings were about 10cm in length. The eggs, grey in colour with the inferior pole white, had a diameter of about 3mm and were distributed irregularly in the jelly. They hatched in one week.

Table 1.

Dimensions of the Common Spadefoots *(Pelobates fuscus insubricus)* referred to in the text

Sex	Length, in millimetres	Weight, in grams
male	45	15
”	44	12
”	45	12
”	42	9
”	42	10
”	39	7
female	45	15
”	51	15
”	54	16

The tadpoles were very small (3mm) and remained attached to the spawn jelly for several days using a particular glandular structure. After this period they moved and suspended themselves on the sides of the aquarium. After five days they started to swim freely in the water with wave motions, feeding actively on the algae growing on the sides and bottom of the tank. At this point I filled the aquarium with water with the same characteristics and the same temperature. In addition to the natural growing algae I gave the tadpoles goldfish flaked food and boiled leaves. They grow very slowly. Some, after four months, have reached a length of 50mm, while others are only 20mm. They can reach a maximum length of about 180mm. Now, at this point, I would like to put a great number of these tadpoles in the mentioned pool, and I will keep in the aquarium only a small number in order to photograph the metamorphosis.

I will follow the progress of this new population and I hope to put the progeny of future spawning in this new place. I will report results in this *Bulletin*.

REFERENCES

Arnold, E. N. & Burton., J.A. (1978). *A Field Guide to the Reptiles and Amphibians of Britain and Europe.* Collins: London.

Baumgart, G. (1982). Batraciens et reptiles des forets riveraines du Rhin en Alsace *Aquarama n.* 64-66.

Billings, D. (1980). Keeping and breeding the European green toad *(Bufo viridis) British Herpetological Society Bulletin* **2:** 31-32.

Billings, D. (1981). Notes on the husbandry and a further captive spawning of the European green toad *(Bufo viridis). British Herpetological Society Bulletin* **4:** 38-39.

Bruno, S. (1970). I Pelobatidi. *Boll. WWF Italia* n1 (8) pp. 15-16.

Bruno, S. (1983). Lista rossa degli anfibi italiani. *Riv.piem.St.Nat.* pp. 5-48.

Bruno, S., Burattini, E., Casale, A. (1974). Il Rospo bruno del Cornalia. Vol. III atti IV *Simposio nazionale sulla conservazione della natura,* Istituto zool, Università di Bari. 23-28/4 pp.33-56.

Capula, M. (1982). Prima che gli anfibi scompaiano. *Panda* **1:** 3-5.

Cochran, D.M. *Il mondo degli animali: Gli anfibi.* Arnoldo Mondadori Editore.

Davies, N.B. & Hallyday (1979). Competitive mate searching in male common toads *Animal Behaviour.* **27:** 1253-1267.

Lanza, B., Tortonese, E. (1968). *Pesci, anfibi e Rettili.* Martello.

Morisi, A. (1983). *Guida agli anfibi e rettili della provincia di Cuneo.*

Vandoni, C. (1914). *Anfibi d' Italia.* Ulrico Hoepli Editore.

NOTES ON THE GENUS *BOMBINA* OKEN

(Anura: Bombinatoridae):

II. LIFE HISTORY ASPECTS

MATHIAS LANG

Zoologisches Forschungsintitut und Museum Alexander König, Adenaueralle 150-164, D-5300 Bonn I, Germany and Museum of Natural History, The University of Kansas, Lawrence, K.S., USA 66045-2454

INTRODUCTION

This paper represents the second portion in a three-part series of papers summarizing pertinent information available on *Bombina*. Overall the series synthesizes information on distribution and characteristics of recognized species of *Bombina*, together with aspects of external appearances, morphology, life history, systematics and taxonomy. This paper focuses on the life history aspects of the species of *Bombina*.

LIFE HISTORY ASPECTS

No life history data has been recorded for *microdeladigitora* and *fortinuptialis*, therefore the following descriptions pertain to the remaining four species of *Bombina*: *bombina*, *maxima*, *orientalis* and *variegata*.

HABITAT

These semi-aquatic to aquatic toads live in shallow permanent to periodic bodies of water and are predominantly diurnal although also active at night. *Bombina orientalis* is frequently found in swamps and rice paddies or low mountain streams. *Bombina maxima*, in contrast, inhabits mountainous regions and is found in small pools and ponds, especially those with dead vegetation. This species is less commonly found in small mountain streams. *Bombina variegata* is found from sea-level up to 1800 m. and is very salt-tolerant (Parent, 1979); *bombina* at lower elevations, found in a variety of shallow bodies of water such as ponds, drainage ditches, pools and slow streams. *Bombina fortinuptialis* is found at elevations from 1200 to 1640 m in Guagxi, China (Tian and Wu, 1981). Excellent descriptions of habits of the European species can be found in Arnold *et al.* (1978). Day and night activity are predominant at temperatures between 10 and 30° C in spring and summer.

HIBERNATION AND BREEDING SEASON

European *Bombina* hibernate on land in animal burrows or in loose soil. These species emerge from hibernation at different times depending on temperature and the amount of rainfall; usually by mid or late April.

The breeding season of *Bombina orientalis* in Korea is May and June, but eggs can be laid all year round. The breeding season of *maxima* is rather short and is usually restricted to early May.

NUPTIAL PADS

Nuptial pads are prominent on the inner aspects of the forelegs, palmar tubercle and first, second and third fingers during the breeding season in *bombina, variegata* (Berger and Michalowski, 1971), *maxima* and *orientalis* (Stejneger, 1907). In addition *variegata* has nuptial pads on the toes of the hind leg (most frequently on the third toe).

VOCALIZATION

Vocal sacs are present in *B. bombina*[1] but are completely lacking in *B. variegata, B. orientalis* and *B. maxima.* Conditions in *fortinuptialis* and *microdeladigitora* are not known.

Vocalization occurs at night or during the day (when reproductive activity is at its highest peak) in warm pools, ponds and ditches. Males occupy a specific position along the bank for weeks. Interspecific distances are maintained by calls. These distances are 3 m in *bombina* and slightly less in *variegata* (Löcher, 1969). A solitary male *variegata* calls with a temperature determined call. Call repetition rate and pitch in *bombina* and *variegata* show a positive rectilinear correlation with temperature. The duration of the call itself is negatively correlated with temperature (Zweifel, 1959; Akef and Schneider, 1985; Schneider *et al.,* 1986). There is also a difference in frequency of calls. For example a frequency of 80 calls per minute at temperatures of 20°C for *variegata* versus 18 per minute of *bombina* under identical conditions. The calls of these two species can be easily differentiated because *variegata* always has a frequency of more than 40 calls per minute, in addition *bombina* and *variegata* differ significantly in their vocal chord size (Schmid, 1977). Call duration and frequency also changes with animal size, with calls of larger males lower in pitch and longer than those of smaller animals (Akef and Schneider, 1985; Schneider *et al.,* 1986).

European *Bombina* also call while suspended in water. Calling is usually in the evening and may last all night. The minimal vocalization temperature is 11°C and the maximal vocalization temperature is 30°C (Zweifel, 1959). Song in *variegata* is a musical "poop ... poop ... poop", which is brighter and faster than the mournful "oop ... oop ... oop" of *bombina* (Arnold *et al.,* 1978). Mating calls of European *Bombina* as well as hybrids thereof exhibit both intra- and interspecific differences (Schneider *et al.,* 1986).

Male *orientalis* produce five types of calls: normal mating call, modified mating call (= male excitement call), clasping call and male and female release calls. During calling, males distribute themselves in the water in such a way as to maintain distances of a few centimetres from one another. They defend their territories by means of mating calls or aggressive behaviour. The latter takes on three forms: frontal attack, attack from the side, or jumping onto the opponent's back (Akef and Schneider, 1985). The mating call of *orientalis* is a monotonous "uuh ... uuh ... uuh", sounding like the tinkling of a small bell, that can be rather loud when males use body cavities as resonance chambers on the surface of the water. As is the case with *bombina* and *variegata,* call repetition rate and pitch in *orientalis* show a positive correlation with temperature. The duration of calling is negatively correlated with temperature.

Bombina maxima produces a weak croak like the sound of a very young chicken (Liu, 1950).

Antiphonal calling is also observed in this genus. The calls are long, drawn out and monotonous. Frog "choirs" can be initiated by a single individual.

[1] Male *Bombina bombina* have two vocal sacs in the throat area. Tyler (1980) indicated that these were not true vocal sacs but rather that they represent a resonance chamber involving the ventral protrusion of the buccal cavity (and the m. geniophyoideii lateralis) between the superficial manidbular muscles: m. intermandibularis and m. interhyoideus.

Plate 1. *Bombina orientalis* eating Wax-moth. Photo by Peter Curry

MATING

Female *orientalis* respond to mating calls of males by either swimming into the territory of a calling male or by generating water waves towards which the male swims (Akef and Schneider, 1985). The males clasp females in front of the hind legs in inguinal (lumber) amplexus. There may be two to three spawnings throughout the breeding season, but principally in May and June. However, individual females may spawn only once a year (Freytag, 1967; Kapfberger, 1984). *Bombina maxima* mates in inguinal amplexus in water (Pope, 1931, Sparreboom and van den Elzen, 1982). Mating in *variegata* is similar to that of *orientalis* as described above. Birkenmeier (1954) further gives details on mating behaviour in *variegata.*

EGGS AND TADPOLES

Eggs are greyish-brown and measure 2 mm in diameter in *bombina* and *variegata* and 3 mm in *maxima.* The egg with gelatinous envelope measures up to 8 mm. Clutches of 80-100 eggs are reported for *variegata,* in contrast to 100-300 eggs reported for *bombina.* Eggs are laid several times during the breeding season. The eggs are laid with characteristic movements in small clumps on vertical plant stems or grass outside the water *(bombina)* or sink to the bottom of the pool (illustration in Engelmann *et al.,* 1985). Development of the eggs of European species can also occur in temporary rain puddles or drainage ditches. The preferred breeding habitats, however, are small ponds with lots of vegetation, but tributaries with clay and muddy bottoms are also used during breeding. *Bombina maxima* lays its eggmass in open water; the eggs sink to the bottom or attach themselves to the underside of floating vegetation. *Bombina orientalis* attaches its eggs to the under surface of stones in small mountain streams (Liu, 1950).

The fertilized eggs of *orientalis* require 25-30 days before attaining the stage of protrusion of the forelegs at 25°C. The complete development requires between 43 and 48 days. In laboratory studies an average female *orientalis* will produce 100 to 200 eggs per ovulation, when the interval between ovulations is 6 weeks. If the interval is 3 months then the number of eggs expected is 200 to 400. Percentage fertilization of these eggs is 95% (Carlson and Ellinger, 1980).

Eggs hatch after 7 to 9 days. The hatching tadpoles measure 6-7 mm *(bombina* and *variegata*) and up to 10 mm *(maxima),* and weigh from 0.0087 to 0.0013 g.

The metamorphosed young measure 12-15 mm (European species and *orientalis* and 17 mm in *maxima).* The larval development of *variegata* takes about 50 days, with low temperatures and crowding during metamorphosis leading to smaller toadlets (Kapfberger, 1984). Full metamorphosis takes place within 90 days. Larvae at the end of the breeding season, however, will overwinter. The fully metamorphosed young of these larvae usually measure 20 mm or more.

Tadpoles of *variegata* are not inhibited (crowding-effect) by their own species or by 6 other European anurans. In fact, tadpoles of *variegata* that often live in ecological sympatry in temporary rain-water pools with other European species *(Bombina bombina, Bufo calamita,* and *Hyla arborea)* show mutual tolerance (Heusser, 1972).

Life history studies of *Bombina bombina* by Bannikov (1950) indicated rapid growth during the first year followed by determinate growth. Embryonic and larval mortalities were estimated at 45.8% that increased to 97.9% after the first year. The high mortality is due to hibernation death. An estimated population renewal of 3.5 years is predicted. Population studies of *variegata* in northern Bavaria indicate a 1:1 sex ratio (Kapfberger, 1984).

SEXUAL MATURITY AND LONGEVITY

Bombina variegata and *B. bombina* attain sexual maturity in two years, at a length of 30-40 mm (Bannikov, 1950; Madej, 1964; Kapfberger, 1984). Maximal ages of *bombina* of 5 years and 10 months and 2 years 4 months for *orientalis* are reported (Bowler, 1975). Longevity of *Bombina* (sp?) in captivity of 12 years have been recorded. Sexual maturity of *orientalis* is reached at one year in this species and full size is attained at two years.

PREDATORS

Newts and larvae of 4 species of *Triturus* prey on tadpoles of *variegata* (Heusser, 1970).

MIGRATION

Local migrations of *Bombina* have been reported (Mertens, 1928; Madej, 1964). Reasons for migration are various: flooding, drying of bodies of water, looking for breeding sites or food sources and retreats for hibernation (Madej, 1964).

BEHAVIOUR

When disturbed on land, *Bombina* becomes motionless and displays its striking ventral colouration in an "Unkenreflex." The back is arched, the hands are pulled forward over the eyes and the feet are pulled into the mid-section of the body. On occasion the animals lie on their back exposing the venter. Cutaneous poison glands secrete a foamy substance irritable to oral-nasal mucosa even without contact in humans (histaminic effect) and can cause death in amphibians (Gessner, 1926. Csordas and Michl, 1972). When disturbed in water, they will dive and bury themselves in the slime or mud at the bottom of the body of water.

ACKNOWLEDGEMENTS

I wish to thank Wolfgang Böhme for comments and help with references and William E. Duellann and Linda Trueb for reviewing an early draft of the manuscript. This study was supported by a stipend from the Deutscher Akademischer Austausch Dienst.

REFERENCES

Akef, M.S.A. and Schneider, H. (1985). Vocalization, courtship and territoriality in the Chinese fire-bellied toad *Bombina orientalis* (Anura, Discoglossidae). *Zool. Jb. Physiol.* **89:** 119-136.

Arnold, E.N., Burton, J.A. and Ovenden, D.W. (1978). *A Field Guide to the Reptiles and Amphibians of Britain and Europe.* Collins, London; 272 pp.

Bannikov, A.G. (1950). Age composition of a population and its dynamics in *Bombina bombina* L. *Doklady Akad. Nauk USSR,* **70**(1): 101-103.

Berger, L. and Michalowski, J. (1971). *Amphibia.* Published for the Smithsonian Institution and the National Science Foundation by the Scientific Publications Foreign Cooperation Center, Part 2, pp. 1-75.

Birkenmeier, E. (1954). Beobachtungen zur Nahrugsaufnahme und Paarungsbiologie der Gattung *Bombina. Veh. Zool. -Bot. Ges. Wien,* **94:** 70-81.

Bowler, J. K. (1975). *Longevity of reptiles and amphibians in North American collections. Society for the study of Amphibians and Reptiles and the Philadelphia Herpetological Society:* 1-32.

Carlson, J.T. and Ellinger, M.S. (1980). The reproductive biology of *Bombina orientalis,* with notes on care. *Herp. Rev.* **11**(1): 11-12.

Csordas, A. and Michl, H. (1972). On the toxin of European *Bombina* species. *In:* de Vries, A. and E. Kochva (eds.) *Toxins of Animal and Plant Origin.* Vol. 2. Gordon and Breach, Sci. Publ. New York: 493-822.

Engelmann, W. E., Fritzsche, J., Gunther, R. and F. J. Obst. (1985). *Lurche und Kriechetiere Europas.* Neumann Verlag, Leipzig. 420 pp.

Freytag, G.E. (1967). Klasse Amphibia-Lurche (Ordnung Salienta-Froschlurche). *In: Urania Tierreich,* pp. 292-355.

Gessner, O. (1926). Uber Krotengifl. *Arch. exper. path.* Leipzig **113:** 343-367.

Heusser, H. (1970). Differenzierendes Kaulquappen-fressen durch Molche. *Experientia* **27:** 475.

Heusser, H. (1972). Intra- und interspezifische Crowding-Effekte bei Kaulquappen einheimischer Anuren-Arten. *Vierteljahrsschrift der Naturforschenden Gesellschaft in Zürich* **117** (2): 121-128.

Kapfberger, D. von. (1984). Untersuchungen zur Populationsaufbau, Wachstum und Ortsbeziehungen der Gelbbauchunken, *Bombina variegata variegata* (Linnaeus, 1758). *Zoologischer Anz.* **212** (1-2): 105-116.

Liu, C.C. (1950). *Amphibians of Western China.* Fieldiana. Zool. Memoirs, **2:** 1-400.

Löcher, K. (1969). Vergleichende bio-akustische Untersuchungen an der Rot- und Gelbbauchunke. *Oecologia* **3:** 84-124.

Madej, Z. (1964). Studies on the fire-bellied toad *Bombina bombina* (Linnaeus, 1761) and yellow bellied toad *Bombina variegata* (Linnaeus, 1758) of Upper Silesia and Moravian Gate. *Acta. Zool. Cracov.* **9:** 291-334.

Mertens, R. (1928). Zur Naturgeschichte der Europaischen Unken *(Bombina). Zs. Morph. Oek. Tiere,* **11:** 613-623.

Parent, G.H. (1979). *Atlas commente dé l'Herpétofaune de la Belgigue et du Grand-Duché de Luxembourg.* Les Naturalistes Belges. 88 pp.

Pope, C. (1931). Notes on Amphibians from Fukien, Hoinan, and other parts of China. *Bull. Am. Mus. Nat. Hist.,* **61:** 397-611.

Schmid, E. (1977). Der Rufapparat der Rot- und Gelbbauchunke und der Geburtshelferkröte *Bombina bombina* (L.), *Bombina v. variegata* (L.), *Alytes o. obstetricans* (Laur.) (Anura, Discoglossidae). *Zool. Jb. Anat.* **98:** 171-180.

Schneider, H., Hussein, F. and Mamdouh, S.A.A. (1986). Comparative bioacoustic studies in the yellow-bellied toad, *Bombina variegata* (L.), and the relationships of European and Asian species and subspecies of the genus *Bombina. Bonn. zool. Beitr.* **37**(1): 49-67.

Sparreboom, M. and van den Elzen, P. (1982). A preliminary note on the care and breeding of *Bombina maxima* (Boulenger, 1905) in captivity. *Br. J. Herpetol.,* **6:** 269-272.

Stejneger, L. (1907). Herpetology of Japan and adjacent territory. *Bull. U.S. Nat. Mus.* **58:** 1-577.

Tian, W. and Wu, G. (1981). *In:* S. Hu, W. Tian and G. Wu. Three new species of amphibans from Guangxi. *Acta Herpetol. Sinica,* **5**(17): 111-120.

Tyler, M.J. (1980). The evolutionary significance of the vocal sac of the European discoglossid frog *Bombina bombina* (L.) (Amphibia, Salientia). *Acta biol. Cracov. (zool.)* **22**(1): 99-104.

Zweifel, R.G. (1959). Effect of temperature on call of the frog, *Bombina variegata. Copeia,* 1959 **(4):** 322-327.

THE CARE AND BREEDING OF THE EDIBLE FROG *(RANA ESCULENTA)* IN CAPTIVITY

DAVID BILLINGS

Red House Farm, Brakefield Green, Yaxham, East Dereham, Norfolk

DESCRIPTION, DISTRIBUTION AND HABITAT

The edible frog *(Rana esculenta)* is a large, handsome frog which can attain an overall length of 12cm, but a more usual size is 8-9cm for females and 6-7cm for males. This frog has a rather streamlined appearance; the snout is slightly pointed while the long back legs are very powerful. Markings and colouration vary considerably, in fact, no two specimens are ever identical. The back is usually green, brown or a combination of the two; dark brown spots and blotches are usually present on the back and sides and many individuals possess a yellow or green vertebral stripe. The rear part of the thighs is marbled with dark brown and yellow or orange; the underside is white, speckled with grey. There is no dark brown temporal area characteristic of most *Rana* species.

The edible frog is found throughout western Europe ranging as far as southern Sweden, western Russia, Rumania and Hungary. It seldom strays far from water, being extremely aquatic in its habits; it will bask for long periods on the sunny bank of a pond, lake, stream or ditch, splashing into the water with a prodigious leap at the approach of danger. Because of its liking for sunshine it is not usually found in thickly wooded areas.

Although the edible frog is not now thought to be indigenous to Britain, many thousands of adults caught in France and Belgium were released in various localities in East Anglia during the last century. These introduced frogs formed colonies which usually thrived for a few years before disappearing completely. However, I know of an extant colony in the Breckland area of Norfolk which is still thriving; this particular area has contained breeding communities of edible frogs for over one hundred years.

CARE IN CAPTIVITY

In view of the large size of this frog, coupled with a nervous disposition, plenty of room in a large vivarium is essential for its successful maintenance. Added to the above traits, its sun loving propensity means that it should be kept in an outdoor vivarium, be it a reptiliary, greenhouse or large cold-frame.

Whatever type of enclosure is used a pond is an essential feature, the larger the better, but certainly no smaller than 60cm x 60cm x 45cm. It should be well stocked with submerged aquatic plants and several large rocks or stones should be placed

Plate 1. Examples of "Green Frogs".
Left: Adult Albanian Frog *(Rana shquiperica).* Right: Adult Epirus Frog (*Rana epeirotica).* Photos by Silvio Bruno taken from *Bulletin* 29, 1989.

around its perimeter on which the frogs can bask in the sun. The arrangement of the vivarium as regards plants and general layout is, of course, a matter of personal choice, but there should be plenty of ground-cover in the form of low growing vegetation. The depth of soil on the base of the vivarium should be sufficient to ensure a frost-proof retreat during the winter months. I would add that the edible frog is extremely hardy, being well able to endure the severest weather, even when quite small.

Feeding

This can be rather a problem as, with very few exceptions, edible frogs do not become tame. They will dive into their pond in fright whenever their vivarium is approached; however, there are exceptional individuals which do become tame; I have one specimen which is confiding enough to be approached and hand-fed without taking fright. I have, as yet, never encountcred an edible frog which will allow itself to be handled or touched. A further problem is that edible frogs are mainly nocturnal in their feeding habits; it is therefore advisable to introduce large numbers of earthworms, slugs, woodlice, etc., into the vivarium. These will soon reproduce themselves, forming colonies for the frogs to prey upon naturally. The vivarium should be watered each evening to bring out the worms and slugs during the night.

Another useful idea is to grow plants with strong scented flowers in the vivarium to attract flying insects on which the frogs will readily prey. I have often observed my own edible frogs seize and devour bees or wasps without showing signs of having been stung. Presumably they are either immune from or impervious to the sting of these insects.

Breeding

Under the conditions described above, breeding should take place regularly each year; spawning does not occur immediately after emergence from hibernation in mid April but is usually delayed until late May or early June. During the first few weeks after emergence from hibernation both sexes remain fairly inactive, sitting listlessly around the pond or in the water with heads protruding. As the weather becomes warmer the frogs are progressively more active and the males commence their loud, raucous call. They are extremely vociferous during the breeding season, calling throughout the day and night in chorus; one male will start up, triggering off all the others. Where large numbers are present the noise is quite deafening and can be heard from a considerable distance; a passing aeroplane, lawnmower or even thunder will also start them calling.

When thus engaged, the males swim excitedly around in the water seizing any female or male they encounter; a male that is seized emits a "grunt" which is the signal for the other male to release him. Amplexus is axillary but the grip of the male is not particularly tenacious; the pair will usually separate if disturbed or handled. They should therefore be left alone during spawning.

The spawn, usually laid in the early hours of the morning, is deposited on underwater vegetation to which it adheres. It is laid in several small clusters about the size of a golf ball and the eggs themselves are smaller than those of *Rana temporaria*. The vitelline sphere is light brown in colour on the upper surface, white below. The white area gradually diminishes in size until the whole egg is brown, by which time it has become elongated in shape. Within a few more hours the head and tail of the developing embryo are clearly discernible; development is rapid, the tadpoles usually hatch within 48 hours of the spawn being laid. The newly hatched tadpoles are remarkably small resembling minute brown-grey slugs. They cling to the spawn for about 2 days before becoming free-swimming, when they browse actively on algae or other soft, underwater vegetation.

Rearing the tadpoles

During the first three weeks after hatching, edible frog tadpoles are most vulnerable. Mortality can be at a very high level if the correct conditions are not provided during this critical period of development. These conditions are, in fact, quite easy to provide; they are:

1) **Sunshine** – edible frog tadpoles are particularly fond of basking in sunlight just under the surface of the water, diving rapidly to the depths whenever disturbed.

2) **Warmth** – if the tank or receptacle in which the tadpoles are kept is placed in a sunny position in the garden the water will become very warm during the day, to the liking of the tadpoles, but water temperature will drop considerably during the night.

To remedy this the tank can be brought indoors in the evening and taken out again each morning. Alternatively, an aquarium heater and thermostat set at about 24°C can be used, this will prevent rapid temperature changes. By the time the tadpoles have attained an overall length of 2cm, which they should have done within four weeks of hatching, they are hardy enough to be left outdoors, permanently without artificial heat.

3) **Space** – overcrowding must be strictly avoided. About 6 tadpoles per square metre is the optimum number. These tadpoles have enormous appetites, feeding voraciously on flaked fish food, "pond pellets", or pieces of raw or cooked meat and fish. I usually keep a few water snails with the tadpoles to eat any food that is not immediately devoured by the tadpoles.

If the above conditions are met, an overall length of 6-7cm, exceptionally 9cm, should have been reached by their seventh week after hatching. Five or six weeks later the front legs are visible and metamorphosis should be complete within another week. The average size of the froglets when they have absorbed their tails is 20-25mm. It follows that froglets of this size can tackle quite large prey; they are quite capable of eating blowflies, small earthworms or half-grown mealworms without difficulty.

Care and hibernation of the froglets

The froglets are also voracious, so growth is rapid. They can easily attain an overall length of 4cm by the time they are ready to hibernate in early November. They can therefore be allowed to hibernate outdoors naturally. They may well be sexually mature the following year but full size is not usually attained until the year after.

Although the edible frog is a highly excitable, nervous creature which seldom becomes tame, its large size and beautiful colours make it a very desirable inmate for the larger vivarium.

British Herpetological Society Bulletin No. 31. 1990

SPAWNING AND REARING THE PARSLEY FROG *(PELODYTES PUNCTATUS)* IN CAPTIVITY

SIMON HARTLEY

8 Harnorlen Road, Peverell, Plymouth, Devon, PL2 3NU

INTRODUCTION

The Parsley Frog, *Pelodytes punctatus,* is a native to western Europe, being widely distributed throughout France and Iberia and occurring also in western Belgium and extreme north-west Italy. It is closely related to the Pelobatidae, the Spadefoot and Horned Toads, but is now more often placed, together with the very similar Caucasian Parsley Frog, *Pelodytes caucasicus,* which occurs in the north-western Caucasus mountains, in a separate family, Pelodytidae.

It is small, reaching a maximum size of 1½-2" (4-5cm), possesses long hind limbs with unusuallly long toes, which are not webbed, a body covered with small, irregular warts, and a flattened head with prominent eyes, which have a vertical pupil. Colouration, even within one population, is extremely variable, ranging from the drab brown individuals usually illustrated in books, where the green dorsal spots which give the frog its name are often very small and sparse, through specimens with a variety of delicate brown patterns of different shades and red-orange dots along the sides, to others with broad patterns of bright, almost irridescent green on a dark or light background, and with additional dark green markings, the latter types being almost as strikingly coloured as European *Hyla.* Darker individuals often display a lighter X mark across the back, but whatever the dorsal colour, the underside is always a uniform, unmarked cream-white. The sexes are similar in general appearance, but males can be distinguished by their thicker front limbs, slightly broader heads and slimmer build, and also by the presence of nuptial pads on the forelimbs when in breeding condition.

Although Parsleys are extremely agile, and almost compulsive climbers, they are at the same time nocturnal and highly secretive, especially when adult, and while individuals can be heard calling during the day, it is always from cover.

The following is an account of my attempts at breeding and raising *P. punctatus* undertaken in 1988 and 1989. Since the latter produced much more information of interest and value to potential keepers of this species so far as spawning method is concerned than the former, observations made earlier this year will be considered in greater detail than those in the previous one.

As available literature covering Parsley reproduction was inadequate for my purposes, and no accounts of captive breeding could be found, my first efforts were wholly experimental. Tadpoles and froglets, about 1 month metamorphosed, obtained in May 1987 were sexually mature at between half and two-thirds full-grown, by September-October, the first characteristic low-pitched 'krr-ek' calls being heard in August. Partly because no suitable outdoor accommodation was available, partly that Parsleys are recorded as spawning after emerging from aestivation in southern Iberia (Salvador, 1985), the above, 4 males and 3 females, were kept inside at room temperature instead of being hibernated. However, general activity decreased in late November-December, so no attempt to induce breeding was made until the following spring.

BREEDING ACCOMMODATION

The only indication of water depth preferred by spawning Parlsey Frogs was that strands of eggs were apparently wrapped around vegetation in similar manner to Spadefoots, so it was decided to start with 10" (25 cm), which could be reduced if required. An aquarium 25" x 12" x 15" was prepared, filled with water to the above depth, to which clumps of *Elodea densa* were added, and a terrestrial area, covered with clumps of grass, moss and stones, was built up in the middle. The tank sides were raised a further 6" (15 cm) by a temporary glass construction, and the top covered with a combination of curtain netting and plastic aquarium condensation sheets, to prevent escapes. As the frogs were evidently active by day during the spawning period, (Arnold & Burton, 1978), the tank was placed where it could receive strong sunlight from a south-west facing window, and since water temperatures remained in the mid to upper 50sF (c. 12°C) when the above was first set up, no artificial heating was used initially.

SPAWNING

The first attempt at amplexus, which in this species, as with *Pelobates* and *Bombina,* is inguinal, was observed in the second week of March. On closer examination, the females appeared gravid, and nuptial pads, in the form of dark brown patches extending the length of the front limbs to the arm pits as well as on the thumbs and forefingers, were now clearly visible on the males, so they were all transferred to the breeding tank on the 17th.

Within 24 hours the males began producing calls which were much louder, and repeated for much longer periods, than those previously described. They did this either resting amongst plants on the surface at the edge of the island, on the island itself, or even from the bottom of the aquarium, where the effects were somewhat 'muffled', but the sound still quite audible. Pairs were seen in amplexus over the next 4 days, sometimes for up to 48 hours, but nothing more happened, cooler temperatures and lack of sun coinciding with less calling, so a heater-themostat was introduced, raising the water temperature to the mid-60sF (c.18°C), and light spraying, simulating rain, was applied to the island in the late evenings. Frogs kept calling and going into amplexus as described, but producing no spawn, for the following 3 days, so the temperature was raised to 75/65°F (23-24°C) early on the 24th, with a view to turning the heater off at night to simulate a natural fall. Still nothing had happened by then, and as females in amplexus earlier had been released, I decided to give the terrestrial area a much heavier spraying last thing.

The next morning, the 25th, 3 clumps of eggs were found, partly wrapped around roots of grass growing into the water from the island. On examining the frogs, all eggs had clearly been deposited by one female, the smallest, which at only 1" (2.50 cm) was half the size of the others, and apparently the least gravid. Its very dark appearance indicated the spawn had been laid probably a few hours previously, and the temperature at the time of discovery was 68°F (c.20°C). The clusters, each approximately the same size, c.1½-2" close to the island, two being at a depth of 1-2" (2.50-5cm), the third at 6-7" (15-18 cm), where growth of roots and *Elodea* was thickest. Over the next 24 hours the spawn swelled to approx. 2" (5 cm) in diameter, and as removal would have proved difficult without causing damage, it was left *'in-situ'*, where it could in any case be easily observed, and temperatures were maintained in the lower to mid 70sF.

Vigorous calling by the males, plus further spells of 24-48 hours in amplexus with the other females continued, but though the pattern of higher temperature and heavy evening spraying was maintained, no further eggs were produced. The last loud breeding calls were heard on 1st April; by the 6th all the frogs had left the water, and the males' nuptial pads were clearly disappearing, so they were removed to their former quarters and the island was dismantled, leaving the tank for rearing the tadpoles.

TADPOLE DEVELOPMENT

With temperatures as above, the eggs developed quickly and, with the exception of a small number of infertile ones in the centre of each cluster, began hatching in 48 hours. At this stage the tadpoles resembled many other newly-hatched anurans, dark brown with a lighter underside, short tail and small, feathery external gills, and developed in much the same way, remaining attached to the spawn jelly or surrounding vegetation until they became free-swimming in a further 48 hours. During this period, I removed one of the clusters for closer observation, finding that it contained 104 embryos, including 20-30 which failed to develop, indicating that the total of eggs produced was around 300.

Over the next 10 days, the tadpoles assumed a shape, size and colour very similar to those of *Bombina* at the same stage, and, feeding mostly on algae growing on the tank sides and plants, plus good quality tropical fish flakes, they progressed very well over the next month, during which time 80-100 were moved to another tank to avoid overcrowding. However, by 28th April it was noticed that although feeding avidly, the majority, especially the smaller ones, were losing their normal rotund shape and becoming thinner, a process observable in both tanks. On 6th May hind leg buds were visible on the largest tadpole, but many of the others were now very thin, and seemed to be stagnating.

Having raised numerous tadpoles to *Rana, Bufo* and *Bombina* species in similar densities, straightforward overcrowding seemed unlikely to be the problem, so possible causes and solutions were sought from various herpetological contacts, though none had experience with Parsley tadpoles. Mike Linley suggested the cause might be minute organisms living in the tadpole gut, which, in a confined area, could be passed on to other tadpoles via the droppings, some of which would be eaten by the latter, whose digestive system would be effectively blocked by the multiplying organisms, with results similar to those I was currently witnessing. Trevor Beebee has since told me of just such an organism, which appears to be the key to competition between the tadpoles of Common and Natterjack Toads *(Bufo bufo* and *calamita).* His research suggests it could be a protozoan or yeast, but at the time of writing this article, the precise identity of the organism is still uncertain. Charles Snell told me of his experiences with tadpoles of Green Frogs *(Rana lessonae/esculenta/ridibunda* complex), when a small number of larger individuals kept in restricted space would regularly outgrow the rest, which appeared to stagnate. This adverse competition could be avoided, he suggested, by splitting the tadpoles up according to size and making more frequent water changes, the latter to prevent the build-up of whatever substance was causing the problem. This was duly tried, and while the smallest, approximately one third of the whole batch, which were by now clearly the weakest, failed to recover, the rest improved rapidly, the largest individuals reaching 2½" (6cm). However, though they were now maintained in much lower densities, I still found it necessary to keep those of comparable size together, as a few larger ones would, within 12-14 days, start pulling away while their tank-mates would start to fall back as before.

By 23rd May 34 tadpoles had fully-developed hind limbs, with their front ones beginning to come through; within the next 6 days this process was completed, other frog-like features had rapidly developed, and on 1st June they emerged as fully-metamorphosed froglets. The rest continued to come through over the following 6-7 weeks, though many, again possibly as a result of having their development retarded, failed to reach more than 2" (5 cm) as tadpoles, thus metamorphosing at much less than the 15mm attained by the largest individuals, and were evidently not strong enough to survive for long.

REARING THE FROGLETS

With the previous year's experience to go by, this proved fairly straightforward. The young Parsleys were housed in various converted aquarium tanks, furnished with a simple substrate of earth and leaves, to which were added clumps of moss, bark and assorted pieces of wood and stones. A water dish was not provided, but I found from unfortunate experience that, even when adult, these frogs easily desiccate if their accommodation becomes too dry, so it was necessary to keep conditions in the tanks damp by means of regular spraying. Fed on a wide variety of insects and other invertebrates collected from grass/hedge sweepings, supplemented by fruit flies *(Drosophila)* and occasionally small crickets *(Acheta domestica),* the froglets made good progress, some of those retained being half-grown by August; calling first heard on 11th of that month, and the largest 6-7 individuals had reached a size comparable with that of their parents at the same stage by the end of November.

1989

The 1988 experience raised a number of questions, such as why only one of 3 apparently suitable females actually spawned, what really 'triggered' that particular success, and was it more a case of good fortune than providing the correct conditions. Alternatively, in view of the relatively short period of intense breeding activity, there was a possibility that the frogs may have been introduced to the breeding set-up too late, and perhaps the females were not in such prime spawning condition after all. The main task of the 1989 season, therefore, was to try to provide answers to some or all of these.

BREEDING ACCOMODATION

Later in the Spring of 1988, Charles Snell obtained a successful spawning from Parsley Frogs (unrelated to mine) in conditions very different to those I had experimented with, i.e. in an outdoor vivarium, with eggs deposited in much shallower water. I thus decided to try a more natural setting for this year's attempt. Also, since another contact, Pat Thorp, had Parsleys (from the same batch as my original ones) produce spawn, which proved to be infertile, apparently 3 weeks before mine had been set up to breed, this in a heated conservatory, I decided to make an earlier start, which of course meant continuing indoors.

This time a vivarium 40" x 20" x 16" was used, with a half aquatic, half terrestrial arrangement in mind, to which end a glass divider 4" (10cm) high was fitted across the tank, sealed by silicone. The basic furniture was similar to that used in '88, except that small logs and more moss were placed in the water and connected with the main terrestrial area by slates overhanging from the latter. The slates, along with clumps of grass positioned so that strands would hang into the water as in the previous set-up, provided cover close to and overhanging the water, giving the frogs greater security and perhaps better 'calling posts' for the males. The water section was filled to a depth of 3½-4" (8-10 cm). *Elodea densa* was added as before, and the tank was this time covered by a strip of plastic greenhouse shade netting, which was fine enough to prevent not only the frogs but also their food, chiefly flies *(Lucilia* and *Calliphora* species) and crickets, from escaping. Since temperatures were unusually mild when this was set up at the beginning of February, and the tank was positioned where it could receive more direct sunlight than last year, it was again decided not to start with any extra heating.

SPAWNING

The frogs, this time consisting of last year's spawning female (now twice the size it was then) and one male, and the largest of the 1988 youngsters, were in excellent condition by early February, most of the males showing nuptial pads and the females clearly plump with eggs. Therefore, 3 of the total 4 females, the other being a small individual which had developed with only one front leg, to be used only if the rest provided unresponsive, and the 7 largest males, were moved to the breeding quarters on 13th of the above month.

Despite 2-3 attempts at amplexus observed within an hour of being introduced to their new surroundings, disappointingly little happened over the next 3 weeks. Typical non-breeding calls were made by males, usually in the evenings and in response to noise produced by television or radio, but frogs were observed in the water only first thing in the mornings, and none were seen in amplexus. On 25th a heater-thermostat was installed in the water section, bringing the temperature there up to the 1988 spawning level of 68-70°F (20-22°C), but still the only activity of note was prolonged calling by one of two males, slightly louder than before. However, on 3rd March, one such louder call was answered by a much lower-pitched one, later observations confirming this latter as a call made by a female, something not heard in 1988, though it was reported by Arnold & Burton (1978) and Salvador (1985).

Following the pattern of '88, turning the heater off at night to vary the temperature, and persistent heavy spraying was tried, but made no difference to the frogs' behaviour, so on 11th March the water level, which had previously been topped-up as it evaporated, was allowed to decrease over the next 3 days. At the end of this, fresh cold water was poured into the tank last thing at night, along with a heavy dose of spraying applied to the terrestrial section.

Loud, typical breeding calls were heard early on the morning of the 12th, and upon checking the vivarium at c. 7.30, 2 clusters of spawn, one as large as those laid last season around a grass stem, one very small around a leaf of grass, had been deposited. One pair of frogs were also in the water, apparently showing little interest in each other, but it was on this occasion that the female, which by its relatively thin appearance had clearly produced the eggs, was heard answering the male's intermittent vocalizations. The temperature of the water was around 68°F (c.19°C), and since the weather was overcast, there was no strong sunlight.

Periodic calling by the above pair went on until they were back in amplexus 2 hours later, and I was now able to witness the actual spawning process, descriptions of which appear to be totally absent from relevant literature. Fortunately, the frogs chose to perform close to the front of the vivarium, which made for perfect viewing. First the female grasped a strand of grass hanging 2-3" (5-8 cm) into the water, from which the pair hung in a vertical position with the female's hind toes just about touching the bottom of the tank, thus pulling the grass a further 2" (5 cm) under the water. After about 10 minutes, the female began pulling itself up the strand 1-2" and a tightly packed string of spawn was quickly ejected while the female made sideways movements which wrapped the eggs around the grass, the male presumably fertilizing them as they were produced, in the usual anuran manner. All this was completed, considering it was not just a case of dropping eggs onto the vegetation etc., with surprising speed, in less than 5 minutes, whereupon the male released the female, swam to the opposite side of the water section and resumed calling. The same process was enacted again about 15 minutes later, this time with a much smaller cluster of spawn produced, after which the female had clearly deposited all remaining eggs, and promptly left the water.

The above male continued calling throughout the day and well into the evening, but none of the other females responded, and apart from spells of loud calling, mostly at night, nothing more happened over the next 2 weeks; frogs were seen in the water only briefly in the early mornings or late at night, none in amplexus. Heavy doses of fresh water every 3-4 days, plus equally heavy spraying, had no more effect than the latter had done after the 1988 spawning.

During this period, another contact to whom I had supplied Parsley froglets, Colin Melsom, reported a spawning in a set-up very similar to the above, and noted how quickly his frogs had attempted to go into amplexus whilst being moved into the breeding quarters, as had also been the case with mine. In addition, most of the males seen in the water over the past 2 weeks had actually attempted amplexus on the rare occasions one of the females passed close to them, but never pursued them very far, so I began to wonder whether forcing the gravid females into close contact with males might produce better results. As an experiment, a pair were placed in a small container, and within moments they were in amplexus.

Following this idea, on 24th March I decided to try the remaining 2 gravid females in a much smaller, almost totally aquatic set-up, from which they could not easily escape the attentions of the males. Thus, a tank 14" x 8" x 8" was prepared, with a small island built up with tile and rocks in the centre, from which large clumps of grass hung into water to a depth of 5-5½" (12-15 cm). The tank was placed in a back room with no direct sunlight, and 2 pairs of frogs were installed. Within a few hours one male was calling, by evening one pair had gone into amplexus, and ½" (2.2 cm) of fresh water was added last thing. Calling was heard after dark.

The same pair were still in amplexus the next day, and by mid-morning the other pair had done likewise. As an experiment, a one third change of warm water, pushing the temperature up to 85-90°F (30-33°C), was tried as an extra stimulus, last thing on 25th. The following morning at about 8.30, spawn was found, attached to the grass as before and very fresh looking, laid perhaps 2-3 hours earlier. This time it consisted of 2 large clusters, around 2-2½" long, one about half that size, and a very small one of no more than 6-7 eggs. The temperature was then 58°F (14°C), and the other pair were still in amplexus.

With temperatures in the original vivarium now reaching 70°F (22°C) in the afternoons and staying at around 60°F (15°C) at night, it was decided as a further experiment to move the small tank to a position in front of the former, so as to receive maximum sunlight from the window. This was done on 27th, and once again a half change of warm water was tried that night. The remaining pair were in amplexus then, but had separated by the following afternoon, and were only persuaded back together again by means of a half change of cold water last thing at night. Still nothing had happened the following morning, and despite changing half or three quarters of the water for the next three evenings, varying the water depth between 3-5½" (7.5-15 cm), and altering the positions of the rocks and grass clumps, the frogs simply went in and out of amplexus periodically for the rest of the week. On 1st April the water level was raised to its original 5½", and no further alterations were made, the pair being in amplexus last thing.

On the morning of the 2nd, nothing had changed, and little attention was paid to the frogs. However, completely without warning, spawning occurred in mid-morning, at a water temperature of 56°F (c. 13°C), the fact that it had taken place being heralded by characteristic loud calling by the male after it was all over. This proved to be the largest of the three spawnings, consisting of 6 clusters, 2 large, c.3" (7.5 cm), 3 medium, c.1-1½" (2-3.5 cm), and one small, and as was the case with all others, the eggs were attached to grass leaves.

Most of the males remained in breeding condition for 2 weeks following the last success, but there was no reason to try the 'reserve' female, if only because there were already more than enough tadpoles to handle.

TADPOLE DEVELOPMENT

As with that in 1988, each of the '89 spawnings had a high fertility rate. Those eggs kept artificially heated developed very quickly as before, those at room temperatures 3-4 days longer. Including the 30-40 infertile eggs in each batch, the first spawning totalled between 450 and 500, the second, produced by the female which bred in '88, 420-30, and the final one 820-30. Though all were substantially bigger than the '88 spawning, even the last was still well short of the 1000-1600 reported by various authors (Angel, 1946; Fretey, 1975; Van Den Elzen, 1976; Arnold & Burton, 1978; Lanka & Vit, 1985 and Salvador, 1985), but none of the females, even the one from '88, was then fully-grown. At the time of writing they are all noticeably larger, and can be expected to produce significantly more eggs next season.

Needless to say, without allowing the Parsley tadpoles to monopolize my available facilities, attempting to raise over 1500 of them was neither possible nor desirable, so large numbers were distributed among various herpetological contacts, and any further surplus fed to newts. With lower densities maintained in a selection of aquaria, the problem created by competition in '88 never arose, most tadpoles this time developing extremely well. Those retained from the first batch, which had been kept at 68-70°F, first showed hind leg buds on the 16th April, front legs on the 26th, and the first two froglets metamorphosed on the 28th – 46 days from hatching.

Perhaps the most interesting observation concerning the 1989 tadpoles, and one which occurred almost by accident, was that keeping them under different conditions and providing a different diet appeared to have an effect upon the colouration of both tadpoles and froglets. Those reared in the same way as last year, i.e. in tanks indoors, and fed largely on fish flakes, assumed a deep reddish-brown body colour, with no discernable markings until about 2 weeks from metamorphosis. However, others, mainly from the third batch, maintained in a temporary PVC lined pond which was dug in one of my outdoor enclosures to help spread the numbers even further, by contrast developed a lighter, more mottled green-brown appearance. These were still provided with flake food, but also fed on the very considerable growth of algae prompted by the strong sunlight the pond received. I originally put the above down to the fact that the pond liner had a light brown colour, but later it became increasingly clear that not only did the tadpoles here rarely resemble the ones developing elsewhere, but there were also far greater numbers of froglets with bright green markings emerging from this pond than anywhere else. Unfortunately, with so many other breeding amphibians dividing my attention at this time, the significance of the above only occurred to me when, along with those reared indoors, many of the tadpoles and froglets from the pond had gone to contacts as described or been released into outdoor enclosures, so it was too late to make reliable comparisons by monitoring closely the development of large numbers in each area, although among those that were left the differences were quite noticeable. Later in the summer, a similar experience occurred when Yellow-Bellied Toad *(Bombina variegata kolombatovici)* tadpoles were reared in an aquarium situated in a position receiving strong enough sunlight to produce algal growth similar to that in the Parsleys' pond. These developed a green appearance never previously seen in the many hundreds of Yellow-Belly tadpoles handled in recent years, the metamorphosed toadlets retaining green dorsal colouration, of which the parents showed no trace. There may also have been genetic factors involved here, but this further convinced me that the high degree of algae in the diet of Parsley tadpoles in the pond had affected the latter as previously described. Certainly this is a theory I look forward to testing next Spring.

Apart from the colouration element discussed above, 1989 produced no information on raising the froglets worth adding to the relevant 1988 section, so there is no need to describe this aspect again.

CONCLUSIONS

As a result of the preceeding survey, a set of conditions required in order to reproduce Parsley Frogs successfully using indoor vivaria can now be summarized, with the addition of a few suggestions (some possibly rather speculative!) as to how my experiences may relate to their behaviour in the natural state. However, this is in no way intended to be definitive, merely what has worked for me, and information on any alternative methods offered by readers of this article would be welcomed.

(1) The evidence of the 1989 season in particular strongly suggests that sudden changes in the frogs' environment will trigger spawning. In contrast to the males, females always seemed much more reluctant to enter the water, which suggests that perhaps in their natural habitat sudden heavy rainfall stimulates them into activity near the breeding sites, where they then come into close contact with males.

Thus, a small aquarium-vivarium set-up, i.e. one which keeps the sexes in continual contact, and with frequent water level changes etc. as described, is most likely to produce the required results.

(2) A water depth of no more than 3-5" (7.5-12 cm) is necessary, as none of the spawn clusters were deposited at more than 6" below the surface. It is highly probable that the frogs prefer spawning in shallow water near the edge of ponds, ditches etc. because of (a) the greater abundance of suitable overhanging vegetation, and (b) in view of what was observed during the first spawning of '89, the actual spawning method seems better adapted to shallow, thickly vegetated surroundings. This also suggests one possible reason why the two larger females failed to breed in '88 was that the much greater water depth, combined with much thinner density of grasss etc., meant they lacked the extra support the above conditions would have provided, and so were unable to balance properly in order to deposit the eggs. Although I had no way of knowing which male was involved in the '88 spawning, it may well have been one of the smaller individuals, as the pair would then probably have been light enough to gain sufficient support from the grass hanging from the island.

(3) As regards temperature and light, spawning conditions were extremely variable, so success can be expected at anything between the mid-50s and upper-70sF (12-25°C). Though it is quite probable that increasing day-length helps bring the frogs into breeding condition, and they are certainly less nocturnal when spawning, on the evidence above strong sunlight is not essential.

(4) Tadpoles may be reared in much the same manner as those of most other anurans, and no problems should occur so long as overcrowding is avoided. Suitably accomodated and fed as described, the young frogs can be ready to breed in as little as 7-8 months.

However reliable the foregoing prove to be in the future, I have no doubt that the Parsley Frog, with its small size, simple requirements and fascinating colour variations, is to be recommended as a highly interesting and rewarding subject for the amphibian enthusiast.

ACKNOWLEDGEMENTS

My thanks are due to Charles Snell, Mike Linley, Colin Melsom, Trevor Beebee and Pat Thorp for the valuable information, advice and observation they contributed at various stages of the events described, and also to Howard Turner for his help with various items of essential equipment.

REFERENCES

Angel, F. (1946). *Faune de France. Reptiles et Amphibiens.* Lechavalier, Paris.

Arnold, E.N. & Burton, J.A. (1978). *A Field guide to the Reptiles & Amphibians of Britain & Europe.* Collins, London & Glasgow.

Fretey, J. (1975). *Guide des Reptiles et Batraciens de France.* Hatier, Paris.
Lanka, V. & Vit, Z. (1985). *Amphibians & Reptiles.* Hamlyn, Feltham, Middlesex.
Salvador, A. (1985). *Guia de los Anfibios y Reptiles de la Peninsula Iberica, Islas Baleares y Canarias.* Leon, Spain.
Van Den Elzen, P. (1976). Remarques sur la biologie de *Pelodytes punctatus,* Daudin 1802 (Amphibia, Pelobatidae), en Camargue'. *Revue Francaise Aquariologique et Herpetologique,* **3.**

British Herpetological Society Bulletin No. 14. 1985

OBSERVATIONS OF THE BREEDING OF A MARSUPIAL FROG, *GASTROTHECA MARSUPIATA*

BARRY R. KIRK

11b Hull Road, Hessle, East Yorkshire HU13 9NG

In early January 1985 I obtained two tropical frogs complete with vivarium through an advertisement in the local paper. The previous owner had housed the frogs in her kitchen, the background heat of which provided the animals with an adequate living temperature. This was supplemented each evening by a 150w spotlight mounted inside the 460mm x 300mm x 300mm vivarium. The frogs had been sprayed twice daily with water and a constant supply of crickets had been provided. The owner commented that one of the animals had been heard calling on several occasions and that an attempted mating had been observed. She could not provide any details regarding the identification of the frogs, only that she had purchased them as Brazilian Tree Frogs.

The animal presumed to be the female was 60mm from nose to vent and some 10mm larger than the male. Both frogs had an overall buff background colour with two bright green bands running from vent to head. The bands on the male were wider than the female's. The male also had more green on the snout, head and flanks than did the female. The flanks of the male were speckled green while the female had an irregular dark green stripe on her flanks. The male possessed a throat sack of considerable size which inflated when he called.

When the female produced young I then realised that the animals were in fact a species of South American marsupial frog and I identified them as *Gastrotheca marsupiata* from Ecuador and Peru.

I installed the frogs in their vivarium which was sited, with my collection of amphibians and fish, in a space heated room. As the previous owner had observed an attempted mating I tried to follow a similar routine to her. I did however stop using the spotlight in the vivarium for fear that the frogs might climb onto it while it was in use. The temperature was an average of 24°C in the room with a temperature drop of about 2°C at night. The frogs proved to be nocturnal and spent all day together on a piece of cork bark in the top corner of the vivarium. A constant supply of crickets was provided of which a surprisingly large number a day were consumed. Two water containers were provided, one of which the frogs could fully submerge in. Shortly after I obtained them the male was heard calling.

When I inspected the frogs on the morning of the 11th February 1985, the female was observed sitting in the smaller of the two water containers, a coffee jar lid, surrounded by 50+ tadpoles each of 15mm length. She was observed using her longest rear toe to empty the young out of the pouch on her back. The opening to the pouch was sited near the vent. At no time whilst I had these animals had there been any visible indication that the female had been carrying young. It may be that she was already carrying the young when I obtained her. Due to shortage of tank space the majority of tadpoles were placed in fish tanks which had recently held young fish. These tanks were situated high in the space heated building and had a temperature of 28-30°C which was higher than I would have liked. The tanks were filtered by undergravel biological filters. Unfortunately all the tadpoles in these tanks died before metamorphosing. They appeared to fill up with fluid in the body cavity. This resulted in their death.

These losses may have been due to one of the following factors, a) the high water temperature, b) the fish wastes already present in the tank water or c) the salinity of the water. One teaspoon of sodium chloride per gallon had been added to the tank water when it held fish.

Luckily I had also placed about 20 tadpoles in an aquarium, 350mm x 200mm x 200mm, containing fresh tap water which in my area is hard and alkaline. The tank was provided with light aeration and maintained at a temperature of 25°C. The tadpoles were fed with crushed lettuce, tropical fish flake food and fish fry food. All food offered was readily consumed and regular water changes had to be carried out because of the amount of waste produced. The tadpoles grew quickly and the back legs began to appear after only one week.

After 3 weeks the back legs were well developed and some colouring on the tadpoles' backs began to show. At the same time the front legs emerged complete.

On 5 March 1985 the first froglets started to climb out of the water onto a rock provided above water level. These still had a considerable amount of tail remaining. Once this had been absorbed, the froglets were placed in a vivarium with a covering of peat and gravel.

Plate 1. Adult pair of *Gastrotheca marsupiata.* The female is the large frog on the right.

Plate 2. Young *Gastrotheca marsupiata,* four months old.

Initially the young frogs were fed hatchling crickets and fruitflies but these proved rather small and a larger size of young cricket was found to be more satisfactory. Cleaned anglers maggots, first pricked with a pin, were provided when no crickets were available.

The young frogs have proved to be delicate and at four months of age only eight have been raised but these appear to be strong and healthy and are consuming large numbers of small and medium sized crickets.

A further attempt will be made to breed these frogs again in the hope of improving the survival rate among tadpoles and young frogs.

REFERENCES

Breen, J.F. (1974). *Encyclopedia of Reptiles and Amphibians,* T.F.H.
Longman Illustrated Animal Encylcopedia, (1984). Guild Publishing.

British Herpetological Society Bulletin No. 17. 1986

A NOTE ON THE "WHISTLING FROG" IN CAPTIVITY

PAUL BECKWITH

Dept. Biology, University of Essex, Wivenhoe Park, Colchester, CO4 3SQ

Eleutherodactylus johnstonei (Barbour, 1914), is a member of the Leptodactylidae, and is native to the numerous islands of the West Indies, for example, Antigua, Barbados, and Martinique. It is a small, plainly coloured species, the females up to 2.5cm in length, the males slightly smaller. However, it is fair to say that what it lacks in size, it more than makes up for with vocal prowess. In fact, it is rumoured that a remarkably similar species, *E. martinicensis,* was introduced to Barbados by an irate local to annoy a neighbour, with whom he was no longer on speaking terms. Anybody who has heard these anurans calling can easily understand why they could be an annoyance!

An interesting aspect of their life history, along with many other *Eleutherodactylus* species, is that they are terrestrial breeders, i.e. the larvae complete the cycle on land, bypassing a free swimming tadpole stage. Few eggs, (each of about 4mm diameter), are laid on damp soil, and development of the young frogs occurs within the egg, until fully formed froglets emerge, using their egg tooth, and are immediately ready to feed. The only major hazards facing the developing young in the egg are desiccation and fungal attack. Both are prevented to a certain degree by the parent, in choice of egg laying site being clean and free from spores, and the presence of the male remaining with the eggs to moisten them with a watery excretion should they become too dry.

I happened to have my first experience of these animals in September of 1985 when a rather dry, neglected vivarium of size 48 by 15 by 12 inches, was given to me to maintain in our department foyer. At that time it contained 5 unknown frogs, *(E. johnstonei)*, and a large female Warty newt, *(Triturus cristatus)*, all huddled together in the only moisture available, underneath the empty water tray. The newt was released into a pond containing a breeding population, the frogs transferred to a temporary holding tank whilst the other was cleaned out. Fresh soil, plants (including 'Maidenhair' and *Nephrolepis* sp. ferns), logs and a water container were added, and a layer of muslin was placed across the top of the tank, under the tube, to reduce the light intensity.

Although no heater was installed the tank remained at the temperature of the foyer, (about $23^0 \pm 2^0$C), and the animals were fed a constant supply of *Drosophila*, and various other invertebrates.

After a period of about 2 to 3 weeks in their new, damp environment, the males were heard calling. This only occurred at night at what appeared to be a regular calling site, on the leaves of an exposed fern about 6 inches off the tank floor.

No amplexus was observed, and it was assumed none had occurred. However, on the morning of February 25th 1986, a small (5 to 6mm) froglet was found drowned in the pool, which was then lowered to make it very shallow, and a search of the tank was undertaken. This revealed a further two froglets and a clump of approximately 15 to 20 fresh, unpigmented eggs laid under one of the logs. Bayley (1950) states that *E. martinicensis* froglets hatch after 10 days, however, the eggs in my care took just over 8 weeks, to eventually hatch on the 18th April. The froglets remained hidden and secretive until a week after hatching, and were 2 to 3mm long. Contrary to the adult behaviour, the froglets were not nocturnal and were often seen foraging during the day. Being so small they could not eat the adults' food and were fed on invertebrates contained in floor sweepings from a nearby copse. The two older froglets were now 6 to 7mm long, and could be sexed via their markings, which corresponded with the adults. (Females being a drab, uniform, light brown, the males having a darker, dorsal stripe extending from the midline of the eyes to the vent). It is hoped that these juveniles will grow to a breeding stock.

In order to maintain these amphibians in a healthy condition with the ultimate view to breed, the following is worth remembering:

1. The frogs must feel comfortable in their tank, and this is best achieved by emulating their natural conditions. In this case it involves a vivarium with shaded light levels, a variety of hiding places, damp soil, (a shallow water container can be added, but it is not essential), correct temperature of about 23^0C, and a plentiful food supply. However, it must be realized that as these are nocturnal animals, and if sufficient hiding places are available, you are unlikely to see them at all during daylight hours, and any forced exposure to daytime activity will decrease the chances of breeding.

2. During the night period *E. johnstonei* is a very active and agile animal. It is, therefore, essential that a secure, tight fitting lid is used, otherwise escapees will be inevitable!

3. The natural breeding season on the islands is the rainy season between April and May, the stimulus being an increase in humidity and rainfall. This can be mimicked in the vivarium by periods of relative dryness, lasting about three months, interspersed with a wetter period involving regular spraying with de-chlorinated water to increase the humidity.

4. If the eggs are obtained it is a good idea to transfer them to a rearing tank, in case the adults eat the emergent froglets.

It is hoped that this may be of small benefit to anyone who has these, or similar, animals but is unsure of their requirements and habits.

I would like to thank Brian Banks, Colin McCarthy and Ron Long.

REFERENCES

Bayley, I. (1950). The whistling frogs of Barbados. *Jnl. of the B.M.H.S.* **17**(4): 161-170.

Mattison, C. (1982). *The Care of Reptiles and Amphibians in Captivity.* Blandford Press, Dorset.

British Herpetological Society Bulletin No. 15. 1986

REPEATED SPAWNINGS IN *HYPEROLIUS MARMORATUS*

CHRISTOPHER MATTISON

138 Dalewood Road, Beauchief, Sheffield, 8, U.K.

Hyperolius marmoratus is a polymorphic reed frog from southern Africa. Adults are usually coloured brown and cream, the colours being arranged either as brown mottling on cream, or as brown stripes on cream (i.e. 'humbug-style') but occasional males apparently retain the plain brown juvenile markings into maturity. In an attempt to investigate the genetics and significance of these variations, a small group of adults was obtained from Mtuzini in Natal. Unfortunately, the work was never completed but the reproductive data obtained may be of some interest.

12 adults from the same locality had the following markings:

males – 6 striped; 1 brown
females – 3 striped; 2 mottled

Plate 1. Juvenile *Hyperolius.* Photo Peter Curry

All possible combinations of these markings were paired, but the brown male never attempted to breed and was not heard to call – this may or may not be significant.

The animals were originally housed in large plastic lunch boxes containing a pad of damp filter paper and a small petri-dish of water. This method was used successfully by Richards (1977) to breed *H. viridiflavus,* the only previous report of captive breeding in *Hyperolius.* However, both productive pairs laid infertile clutches on the bottoms of these boxes and were subsequently moved to larger cages. These consisted of glass aquaria measuring 18 x 10 x 10 inches, containing about 2.5 inches of water. A thin styrofoam platform was wedged across the tank at surface level to give a dry area (for the introduction of food) without affecting the volume of water. A small clump of Java moss *(Vesicularia dubyana)* was placed in the water and this was changed each time that spawning occurred. The adults were fed daily on crickets and houseflies dusted with 'Vionate', a powdered vitamin-mineral supplement.

Temperature was kept at a constant 72°F and the photoperiod was 14 hours light: 10 hours dark. As the room received no natural lighting, only a single fluorescent lamp, a covered desk lamp was left on permanently in order to avoid total darkness at night.

Males (whether paired or not) began calling soon after 'lights-out' each night, usually while clinging to the glass sides of the aquarium. The call was a high-pitched 'peep-peep-peep', best likened to a squeaky wheelbarrow being moved about. Spawning was never observed and invariably occurred during the night, the spawn being deposited in several small clumps, attached to the Java moss, each containing about 20 eggs.

Plate 2. Young larvae of *Hyperolius marmoratus* in rearing container containing Java moss

Spawn and tadpoles were raised in small plastic boxes containing 'their' Java moss; aeration was provided via a hypodermic needle attached to a plastic air line. The tadpoles were fed on a good quality tropical fish flake and were kept clean by periodically changing about 30 per cent of their water. Local tapwater (pH 6.6) was used throughout. At metamophosis they were transferred to an 18" x 10" x 10" aquarium lined with moist tissue and fed on small crickets. Although they grew rapidly, it was necessary to dispose of the colony before any reached reproductive size. All juvenile *Hyperolius marmoratus* are brown in colouration.

HYPEROLIUS MARMORATUS – BREEDING DATA

	Date laid	Date hatched	No.	Date first metamorphosed
Female 1	29.12.81	infertile*		
	16. 1.82	infertile*		
	26. 1.82	30.1.82	200	7.4.82 (66 days)
	5. 2.82	9.2.82	241	Died
Female 2	4. 1.82	infertile*		
	22. 1.82	26.1.82	333	31.3.82 (64 days)
	1. 2.82	6.2.82	230	12.4.82 (65 days)
	13. 2.82	17.2.82	190	24.4.82 (66 days)
	28. 2.82	3.3.82	186	10.5.82 (61 days)
	11. 3.82	15.3.82	179	26.5.82 (62 days)
	22. 3.82	26.3.82	–	
	6. 4.82	10.4.82	–	
	16. 4.82	infertile**		
	26. 4.82	infertile**		
averages	11.2 days	inter-clutch	223	64 days

* clutches of eggs laid in plastic boxes

** male died shortly after the last of these two infertile clutches

DISCUSSION

Hyperolius marmoratus breeds readily and prolifically under simple conditions (although I have since been unable to induce commercially obtained specimens to reproduce or even to stay alive for any great length of time). Their enormous breeding potential and polymorphism could be of value to geneticists and behavioural ecologists (as well as to persons requiring large numbers of small frogs as snake-food etc.). It would be of great interest to see if this reproductive potential occurs in the wild as well as under controlled conditions – if so, this, and other similar species undoubtedly contribute a significant biomass to the lower and middle trophic levels of the eco-system.

ACKNOWLEDGEMENTS

The animals were collected for me in South Africa by Arthur Stevenson of the University of Wales, Cardiff.

REFERENCES

Richards, C.M. (1977). Reproductive potential under controlled conditions of *Hyperolius viridiflavus,* a Kenyan reed frog. *Journal of Herpetology* **11** (4): 426-428.

British Herpetological Society Bulletin No. 1. 1980

A NEW SPECIES OF ANURAN, *RANA MAGNAOCULARIS,* THE POP-EYED FROG

RANK FROSS

Loyal Ontario Museum

Night collecting on roads in Ontario has revealed a new species of frog strikingly characterized by enormous eyes and a flattened body. The species is described below and the adaptive significance of its diagnostic features are discussed.

Rana magnaocularis
Holotype:

Loyal Ontario Museum 12854, adult male, collected on Highway 401 five miles north of Toronto, 10 May 1973.

Diagnosis:

Eyes enormous, protruding tongue usually extended, body and limbs highly flattened dorso ventrally. Dorso lateral fold absent. Otherwise resembles *Rana pipiens.*

Description:

Body subdiscoidal. Depth of body 1-2mm. Snout-vent length 6 inches. Maximum body width 3 inches. Skin somewhat cornified usually with a series of polygonal indentations running transversely across the body. Colour green or brown, marked with large circular dark spots (which occasionally run together) with light margins. Underparts white.

Habitat:

Found on or sometimes beside asphalt roads where traffic is fairly heavy. Most common in spring.

Discussion:

Three questions require attention. Of what significance is the peculiar morphology, why is it restricted to a single habitat and how does it move?

Why is the body so flattened and why are the eyes so large? We believe that these are adaptations to the peculiar habitat. Normally frogs are at least partially hidden from potential predators by reeds, grass or bushes. On the road they are completely exposed, however. In evolving a two-dimensional body, the pop-eyed frog is enabled to escape the attention of all predators excepting those immediately overhead. Were the eyes also two-dimensional, they would be incapable of lateral vision. So instead they are enlarged to make up for the loss of view resulting from the recumbent body.

Obviously, locomotion is difficult with a discoidal two-dimensional body. This may explain why they are not found off the road – they are incapable of surmounting rough surfaces.

We were at first puzzled as to how it moved from one place to another, observations on live specimens being lacking. Initially we found the tread-like markings found on the upper surface puzzling. Of what use were the treads in locomotion when they were not in contact with the ground? Analogy with the hoop snake offered a hypothesis; the frogs roll themselves into a ring, insert the extruded tongue in the posterior, and roll themselves neatly along, thereby engaging the treads with the road surface. A colleague has suggested alternately that the ridges may permit turbulent air from passing cars to lift the frog into the air, leaf like. Steering would be possible by lowering one leg or the other like aeroplane flaps.